SPACE FLIGHT

SPACE FLIGHT

Satellites, Spaceships, Space Stations, and Space Travel Explained

CARSBIE C. ADAMS, 1922–
President, NATIONAL RESEARCH AND
DEVELOPMENT CORPORATION

WITH THE COLLABORATION OF

FREDERICK I. ORDWAY, III
Director, ORDNANCE PROJECTS
GENERAL ASTRONAUTICS CORPORATION

HEYWARD E. CANNEY, JR.
Founder and Chairman of the Board
GENERAL ASTRONAUTICS CORPORATION

RONALD C. WAKEFORD
Director of Research, ASTRONAUTICS
DIVISION, NATIONAL RESEARCH AND
DEVELOPMENT CORPORATION

McGraw-Hill Book Company, Inc.
NEW YORK   TORONTO   LONDON   1958

ASPF

To

LAURA SUE HAWKINS

and her fellow teachers

who first reveal to young and eager

minds the wondrous worlds of science

Foreword

Ever since the summer of 1955, when both the United States and the Soviet Union announced plans to launch a series of artificial satellites within the framework of the International Geophysical Year, a veritable spate of space-flight literature has overwhelmed the American public. And it may be expected that this tide will further rise in the wake of the Sputniks, Explorers, and their counterparts.

Most of these publications were written with particular groups of readers in mind. There have been space books for children—our present space cadets and future rocket pilots. There have been books for students of science and engineering, and books designed to familiarize the general public with the colorful history and the bright future of man's greatest venture.

I do not know what kind of reader Carsbie C. Adams had in mind when he prepared the manuscript of the present volume, but I have no doubt that "Space Flight" will become the spaceman's book on space flight. And I am certain that it will soon attain the stature of one of the few great classics on this fascinating and many-faceted subject.

Dr. Adams's book begins with a historical review. It is not only well written, but it introduces us to several persons and incidents of the more remote past that, to my knowledge at least, have never been uncovered before.

When we come to the more recent past, Carsbie Adams displays good judgment in appraising performances, personalities, and controversies (all of which are so indispensably needed for progress).

The ensuing chapters on rocket propulsion and celestial mechanics are clear and cover difficult subjects with a refreshing scarcity of mathematical formulas.

Whereas the first half of "Space Flight" is an unusually happy blend of historical review and scientific treatise on the astronomical and engineering fundamentals of astronautics—the latter presented in a language comprehensible to anyone who has gone through high school—the second half offers a broad outlook into the future of space flight which far transcends the mere technological aspects. There is a challenging chapter on the human and biological factors in space flying, with revolutionary new concepts on feeding and air and water recuperation aboard spaceships. There is a chapter on communications in space, wherein we learn of Dr. Adams' proposal to make practical use of the so-called Trojan points on planetary orbits which were discovered by the French mathematician Lagrange as early as 1760. Specifically, Dr. Adams suggests to improve radio communication with interplanetary expeditions by placing radio booster stations into these "stable" orbital positions, thus permitting uninterrupted radio contact even with planets temporarily hidden by the sun.

You will find many more creative suggestions in this most stimulating book. Read it and you will be reminded of Rudyard Kipling's immortal "The Elephant's Child":

> *I kept six honest serving men*
> *They taught me all I knew.*
> *Their names are What and Why and When,*
> *And How and Where and Who.*

Dr. Wernher von Braun
Director, Development Operations Division
Army Ballistic Missile Agency
Redstone Arsenal, Alabama

Preface

On October 4, 1957, the Russians took the first definitive step into space by launching their Sputnik unmanned artificial satellite of the earth. Scientists had long predicted such an achievement although it had been suspected in many quarters that 1958, and not 1957, would be the remarkable date. It had also been widely believed that the first satellite launching would take place in Florida, U.S.A., so it was with considerable surprise that the world accepted the smashing Soviet triumph at the space frontier.

More ambitious programs became evident as the space age entered infancy. Russia surprised the world again on November 3, 1957, with the launching of their 1,118-pound animal-occupied Sputnik II. The United States followed quickly with the launching of its first satellite, Explorer I, on January 31, 1958. That full-fledged space flight is somewhere not too far around the corner seems certain. Man will probably leave the earth and take up residence in a space station during the next five years, and within twenty or twenty-five years, we shall probably have set foot on the moon. It seems likely that instrumented probes, and perhaps even man, will voyage to the planets during this century.

It is now our problem to consider immediately the many ramifications and consequences of the imminent progress of aviation and rocketry. We can no longer leave space flight to our grandchildren —we must do it ourselves. It is no longer possible to avoid the many questions that confront us, even in our initial phases of space flight.

In April, 1939, the German pilot, Fritz Wendel, set a record of 469 mph, with a Messerschmitt 109-R fighter. Soon after the war,

British Group Captain H. J. Wilson made a record flight with a twin-engine Glouster Meteor Jet flying at 606 mph. The present published record is that of Bell's X-2, which was rocketed to a speed of 2,200 mph by Lt. Col. Frank K. Everest and to an altitude of 126,000 feet by Capt. Ivan C. Kincheloe. Our rockets have reached nearly 15,000 mph and 700 miles out into space. Man has already flown over 98 per cent of the way up through our atmosphere, touching the "veil" of outer space. Man-made moons have been launched which circle the earth every few minutes. The next step is to launch missiles carrying man into space. The idea of rocketry and astronautics has had such an effect on society that it was possible for The Southern Research Institute to hold a conference in 1957 on their impact on our times, something that would not have been even feasible a few years earlier.

These are great accomplishments for so short a period of time. Yet the skill, resolution, and enterprise that have created our modern world will carry us forward at an even faster rate. Given a sufficiently powerful motivation, there is apparently no limit to what the human race can do. No load is too heavy, no road too long; the pyramids of Egypt and the Manhattan Project are examples of history. The prime consideration is, of course, the motive. The power of religion built the pyramids; the pressure of war made the atomic bomb. The reader may already have asked: What will be the motives which will prod men into outer space? Why should we go outside our atmosphere? Why should we go to other worlds?

It is possible to list many practical reasons why mankind ought to conquer space, and the development of the atomic bomb has created new urgency in relation to some of them. Many feel that *the nation controlling space will control the peace*. Indeed, Air Force ballistic-missile expert General Shriever has forecast future battles in space, holding that superiority there may ensure national security. Secondly, the physical resources of our planet are limited. Also, dozens of tremendously important scientific procedures and experiments would become possible immediately upon the completion of the space station. Complete, detailed, accurate weather reporting could be made from an observatory on the space station—no more unexpected "weather." Research in all the fields of medicine could be facilitated at a laboratory on the space station—perhaps a cure for cancer, tuberculosis, polio, and, who knows, even "old age" would be an easy "find" in the cosmic rays of outer space. Opportunity for astronomical study would perhaps be one of the greatest advantages of the space station. Once astroscientists rid themselves of our atmosphere, they will not only be nearer the planets, stars, and nebulae, but they will for the first time be able to get a clear, unbroken view of the astral bodies. For, while our atmosphere is a protective blanket, it is also a screen which hinders the scientist from detailed observations.

A space station would serve as a "launching station" for space ships to the moon, saving fabulous amounts of precious fuel. Worldwide television would be possible by relay to the space stations; direction of lost-aircraft rescue missions would be simple and accurate from them. Any one of these many factors might be considered by some to be adequate motivation for space travel, and yet there is one factor disregarding all these, still unmentioned, which alone would drive man into space. That motive is his aggressive pioneering instinct. Space travel offers a permanent outlet for that intense desire to "see what's over the next hill." Space travel is now the only form of "conquest and empire" compatible with civilization.

There is yet another drive associated with this "aggressive drive," as was once stated by the anthropologist J. D. Erwin: "There is no trace of any display of productive energy which has not been *preceded* by a display of *expansive* energy." Sir James Frazer further stated, "Intellectual progress which reveals itself in the growth of arts and sciences receives an immense impetus from conquest and empire." Consequently, we may assume that with space travel and the expansion of the world's mental horizons may come the greatest outburst of creative activity this world has ever known.

The author has designed this book to give the intelligent layman, the student, and the practicing engineer and scientist a complete, well-rounded account of (1) the history and background of the astronautical sciences, (2) the many subsidiary fields that compose these sciences, and (3) detailed information on many of the most important world-wide developments of astronautical significance.

The book is further intended to offer exceptionally complete coverage of introductory space flight material, assess the present state of the art, and present a penetrating look into the future potential of astronautics. It is hoped that "Space Flight" will perform the important generalizing function of bringing into focus the contributions of many fields of endeavor as they affect astronautics. Thus, key progress in astrophysics, communications, geophysics, materials, space medicine, chemistry, and other areas will be shown to form the ever-broadening base of astronautics.

The author hopes this book may serve to stimulate additional interest in astronautics. As space travel is itself a sufficiently sensational subject, embellishments are by no means needed, and any speculations by the author will be based upon facts, or certainly upon probabilities.

My sincere gratitude is expressed to Willy Ley for his valuable comments and criticisms. Appreciation is extended especially to Dr. Wernher von Braun for his interest and invaluable aid in many aspects of this book, and particularly for his generosity in providing rare historical photographs.

Carsbie C. Adams

Contents

SPACE FLIGHT

1

The History of Astronautics

Glimmerings

Disregarding any random musings of primitive and prehistoric men, the time span of the mental evolution of space flight may be said to cover nearly 4,000 years, and may be divided into three overlapping phases: the religious phase, 2000 B.C. to A.D. 1850; the question phase, 1638 to 1895; and the thinking phase, 1890 to the present.

The religious phase began with the discovery of bodies moving in the heavens, the origins of astrology, and the obscurantism of primitive religions, which demand anthropocentric interpretations of the universe. Examples of this sort of thinking can be found in the folklore and mythology of the world (relieved by a brief span of clear thinking in ancient Greece) and the ascendancy in the Western World of the Christian Church, which eventually forbade men even to think about the possibility of other worlds and their habitability. Swift retaliation by the church made men cautious as late as 1850.

The beginning of the question phase can be placed in 1638, with the publication by Bishop (!) John Wilkins of a serious treatise on the moon and the possibility of actual flight to it. Early balloon flights by the Montgolfiers turned eyes skyward with a new interest. Tales of flight between the planets, which had started in antiquity as fables, developed, in the nineteenth century, into science-fiction novels, and may perhaps have been responsible also for a good deal of speculation on how to communicate with possible beings on other

1

bodies. These attempts to signal were very important, as they were the first popular impulse to do something concrete about the separation between the planets. People keenly wanted to find men on the Moon and Mars, and this desire precipitated a number of hoaxes or well-intentioned misconceptions akin to the present-day comedy of errors over the "flying saucer." Jules Verne reflected the new, cocky mood of science and produced what may loosely be called the first space-flight proposal. By the end of the century, a German novelist, Lasswitz, introduced the startling innovation of a station in space.

By this time the thinking phase had started. There were no further religious qualms over thinking about other planets. The rocket had emerged from a motley assortment of possible propulsive agencies as the basis of interplanetary flight; man's concept of his world and its relationship to the universe had matured; and, most important, technology had been able to build enough on the foundations of pure science to begin producing machinery and raw materials that man could trust.

Man could almost feel the advent of flight. The first thinker was a Russian, Konstantin Ziolkowski; he was followed by Prof. Hermann Oberth, of Germany, who began his work about the time that a world movement to form interplanetary societies got underway. When World War II began, technology had gained a firm mastery of ways and means. Deadly aircraft spat bullets and bombs in smothering profusion, while in Germany the Nazi war machine developed a fearful weapon, the guided missile. America developed the atomic bomb.

Today the world sits in the novel tension of the convicted murderer, wondering if the governor will grant him a pardon, or at least a reprieve. Guided missiles grow in size and so do nuclear bombs. The two of them together constitute the superkiller of all time: the intercontinental ballistic missile with a hydrogen warhead. Thoughtful men believe they can see a way out. These huge missiles behave almost like spaceships and actually do fly in space over part of their trajectory. It is more than conceivable, they think, that the current satellite successes may precipitate a race to the planets, and man will channel his energies into this rather than into self-destruction. Russia's success with Sputnik gives weight to this belief, as do repeated statements and prophecies emanating from the Soviet Union.

The Religious Phase

To find whether there is any basis for such an optimism, we should look back into man's own record, to the dim past where the strong lens of the historian's mind can no longer resolve the difference between fact and fiction, if, indeed, there was in those dim days any meaningful difference. Ananoff [1] considers the Hindu Vedas (2000 B.C.) typical of the germ plasma of astronautical thinking. Souls, say the Vedas, wander about in space. This tradition is also detectable in the lore of the Eskimos and other primitive peoples, though space travel with them seems confined to the moon. The Sanskrit Bhagavata, written during the fifteenth century before Christ, depicts Yogi making this trip. Again, in the writings or traditions of the Mayans and Incas, are flights to the moon—this in the period to A.D. 1000. The Japanese god Suzano was thought to have lived in the moon before coming to earth. The Egyptians were reported to have thought, at one time or another, that all the planets and satellites were habitable. Persian literature, particularly that related to the tenth-century Ferdousi, mentions flights into space. The medieval Finnish epic Kalevala (Finland), published by Lonnrot, in 1835, relates how the hero, Vainamoinen, compels the evil Louhi to release the sun and the moon he had imprisoned within a copper mountain. And so on.

Aside from these scattered examples, one can start in conventional historical fashion with the Babylonians and trace the spread of the idea through the whole matrix of Western culture, remembering that any serious notion of flight to another planet naturally awaited the discovery or decision that these other planets were solid bodies.

The motions of the planets, of course, were known to the Babylonian astrologers, who regarded the planets as the homes of the gods. Some idea of system was evolving in the late centuries before Christ. In 360 B.C., Heraclides, of Pontus, proposed a system in which Mercury and Mars revolved around the sun, but in which all

[1] Alexandre Ananoff, "L'Astronautique," p. 18, Librairie Arthème Fayard, Paris, 1950.

4 THE HISTORY OF ASTRONAUTICS

these revolved around the earth. Aristarchus, of Samos, proposed a heliocentric solar system in 280 B.C., over 1,800 years before Copernicus.

Eratosthenes, of Alexandria, some time after 240 B.C., proposed the concept of a spherical earth and calculated the earth's circumference to a surprisingly close 24,000 miles. Just how close he came depends on the length of his unit of measurement, the *stade,* and this has yet to be precisely determined.

During the last five centuries before Christ, a debate on the plurality of solar systems raged among Greek philosophers, but by the Middle Ages and the Renaissance it had degenerated into the question of plurality of planets. The Pythagoreans had propounded, as early as 500 B.C., a counterearth which was earth's duplicate, in every detail, and moved with it. The moon was regarded by many Greeks as a junior earth with superior men and animals. Aristotle rejected plurality of planets, without giving any reason, and the Christian Church's reliance on Aristotle's imagined omniscience made things difficult for scientists for centuries.

Plutarch, who died in A.D. 120, regarded the moon as solid, a smaller earth, and inhabited by "demons." Lukian wrote a satire entitled the "True History," in which a vessel is swept up by a whirlwind and travels for a week, coming finally to "a great countrie in the aire, like a shining Island" (the moon). He depicted it as populated by warlike but antiseptically clean beings. In another tale of Lukian, the hero, Icaromenippus, flies with bird's wings to the moon, and then, after three days, to heaven. The church discouraged such speculations as these, and, in 1145, banned them as heresy.

Copernicus, Kepler, and Galileo were under stern pressure by the church. Nikolaus Copernicus reversed Hipparchus, of Samos,[2] by placing the sun in the middle and the planets in epicyclic orbits around it. Johannes Kepler's observations of Mars disagreed with Copernicus and showed the planet to travel in an ellipse. Galileo Galilei, making a special telescope for the purpose, examined the planets and found them to present disks like the moon. But astronomy prospered mainly in Protestant countries in those days.

[2] The geocentric universe is wrongly ascribed to his "managing editor," Ptolemy.

Kepler wrote a book, entitled "Somnium," in which both the earth and moon are populated by demons who can traverse the shadow between the earth and moon during eclipses and take human beings with them. Kepler's Lunarians, like the trolls of medieval mythology, could not endure sunlight and built ringed walls (the "craters") to protect themselves. All of this is learned allegory which the sophisticated astronomer has little trouble in decoding. The book was based on solid mathematics of orbital mechanics and was valid only without the element of friction. Thus the medium of a connecting atmosphere between the earth and the moon was eliminated.

About the time of "Somnium," Bishop Francis Godwin, of England, published a tale called "The Man in the Moon." The hero, Domingo Gonzales, sounds a little like Kepler himself. Godwin's solar system is a throwback to Hipparchus, but, like Kepler, speaks of gravity as magnetic in character. The hero trains geese to carry a framework on which he sits. They take him by surprise to the moon, which has the paradisaic landscape and population of Lukian.

The Question Phase

Another book, appearing at nearly the same time and by another Bishop (John Wilkins), was a straightforward analysis of a flight to the moon. Two years later Wilkins appended the prediction of a chariot carrying several men by some yet undiscovered power to any height, even to the moon. In 1638, this took some courage.

About the middle of the seventeenth century, Cyrano de Bergerac (the swordsman) wrote two novels about flights to a somewhat Lukianesque moon. Several methods were used by different heroes —bottles of dew (which vanished sunward in the morning), an iron vehicle drawn by a series of lodestones thrown ahead (a blunder akin to that made later by Eyraud), and finally a box with an array of rockets attached to it. Cyrano had innocently stumbled on the secret: reaction.

Bernard de Fontenelle published "Discourses on the Plurality of Worlds" in 1686, and it became a best seller. It was fanciful indeed, but important for the idea that each planet was inhabited, with the people differing as the conditions prevailing on the planets differed. De Fontenelle doubted the moon to be inhabited, basing his doubt on recent findings by Johannes Hevelius which indicated a world weirdly marked and apparently without air and water.

In 1738 the Montgolfier brothers flew hot-air balloons. Some rudimentary but real flight by man had finally taken place.

In the middle of the eighteenth century, the beings of other worlds were still spiritual (abstract in nature) as typified by "Micromegas," of Voltaire, and the "Arcana coelestina," of Emmanuel Swedenborg. In "Philosophe sans pretention," Louis Guilliaume de la Follie depicted real people (on Mercury) making an actual flight in a space vessel to earth, propelled by some vague force akin to static electricity. By a quirk of fate, this notion of electric propulsion happens to be one of the most advanced propositions of astronautics, judged even by today's sophisticated standards.

In 1835, Richard Locke, of *The New York Sun,* concocted an entertaining hoax that purported to be the report of Sir John Herschel completing a catalogue survey of the heavens begun by his father, the great Sir William. Any informed person of the day knew that Sir John was then on an expedition in South Africa, but the hoax was nonetheless a fabulous success. Describing a fictitious 288-in. reflector used in conjunction with some sort of image intensifier,[3] Locke told of trees resembling the yew (a commonplace for a large tree, since everything on the low-gravity moon, according to the tradition, was supposed to be bigger). The moon was populated with bat people.

Readers were in a mood to expect new instruments and new astronomical discoveries. Planets, solar systems, and galaxies were coming into the public consciousness. Laplace had recently published the fifth volume in a work of dazzling genius, "Mechanique celeste," in which he expanded on Sir Isaac Newton's "Principia mathematica." Meanwhile, unfortunately, although the universe had grown in estimated size, the celestial bodies had increased vastly in number. There was an inkling that this somehow im-

---

[3] As it happens, an electronic device of this type, resembling a television image orthicon, has been developed by Morgan and Sturm of Johns Hopkins University. Introduced for X-ray work, it has already achieved some success with astronomical telescopes.

proved the probability of populated planets, but the only flying machines in the middle of the nineteenth century were balloons, and these could rise only a few miles. Science fiction on space travel waned. Apparently nothing could be done against the vast, implacable cosmos.

But if nothing could achieve flight, perhaps, at least, the planets might exchange messages. This assumed that one of the other planets was populated, since there had to be an intelligent recipient on the other end to provide a reply. Such beings were not known, but the attempt might reveal if they existed—subject to several provisos:

1. The means of signaling must reach the other body readably.
2. The message must be identifiable as a message.
3. The content of the message must be understandable.
4. The nature of the message must be susceptible of reply.

It was an interesting problem. If the signaling was to reach the other body readably, the signals must be very powerful, the other body very close, or both. The telegraph (the first fundamental improvement in the history of communications since the invention of writing) had been invented, in 1837, but was of little help because it required a wire. If the wire could be established, space travel would already have been achieved. What remained was a variety of visual equipment such as semaphores and lights. The semaphore, here, would be a mark on the land. Lights could be made with fires. Light had its limitations, for its intensity was known to decrease rapidly with distance. The biggest fires man could build would be visible only to the nearest planets, but this seemed good enough.

The possible recipients of the message, of course, would have to know that they were being signaled, which further meant that they would have to be looking at the earth at that time. Here, permanent "earth writing" might be better than expensive fires. A million dollars worth of oil might be expended on a night when "the other people" did not happen to be looking at us. Repeated examinations of an earth marking by telescope would establish it as definitely existing, and then would provide time to figure it out after having identified it as a message. On the other hand, a marking, while suggesting intelligence, might not suggest a signal. This is one advantage of the fires, since a titanic fire in some regular pattern would be no coincidence.

The beings, if they existed, would not only have a different language, but very possibly a different basis of thought. At the very least, they would likely have a different mechanics of language. An examination of such languages as Chinese [4] and Nootka [5] will show that practical communications will not be an easy matter. If these extraterrestrial beings are to understand, the message must obviously be a masterpiece of clarity, but what can we possibly have in common with them? It is our elementary reaction to observed facts, which can be expressed in terms of mathematics (and it is interesting that mathematicians are chief among those who are interested in interplanetary communications).

The message, having been received, must be responded to in a way that the sender can identify as an answer. It must fulfill all the previous requirements of communications, and, in addition, be related to the original message so that the sender knows that his message has been received, that it has been understood, and that what he perceives is a reply. Due to the nature of the messages and the means at hand, the message content must be simple, yet not so simple that a reply would be ambiguous.

The great mathematician, Karl Gauss, suggested a Pythagorean triangle laid out in the wilds of Siberia—the dark line to consist of a pine forest 10 miles wide, and the center of the triangle to be planted with wheat for contrast. His proposal had the advantage of permanence, relatively, considering the rate of growth in the wheat crop. Any beings intelligent enough to build telescopes would recognize the relationship. If they observed it over a season, they would note a change in contrast and know that it was a device created from vegetation.

A regular pattern like this would make them ponder, but would they recognize it as a message? It might be regarded as a cabalistic

---

[4] Rudolph Flesch, "The Art of Plain Talk," chap. 2, Harper & Brothers, New York, 1946, provides an inkling of Chinese thinking processes, without a hard study of Oriental grammar.

[5] G. R. Shipman, How to Talk to a Martian, *Astounding Science Fiction,* pp. 112–120, October, 1953. A discussion of Nootka Indian language of Vancouver Island based on writings of Benjamin Lee Whorf. The author shows that even mental telepathy, if possible, would be a treacherous aid.

device of a culture equivalent to, say, the early Egyptians. Perhaps not, for a low civilization might not be expected to do things on so large a scale; and by what coincidence did it happen to be of such size and location that it was conveniently observed from outside?

The reply to the message would be a problem. Although it might logically consist of domestic notation for the geometric theorem sent as the message, the notation might not be identifiable as such. Contrasting marks on a surface may not be the only means of writing. The beings might respond merely with the same design. This would take time to prepare, but they would be in no hurry since, if the earth really were signaling, the earth beings would also know the magnitude of preparing the signal and wait some time for a reply in kind.

Intrinsically, this message would not mean much, but the implications would be tremendous. It would prove to each planet that the other was inhabited, intelligent, and eager for communication. The galvanic effect this would have on each civilization and the progress of space travel would be dramatic indeed.

One Littrow, of Vienna, is said to have proposed water-filled, circular, square, and triangular designs drawn with "narrow" trenches on the Sahara measuring some 20 miles in diameter, or on one side, supplied with kerosene, and each design, on succeeding nights, burned for 6 hours. This suffered from certain logistical difficulties. Elementary calculations would show water areas running to a good many square miles, and hence a fantastic amount of kerosene or oil, even for these days. It would involve more capital outlay than private means could have mustered, and governments of the mid-nineteenth century could not likely have been interested in the project. Today, luckily perhaps, we have radio or radar agencies which may be put to use, and Prof. L. Hogben of England[6] has devised a type of mathematical "Morse code" which may be employed, provided other planetary beings have suitable equipment to receive it.

The matter of looking for markings and lights, however, runs into difficulty. In 1822, Franz Gruithuisen, of Munich, announced

---

[6] L. Hogben, Astraglossa, or First Steps in Celestial Syntax, *J. Brit. Interplanet. Soc.,* vol. 11, no. 6, pp. 258–274, November, 1952.

he had seen a walled city on the moon, based on an odd formation he thought he saw north and somewhat east of the crater Ptolemy. It looked artificial to him, as did the Straight Wall, near the crater Thebit, to others, and the lack of comparable formations on earth stirred speculation that they were intelligently built. Many arguments, both old and new, sprang up on each side of the question. Gruithuisen also propounded a reason for some mysterious lighting effects on Venus: pyrotechnic or other fiery displays on the grand scale. It could simply have been, as Willy Ley suggests, an aurora.

A Frenchman, Charles Cros, suggested a large burning mirror to write fused-glass messages on the sands of Mars, and tried his whole life to interest the French government in the project. A German astronomer, Plassman, once speculated that Martians equipped with telescopes equal to the 100-in. Hooker model could not be quite sure that they saw light where the Earth's greatest cities stood. With a "200-incher" they would be sure.

Prompted by Gruithuisen's speculation about Venus came a novel by Archile Eyraud, "Voyage à Venus," 1865, containing the first detailed explanation of a spaceship. Eyraud correctly proposed a reaction engine but made the error of collecting the water ejected as reaction mass. This same error was made as late as 1927 by Abdon Ulinski. As Willy Ley points out, the novel was important in that it expressed the feeling that one branch of science (engineering) could bridge the chasm created by another (astronomy). Ley notes in Jules Verne both romanticism and the new feeling of scientists that theirs was a powerful and productive calling.

Jules Verne's genius lies fully as much in his thoroughness and accuracy of research as in the drama of the tales he tells. His "De la terre à la lune," which appeared the same year as Eyraud's book, is chiefly a technical description of preparations to fire a projectile at the moon from a large cannon. We know today of a host of reasons why it would not have worked, but this is no derogation of Verne. He did what no one before him had done: made a highly systematic analysis of a problem in space flight. It is not likely that this story, or any of his others, was intended as a serious proposal. He was expressing a mood of scientific people and reflecting a philosophy of the time.

The errors Verne made and the fact that his stories are science fiction may cause many people to belittle his genius. But this arises from taking note of specific errors rather than considering the over-all intent of the work (a common failing, even among highly trained minds) and from a misunderstanding of science fiction itself. Even the most sophisticated science-fiction writer of today does not mean to imply that the technical basis of his story is a proposed hypothesis. Like Verne, he makes his hypothesis as accurate as he can, and then proceeds to examine the consequences of the scientific problem at hand and, in the process, make the examination interesting by weaving a story around it. Good science fiction, taken in the right spirit, is one of the most important sources of scientific thought.[7]

"De la terre à la lune" is well worth the reading in this light. Verne examines the problem of getting to the orbit of the moon— the velocity required and the means to attain the velocity. Velocity required power, and Verne chose the cannon as a power agency which could theoretically be scaled up to produce the necessary velocity in a projectile big enough to carry passengers. Verne described the design and construction of the cannon and projectile in considerable detail. The drama of the proposition is inescapable, for it represents a great mind attacking a great problem, systematically and confidently. The hero of the nineteenth century seems clearly to have been the scientist.

A number of stories of this time dealt with meteors as objects containing messages.[8] The meteoritic aspect stemmed from the fact that, some years before, a scientist had finally convinced the

[7] William O. Davis, formerly USAF Deputy Commander for Operations, Air Force Office of Scientific Research, "Fundamental Basis for Space Flight," a paper given at the Annual Meeting of the American Astronautical Society, New York, Dec. 1, 1955. The fundamental basis, he shows, is creative imagination. See also *J. Astronautics,* vol. 3, no. 1, p. 9, 1956; an interview, *Missiles and Rockets,* p. 103, June, 1957; and "A New Approach to Space Flight," *Missiles and Rockets,* p. 64, December, 1956.

[8] The idea of finding coded messages is no doubt linked with an older scientific notion that the greatest wisdom is locked in the past and can somehow be learned by decipherment, as in the Rosetta Stone researches of Champollion. Science-fiction stories as late as 1924 use this theme. See, for example, R. M. Farley, "The Radio Man," reprinted as "An Earthman on Venus," Avon Books, New York, 1950. The basis of decipherment is often naively at variance with basic semantics.

world that meteorites actually had their origin in space. An anonymous novel, "Voyage à la lune," introduced another idea which now enjoys a perennial vogue: negative gravity. In the 1880s, Venus and the moon had been given up by science fictioneers, and this trip (to Mars) uses the first version of negative gravity, "apergy."

The century had produced some basic ideas. Wöhler, in 1828, showed that organic and inorganic matter consist of the same basic elements. Kirchhoff developed the spectroscope and, in 1859, showed that not only stars but also other planets consist of the same elements as those on earth. Darwin not only showed that all life is interrelated but also implied that, under the right conditions, life of some sort must of necessity appear. Allowing for variation in the basis of life and a few obvious extremes of temperature, pressure, and the like, any planet in the universe is technically able to sustain it.

In 1877, Schiaparelli reported *canali* (grooves) observed on the surface of Mars. What he actually saw is still the subject of spirited debate, but the popular mind, eager to believe in people of other planets, construed these *canali*, literally, as canals, and Mars became the favorite planetary neighbor. It still is; the Martian is still synonymous with an other-worldly being. Many people looked frantically for signals from Mars, and a few thought they saw some. Near the turn of the century, a Prix Guzman had been established in Paris, offering what would now amount to $20,000 to the first person proving successful two-way communication with another planet. The belief about Mars and possible Martians was then so optimistic that the planet was ruled out on the ground of being too easy. It need hardly be said that the prize was never claimed.

In 1897, a German named Kurd Lasswitz published a novel "Auf zwei Planeten," which introduced another aspect of space flight: the space station. In the novel, the Martians establish a space station one earth radius above the North Pole. Earth explorers (traveling in a free balloon) are caught up in a maelstrom —but this time with a new twist. The maelstrom is an antigravity ray supporting the station, emanating from a building on the pole, and based on the same general principle as the propulsion of the Martian's spaceship. This ship is constructed of a special substance that causes the entire vessel to become weightless when the outer surface is unbroken, because gravity will then flow around rather than through it. Thus the ship can float from planet to planet. Stopping, starting, and steering are accomplished by "repulsors" producing a regulated explosion.

The term "repulsor" later became a favorite among the experimenters of the German Rocket Society as a general term meaning "rocket engine." Lasswitz had made a fundamental improvement on Verne in replacing the shattering jolt of the cannon with the somewhat gentler push of the rocket engine, and had delineated the problem of transfer between orbits as one of timed free fall (Chap. 7).

There are two interesting things about this novel: the use of antigravity and the position of the space station. The two actually depend on each other. Antigravity, an astonishingly sophisticated prediction,[9] was needed to support the station because, although it was what can be regarded superficially as a space station, it was not a satellite vehicle. It was not in motion, as a satellite vehicle must be to stay aloft. Although a satellite can be stationary with respect to a point on the earth's surface, to do so it must be at an altitude of 22,300 miles and in the plane of the earth's equator, the orbit, of course, being from west to east.

Lasswitz's Martians were using the station for observation of the earth; and this, as a prediction of utility, was a masterpiece, since it may well develop that observation will be the justification of artificial satellites. A number of important theoretical contributions to the proposition of the satellite vehicle were made, after Lasswitz, by Oberth, Hermann Noordung, Guido von Pirquet, Hohmann, Smith and Ross, Clarke, and von Braun. These will be treated in detail in Chap. 4, since they would require too large a digression here.

H. G. Wells, who in many ways was far more modern than his predecessors, had a number of odd throwbacks in his work. One was the use of cannons for ship launching by octopoid Martians

[9] The Martin Company of Baltimore, prime contractor on the project Vanguard, satellite vehicle, has established a subsidiary, RIAS, Inc., which will have among its chief missions the investigation of gravity, with an eye to its eventual control.

who had come to wage annihilating war on the Earth ("War of the Worlds"), thus introducing a whole new type of science fiction using either the invasion idiom or the bug-eyed monster. Up to this time, alterplanetarians were regarded as somewhat human and not especially hostile to our world. In another story, "The First Men in the Moon," the moon beings were literally insects, akin to termites, who captured the explorers. The explorers, it turns out, used "cavorite," a substance like that used by Lasswitz's Martians. The scientific novels of this type were overtaken, in a sense, by the achievements of actual science, and science fiction since has prospered only moderately, and in the form of the short story. But what it lost in majesty, such as it had in the latter nineteenth century, it gained in range and subtlety.

This range and subtlety, unfortunately, made it more elusive; and a welter of shoddy pseudoscience stories featuring violence, technical jargon, and finally sex has since made its appearance. This has so confused the situation that it does not enhance one's reputation today to admit a fondness for science fiction. The field now has become jaded on the question of propulsion and tends to deal with novel technical trends such as cybernetics, with psychological subtleties, and with sociophilosophical questions. Geographically it is now cosmic in its sweep.

Meanwhile, a parallel history, that of rocketry (noted at some length in the next chapter) contained a chain of events that led to a joining of forces with astronautical thinking about the turn of the century. Simple reaction devices were known to antiquity and eventually gave rise to a series of steam-reaction vehicles (in proposal at least), such as those of Gravesande (1721), Perkins (1824), Golightly (1841), Phillips (1860), and an anonymous inventor [10] (1867). These vehicles have led to serious and promising experimentation with steam rockets for JATO (jet-assisted take-off) applications at the Research Institute for Jet Propulsion Physics, at Stuttgart Airport, Germany. The history of rocketry

[10] Willy Ley, "Rockets, Missiles and Space Travel," pp. 86–91, The Viking Press, Inc., New York, 1957. This book, particularly the first seven chapters, is a fine work of historical research. It is very hard to find an historical item not already uncovered by the author's labors. In this aspect of the subject, his book is unsurpassed. See also the works of Marjorie Nicolson, in the bibliography.

itself stems from its introduction by the Chinese and records the rocket developing spasmodically as it went in and out of favor, variously as a weapons agency, a pyrotechnic device, or a useful vehicle for carrying messages, lines to foundering ships, or instruments to inaccessible places.

So it appears that three tributaries make up the stream of astronautical development: man's speculations on planetary space and how to conquer it, the development of the notion of reactive force, and the physical evolution of the rocket through experiment and development. The latter two elements merged first, about the time that Sir Isaac Newton explained the nature of reaction.[11] Until the notion of reaction crystallized, it could not be understood that the operation of a rocket is independent of environment, and, in fact, is best in what amounts to *no environment,* the near-total vacuum of outer space.

At first the application of the reaction-rocket idea was limited to attempts at terrestrial flight. Even in fiction—going back to de la Follie in 1775, when space travel was taken for the first time out of the spiritual realm—rockets had not been seriously connected with space propulsion. The ship of Eyraud was not detectably a rocket, although it was reactive (and self-immobilizing). Jules Verne used a cannon, also oddly favored by late-comer H. G. Wells. Then followed negative gravity ("Across the Zodiac," 1880). Finally, in Lasswitz, in 1895, reaction engines were coupled with antigravity for propulsion, and it was in this era that the merger of rockets and space travel also took place in the minds of scientists and scholars who were studying the proposition as an engineering undertaking.

Until that time rockets had been used for a variety of projects, including attempts at terrestrial flight dating from the legend of Wan Hoo, in A.D. 1500. (Chap. 2), to Jir, Tretesskij, Lepsius, von Siemens, Battey, and Kibaltchitch.[12] Herman Ganswindt invented

[11] Curiously, it was not until 1915 that this was proven experimentally, by Dr. Robert H. Goddard, who did so by showing that rockets can move in a vacuum.

[12] Miollan and Janninet of Paris, in 1783, tried unsuccessfully to use the reaction principle to propel a hot-air balloon horizontally by opening a vent in the side. The idea was good, but they had the bad luck to choose a day so hot that the balloon could not even be inflated.

a spaceship propelled by a series of solid explosive pellets injected into a firing chamber at high frequency. This seems to have occurred about 1890, when Lasswitz published his novel. The idea may simply have been in the air at the time.

The Thinking Phase

Konstantin Ziolkowski, of Kaluga, Russia, was self-educated, and, like Ganswindt, was early interested in lighter-than-air craft. He had pondered space flight as a youth, possibly as early as 1871, and in 1895, he published an article hinting at its possibility. The article was apparently well received, since its author then plunged into deep study of the matter. He wrote a study on the requirements of a vessel capable of traveling in space, and, in 1898, he published a finding that was of transcending importance: that liquid propellants are more efficient than solid propellants.

Little attention was paid at the time, since Ziolkowski had just been eclipsed in the matter of dirigibles by Count von Zeppelin, in Germany. More works on the subject appeared up to the eve of World War I, when Ziolkowski's work stopped for the duration. After the Russian Revolution, the Soviet government sponsored his work in a very mild way. How mildly may be noted from the fact that Ziolkowski's work was virtually unknown outside Russia until Hermann Oberth, in Germany, published his first book on space flight, in 1923. The Soviet press then put up the familiar cry "we did it first," and for once they were right.

Meanwhile, in 1919, Robert H. Goddard, then a professor at Clark University, Worcester, Massachusetts, stumbled into the astronautical limelight in a cautious study on rockets entitled "A Method of Reaching Extreme Altitudes," published by the Smithsonian Institution. It dealt chiefly with principles, ways, and means of high-altitude research above the range of balloons. As inevitably happens, it was an illustrative example and not the basic proposition that was reported in the newspapers. Goddard mentioned the possibility of a rocket flying to the moon and announcing its arrival with a flash of exploding powder.[13] The paper itself attracted little

---

[13] In the 1919 Smithsonian report he wrote, under the section Calculation of Minimum Mass Required to Raise One Pound to an 'Infinite' Altitude, that the only reliable procedure would be to send the smallest mass of flash powder

attention. Goddard was just as happy, at least about the moon rocket, and proceeded to make a monumental name for himself in practical rocket development.

In 1923, as mentioned, Prof. Hermann Oberth, a German living in Rumania, published "Die Rakete zu den Planetenräumen" ("The Rocket into Interplanetary Space"). It was, generally speaking, cautious, formidable, and scholarly, but to the surprise of its author, it was a sort of small-scale best seller. As Willy Ley points out, it failed in one sense: it appealed to the "astronautical profession," in effect, for criticism and possibly for approval, but, unfortunately, there was as yet no such profession to render opinions. Its three parts dealt with general principles of rocket operation and flight, high-altitude research proposals, and space flight, including some theory on space stations. What little critique appeared was negative and contained false objections by scientists who should have known better. Unnecessary objections were posed: "a rocket could never exceed the speed of its own exhaust," it was claimed,[14] and "could not work in the vacuum of space."[15] There were many others, but they are properly dealt with in a formal text. At any rate, Oberth rightly chose liquid fuels for their higher exhaust velocity, as Ziolkowski had done 20 years before. Oberth actually performed some rocket-engine experiments in Berlin about 1930, with the German Rocket Society, aided by a number of members who have since become famous, such as Dr. Wernher von Braun and Willy Ley. The society generated a popular interest, probably from the original intellectual impetus of Oberth himself. In this

---

possible to the dark surface of the moon when in conjunction (i.e., the 'new' moon) in such a way that it would be ignited on impact. The light would then be visible with a powerful telescope. He cautiously ended the discussion with the following: "This plan of sending a mass of flash powder to the surface of the Moon, although a matter of much general interest, is not of obvious scientific importance. There are, however, *developments of the general method under discussion, which involve a number of important features not herein mentioned,* which could lead to results of much scientific interest. These developments involve many experimental difficulties, to be sure; but they depend upon nothing that is really impossible." It is interesting to note that S. F. Singer, well-known physicist, proposed (at the Eighth Congress of the International Astronautical Federation, at Barcelona, Spain, October, 1957) that ICBMs be used to land a thermonuclear charge on the moon.

[14] See Chap. 3, Rocket Vehicle Calculations.
[15] See footnote 11.

sense, Oberth may be regarded as the true father of practical astronautics.

In 1925, there appeared a book by Dr. Walter Hohmann, a classic and archetype of that breed of technical paper which seeks to protect the author from unfavorable opinions by a massive rampart of differential equations. This was "Die Erreichbarkeit der Himmelskörper" ("The Attainability of Celestial Bodies"). Its five-part analysis of the mechanics of space flight was a landmark in astronautical scholarship but did not register on the public mind at all—except for, as the reader might expect, a misinterpretation of an illustration of a "powder tower" intended to illustrate fuel consumption per minute. Because Hohmann failed to annotate the picture, the myth of a Hohmann spaceship, shaped like a chess pawn, is still repeated by publications which do not take the trouble to research their pictures properly.[16] This editorial sin is today a very damning one, because of the popularity of pictorial treatment.

Max Valier, a member of Oberth's society, popularized Oberth's work in a book entitled "Der Vorstoss in den Weltenraum" ("The Plunge into Interplanetary Space"). Valier later performed many spectacular experiments in attempts to rocket-propel automobiles, gliders, and rail cars. Many students of the subject feel that the experiments added nothing to rocketry and only embarrassed Valier's colleagues. Another work, published by Willy Ley in 1926, "Die Fahrt ins Weltall," also popularized astronautics, probably more clearly than Valier and without a mass of mathematics.

In 1927, a famous French scientist, Robert Esnault-Pelterie, lectured on space flight (paper published in 1928) and from then on devoted much of his time both to this problem and to practical rocket experimentation. Professor Nikolai Rynin, in Moscow, began publication of a massive nine-volume work, "Interplanetary Travel," published in Russian as "Mezhplanetnia Sobstchyenia," the second word translating literally as "communication." The Russians apparently include the notion of transportation in this word.

The Verein für Raumschiffahrt (German Rocket Society, literally Club for Spaceship Travel, abbreviated as VfR) was founded in 1927, with Johannes Winkler as its first president. Oberth and

---

[16] There is at least one such in "L'Astronautique," *Science et vie,* hors de serie, Paris, 1952.

Hohmann soon joined, and they were followed by Dr. Franz von Hoefft, Prof. Guido von Pirquet of Austria, Rynin, Esnault-Pelterie, and others—the blue book of astronautical scientists. Meanwhile a frenzy of Valier-type experiments spread over the world like an epidemic.

Meanwhile, too, Esnault-Pelterie collaborated with a Parisian banker, André Hirsch, on an annual award entitled the REP-Hirsch Prize for the best work on astronautics. Oberth won the first one. The prize was awarded intermittently from 1929 to 1936.[17]

Oberth was technical adviser on a Fritz Lang film "Frau im Mond" ("Girl in the Moon"), in which a spaceship resembling his theoretical Model "B" was used. A small flying model bearing no resemblance to the movie version was prepared for publicity purposes in connection with the premiere, but, due to misunderstandings, it was not completed. Equipment left over from work on the motion-picture rocket was obtained and became the basis of practical experimentation at Raketenflugplatz, the German Rocket Society's small proving ground in the Berlin suburbs. The society had long recognized the rocket as the agency for space flight and now began an experimental program to see how such rockets, beginning with the smallest one, could be built. A number of flights were made before the Nazi government took over both records and men, in 1933. The development of German war rockets and the saga of Peenemünde are now well known.

Meanwhile, in 1930, the American Interplanetary Society was formed, under David Lasser, in New York. It attracted some competent scientists, as had the German society founded a few years before, and also began a series of rocket-engine experiments. One of the dynamic forces in the American society was G. Edward Pendray, a practical rocket experimenter and a highly gifted public relations man. Experiments continued until World War II, when they stopped.

The society, however, continued, forming sections in various parts of the United States. The present strength is something like

[17] 1929, Hermann Oberth, German; 1930, Pierre Montagne, French; 1933, Pierre Montagne, French; 1934, Louis Damblanc, French; 1936, Alfred Africano, American.

6,000 members, with more than 30 sections throughout the country. Heavy corporate membership had, for some time, made the society more conservative. Its name was changed to the American Rocket Society, and that of its publication *Astronautics* first to the *Journal of the American Rocket Society* and then to *Jet Propulsion*. In July, 1957, the society resurrected the old title *Astronautics,* publishing it as a companion magazine to *Jet Propulsion*. Spaceflight enthusiasts are happy to see the recent reemphasis of astronautics in the society, after a long post-war period of almost militant deemphasis.

In the last few years, the astronautical movement has blossomed anew with the popular premonition about satellite vehicles. One of the newly formed societies is the small, struggling American Astronautical Society, which publishes the *Journal of Astronautics*. Elsewhere a number of small, largely local societies have banded together in a league known as the American Astronautical Federation. Operations of all these are decidedly provincial in character, and it seems unlikely that any will long survive.

More significant is the international distribution of rocket and space-flight societies, which have mushroomed in more than twenty countries and have gradually formed an august body called the International Astronautical Federation (IAF), whose secretariat resides permanently in Switzerland. Congresses have been held every year since 1950, in Paris, London, Stuttgart, Zurich, Innsbruck, Copenhagen, Rome, and Barcelona. The cream of the world's astronautical scientists and other distinguished scholars are represented in the general membership of the federation. Other leading supporters of the IAF are the British Interplanetary Society (publishers of both the *Journal* and the less technical *Spaceflight*) and the German Deutsche Gesellschaft für Raketentechnik und Raumfahrt (formerly Gesellschaft für Weltraumforschung), publishers of *Raketentechnik und Raumfahrtforschung*.[18]

Aviation had been establishing speed and altitude records over the years but mainly as an outgrowth of efforts to improve the performance of terrestrial-flight vehicles. In 1947, the Bell X-1, powered by a rocket engine, surpassed the speed of sound; in

[18] This publication followed *Weltraumfahrt,* which is now available through a commercial publisher in Stuttgart.

1954, an improved sister ship, the X-1A, reached an altitude of more than 90,000 ft. Most recently the X-2 has achieved 2,200 mph in one flight and in another, 126,000 ft. This X-2 subsequently crashed, leaving rocket-airplane testing to the Bell X-1E in the 1957–1958 time period. The next crop of X rocket-research planes will be, like the X-15, designed for the Mach 6, 100-mile-altitude regimes.

The unmanned rocket, a specialist at vertical flight, has increased its capabilities from a possible 0.85 mile, in the time of Congreve, to 132 miles for a V-2, 158 miles for a Viking, 193 miles for an Aerobee-Hi, 244 miles for a two-stage vehicle called Bumper, 650 miles for a Jupiter test vehicle, and 3,000 to 4,000 miles for Farside rockets. The Bumper vehicle consisted of a WAC-Corporal, air-launched from the nose of a V-2 at about 20 miles altitude on February 24, 1949. It is not the latest high-altitude flight, but it was long the highest. Even more spectacular was an Army Jupiter-C test vehicle which, in September, 1956, flew more than 3,000 miles over the Atlantic. It, too, was multi-stage, having a Redstone first stage, a cluster of scaled-down Sergeants, called Recruits, as the second stage, and a single Recruit as the third stage. Since then other Jupiter test rockets, NACA hypersonic test vehicles, three-stage X-17s, and four-stage Farsides have been probing high-speed, high-altitude regimes. The importance of these flights lies in the principle of multistaging. The details of staging are covered in Chap. 8, but the point to remember is that multistaging reduces the size of rocket vehicles one whole order of magnitude.

A three-stage vehicle, proposed by Dr. Wernher von Braun, to reach a 1,075-mile orbit about the earth would stand, at take-off, about 265 ft high (visualize a B-29 on top of a B-52 vertically) and weigh 7,000 tons. This is in the weight class of a light cruiser. But to accomplish this orbit with a single-stage rocket would require a vehicle approximately the size of the dirigible Hindenburg and weighing perhaps many times more than the von Braun rocket. The cost of the von Braun rocket might reach a billion dollars, but the single-stage rocket might cost the equivalent of the national debt, if it could be built at all without collapsing under the weight of the almost inconceivably large load of propellants it would have to carry.

Since the publication of the great von Braun proposal, space-flight protagonists, including von Braun himself, have looked for more economical, minimum schemes of getting into space. Vanguard and the Farside balloon-launched rockets represent this trend, though admittedly they have not the capability of carrying man. The question of propulsion systems, dealt with in detail in Chap. 3, has evolved from chemical propellants, in theory at least, to include atomic energy, ionized particles, photons, electrons, light beams, and "negative gravity." Man's view of the universe had widened, and some scientists, notably Dr. Leslie R. Shepherd, of England; Dr. Eugen Sänger, of Germany; and Dr. S. Fred Singer, of the United States, are now cautiously probing the factors of interstellar and intergalactic flight.

TABLE 1-1   *Chronology*

Year	*Event*
540 B.C.	Pythagoras conceives of a counterearth that duplicates the earth in every respect and moves with it.
384 B.C.	Aristotle rejects plurality of planets; serious handicap to later thinking.
360 B.C.	Heraclides, of Pontus, conceives of a semigeocentric universe: Mercury and Mars orbit about Sun, all orbit about Earth.
280 B.C.	Aristarchus of Samos, conceives of a heliocentric universe. Although correct, he was eclipsed by Hipparchus and long forgotten.
240 B.C.	Eratosthenes, of Alexandria, measures earth's circumference as 24,000 miles—staggering precision for those days.
125 B.C.	Hipparchus, of Cos, proposes epicyclic orbits of planets (Hipparchus was real father of the Ptolemaic system).
120	Plutarch regards moon as a solid junior earth, cautiously populates it with demons.
160	Lukian's "Vera historia" and "Icaromenippus," stories of trips to the moon and heaven banned by church about 1145. The hero finds moon inhabitants warlike but antiseptically clean.

1543   Copernicus puts sun in center of solar system and the planets in epicyclic orbits about it.

1633   Galileo discovers that planets are more than mere points of light; church makes him recant.

1634   Kepler's "Somnium," in which lunarians—demons like the trolls of medieval mythology—traverse shadow between moon and earth and take humans with them.

1638   Wilkins' "The Discovery of a World in the Moone." Story of a trip to the moon by chariot, demonstrates faith in science.

         Bishop Godwin's "The Man in the Moone: Or a Discourse of a Voyage Thither." Story of a trip to the moon in a vehicle propelled by geese, based on the epicyclic solar system of Hipparchus.

1649   Cyrano de Bergerac's "Trip to the Moon," with propulsion by bottles of dew, lodestones, and rockets.

1686   De Fontenelle's "Entretiens sur la pluralité des mondes."

1687   Newton's "Principia mathematica," which explains the laws of reaction.

1752   Voltaire's "Micromegas," travels of Sirius man and Saturnian spiritual beings.

1756   Swedenborg completes "Arcana coelestia," which depicts all worlds as populated by spirits.

1769   Watt invents steam engine.

1775   De la Follie's "Philosophe sans pretention," the first depiction of real people making a flight by space vessel from one planet to another. The spaceship was propelled by static electricity.

1783   Balloon flights by the Montgolfiers.

1796   Laplace's "Exposition du système du monde," expansion of Newton's "Principia mathematica" and nebular hypothesis.

1822   Gruithuisen reports walled city on moon and people on Venus.

1828   Wöhler, by first organic synthesis, demonstrates that organic and inorganic substances are related.

1835   Copernicus removed from Catholic Index.

         Chladni proves that meteorites originate in space.

TABLE 1-1 *Chronology (Continued)*

Year	Event
	Locke's moon hoax, purporting to be report of an eminent explorer (then in Africa) of trip to the moon, populated by bat people.
1837	Morse invents telegraph.
ca. 1840	Karl Gauss, a great mathematician, and not a "crackpot," proposes Pythagorean triangle as signal to Mars.
1859	Kirchhoff and Bunsen invent the spectroscope, which proves the universality of elements.
	Charles Darwin's "The Origin of Species," which demonstrates the interrelationship of all life.
1865	Jules Verne's "De la terre à la lune," a story of earth-to-moon journey by cannon launch that depicted the new mood of science.
	Alexandre Dumas' "Voyage à la lune."
	Henri de Parville's "Un habitant de la planète Mars."
	"Voyage à la lune," of anonymous French authorship.
	"Journey to the Moon," of anonymous English authorship.
	Camille Flammarion's "Les mondes imaginaires et les mondes réels."
1877	Giovanni Schiaparelli, after telescopic study, reports the "canals" of Mars.
1880	Percy Greg's "Across the Zodiac," the story of a journey to Mars (populated by small humanoids) by negative gravity. The propulsion system was built on basis of hieroglyphics on a meteor.
1895	Kurd Lasswitz's "Auf zwei Planeten," the first appearance in literature of the space station. Voyage is from Mars to earth by push of controlled explosion aided by antigravity.
	Konstantin Ziolkowski writes the first serious paper on space flight.
1897	H. G. Wells' "First Men in the Moon," the journey being made by cavorite (antigravity) to a moon populated by hostile termites.
	Wells' "War of the Worlds," which starts the cycle of invasion and monsters from other worlds as a fictional motif. In this novel, octopoid Martians get to earth by cannon launch.

1900   Madam Guzman prize offered for interplanetary communi-
        cation; Mars ruled out as "too easy."

1919   Goddard's "A Method of Reaching Extreme Altitudes,"
        published by the Smithsonian Institution. Misinterpreted by
        newspapers as a proposal of flight to moon.

1923   Hermann Oberth's "Rakete zu den Planetenräumen," a cau-
        tious work heavy with mathematics.

1925   Walter Hohmann's "Die Erreichbarkeit der Himmelskörper,"
        a landmark in astronautical scholarship.

1926   Willy Ley's "Die Fahrt ins Weltall," a popularization, with-
        out a mass of mathematics, of astronautics.

1927   Nikolai Rynin begins his huge encyclopedia "Interplanetary
        Travel."

        Winkler's "Verein für Raumschiffahrt." (Winkler is regarded
        as the father of modern rocket societies.)

1928   Esnault-Pelterie and Andre Hirsch establish the Hirsch prize
        for best work on astronautics during the year.

        Esnault-Pelterie, "L'exploration par fusées de la très haute
        atmosphère et la possibilité des voyages interplanétaires."

1929   Fritz Lang produces "Frau im Mond," the first movie based
        on space flight.

1930   David Lasser founds American Interplanetary Society (now
        the American Rocket Society).

1937   Germans begin a large rocket program.

1942   First V-2 fired.

1944   V-2s bombard Europe.

1947   X-1 flies faster than sound.

1949   Air Force Department of Space Medicine founded; Bumper
        reaches 244 miles.

1950   First International Astronautical Congress, Paris, France.

1951   First Physics and Medicine of Upper Atmosphere Sym-
        posium; International Astronautical Federation founded.

1952   Space Biology Branch, Aeromedical Field Laboratory, estab-
        lished at Holloman.

1953   X-1A reaches 1,650 mph, 90,000 ft altitude.

1954   Viking flies to 158 miles at 4,300 mph.

1955   United States announces Vanguard satellite program.

TABLE 1-1 *Chronology* (*Continued*)

Year	Event
1956	X-2 reaches 2,200 mph, 126,000 ft altitude.
	Aerobee-Hi AGUL-o113C reaches 164 miles.
	Jupiter-C goes over 3,000 miles, 650 miles high, 15,000 mph.
	NACA tests Mach 10, four-stage, 200 miles altitude, hypersonic test vehicles.
	TV-0 (Viking 13), Vanguard test vehicle, is fired.
1957	X-17 flies 600 miles up, reaches 9,000 mph.
	TV-1 (Viking 14), two-stage Vanguard test vehicle, is fired, followed by regular Vanguard.
	Russia announces rocket, satellite plans for International Geophysical Year.
	First IGY rockets fired from Fort Churchill.
	X-IE flight-tested.
	Air Force Office of Scientific Research and Convair-Astronautics sponsor Astronautics Symposium.
	Project Snooper announced; ion-rocket study contract let.
	Navy Aerobee-Hi attains 193 miles, single-stage record.
	First full-scale Jupiter IRBMs fired successfully.
	First Russian ICBM firings.
	First Thor fired successfully.
	Russian artificial satellites launched (Sputniks I and II).
	First successful Farside rocket fired.
1958	First Atlas ICBM successfully tested.
	U.S. Explorer satellites launched successfully.
	Jupiter and Thor placed in production.
	Advanced Research Projects Agency formed.
	TV-4 Vanguard test vehicle launches small satellite.

BIBLIOGRAPHY

Plutarch: "Die facie in orbe lunae," 100. English translation supervised by W. W. Goodwin, Little, Brown & Company, Boston, 1870.
Lukian: "Vera historia," 160. Translated by Alfred J. Church, and with twelve illustrations by C. O. Murray, Scribner & Welford, New York, 1880.

Lukian: "Icaromenippus," 160. English translation in Fowler and Fowler, "Collected Works," Clarendon Press, Oxford, 1905.

Copernicus (Kopernik), Nikolaus: "De revolutionibus orbium coelesticum," 1543. Modern facsimile done by Chiantore, Torino, in 1943. German translation by Fritz Kuback, 2 vol., R. Oldenbourg-Verlag, Munich, 1949. French translation by A. Koyré, "Des revolutions des orbes celestes," Librairie Felix Alcan, Paris, 1934.

Kepler, Johannes: "De motibus stellae martis," 1609. Prague, German edition appeared in 1929 in Munich, with title "Johannes Kepler's Neue Astronomie."

Galilei, Galileo: "Sidereus nuncius," 1610. Published in London, 1653. See "Sidereal Messenger of Galileo Galilei . . ." edited by E. S. Carlos, London, 1880.

Kepler, Johannes: "Joh. Keppleri mathematici olim imperatorii somnium seu opus posthuman de astronomia lunari" (short title, "The Somnium"), Frankfort, 1634. Only translation out of Latin is "Kepler's Traum von Mond," by Ludwig Günther (with scholarly introduction), Leipzig, 1898.

Godwin, Francis: "The Man in the Moone: Or a Discourse of a Voyage Thither by Domingo Gonzales," 1638. Rare photostat of original-manuscript studies by Grant McColley, Smith College Series in Modern Languages, XIX, 1937.

Wilkins, John, Bishop of Chester: "The Discovery of a World in the Moone," 1638. Part I, dated 1638, is entitled "A Discourse Concerning a New World and Another Planet." Part II (the major title) published together with Part I in 1640. Printed for M. Sparke and E. Forrest, London, that date.

More, Henry: "An Essay upon the Infinity of Worlds," Cambridge, 1646.

Hevelius, Johann: "Selenographia: Sive lunae descriptio," published by Gedani, 1647.

de Bergerac, Savinien Cyrano: "Voyage dans la lune," 1649. Published as "Voyage comique dans les états et empires de la lune," V. Lecon, Paris, 1855; translated by Richard Aldington, Routledge & Kegan Paul, Ltd., London, 1923. See also "A Voyage to the Moon" (Bergerac), Doubleday & McClure, New York, 1899.

Borel, Pierre: "Discours nouveau prouvant la pluralité des mondes," Geneva, 1657. Translated to English under title "A New Treatise Proving a Multiplicity of Worlds," London, 1658.

Grimmelshausen, Hans Jakob Christoph von: "Fliegende Wandermann," 1659. May be a part or derivative of his "Der Abenteuerliche Simplicissimus; Und andere Schriften," edited by Max Wehrli, Atlantis, Zurich, 1944.

de Fontenelle, Bernard: "Entretiens sur la pluralité des mondes," 1686.

Published by M. Brunet, Paris, 1694, and by E. Roger, Amsterdam, 1719. An English translation entitled "A Conversation on the Plurality of Worlds," by Addison, published by D. Evans, London, 1769.

Newton, Sir Isaac: "Philosophiae naturalis principia mathematica," 1687. [Short title, "Principia mathematica," not to be confused with the later (and also monumental) work by Alfred North Whitehead.] Any good college physics text carries enough about Newton's physical laws to answer the requirement of elementary astronautics. Further, these laws must be qualified by new aspects of thought introduced by relativity, lest they lead to serious inaccuracies.

Russen, David, of Hythe: "Inter lunare: or Voyage to the Moon," London, 1703.

Defoe, Daniel: "A Journey to the World in the Moon," 1705. Reprinted in Edinburgh by James Watson in "Craig's Closs," 1705.

McDermot, Murtagh (pseudonym): "A Trip to the Moon," Dublin, 1728. Reprinted the same year in London.

Swedenborg, Emmanuel: "Arcana coelestia." Written between 1749 and 1756; modern publication, translated, revised and corrected, is "The Heavenly Arcana," 4 vols., published in New York, 1853, and, in the corrected version, by the Emmanuel Swedenborg Foundation, New York, 1928.

Voltaire, François Marie Arouet de: "Le Micromégas," 1752. See "Micromégas: A Voyage to the Planet Saturn by a Native of Sirius," a translation published by P. Eckler, New York, 1897.

Lunatic, Sir Humphry, Bart., pseudonym of Francis Gentleman of York: "A Trip to the Moon," 1764.

Raumier, Marie-Anne: "Voyage de Milord Céton dans les sept planettes," 1765. Edited by Garnier, vol. 17, in The Hague.

La Follie, Louis-Guillaume de: "Philosophe sans prétention," Clousier, Paris, 1775.

Thomson, William, pseudonym of Thomas Newte: "The Man in the Moon," London, 1783.

Anonymous: "Le Char volant: ou Voyage dans la lune," London and Paris, 1783.

Laplace, Marquis Pierre Simon de: "Mécanique celeste," 1799. English translation, by Nathaniel Bowditch, published by Hillard, Gray, Little and Wilkins, Boston, 1839. Original written between 1799 and 1825.

Chladni, Ernst Florens Friedrich: "Über Feuer Meteore," J. G. Heuber, Vienna, 1819.

Locke, Richard Adams: "The Moon Hoax," 1835, possibly written with the collaboration of the French astronomer, Jean Nicolas Nicollet, in *The New York Sun,* beginning with August 25, 1835.

The complete text is reproduced in *Sky Magazine,* February–April, 1937.

Darwin, Charles: "Origin of Species," 1859. Modern edition by Appleton, New York, 1921.

Verne, Jules: "De la terre à la lune," Paris, 1865. Sequel, "Autour de la lune," published in 1867. See "The Jules Verne Omnibus," Blue Ribbon Books (Lippincott), New York, 1931. Part IV: "From the Earth to the Moon and a Trip Around It," pp. 545–822.

Flammarion, Camille: "Les Mondes imaginaires et les mondes réels," 17th ed., Paris, 1880; originally published in 1865.

Anonymous: "A Journey to the Moon," 1865.

Dumas, Alexandre: "Voyage à la lune," 1865.

Anonymous: "Voyage à la lune," 1865.

Éyraud, Archille, pseudonym of Archille Lafont: "Voyage à Venus," 1865.

Parville, Henri de: "Un Habitant de la planète mars," 1865.

Cros, Charles: "Moyens de communications avec les planètes," Paris, 1869. Possibly published by Gauthier-Villars.

Greg, Percy: "Across the Zodiac," 1880.

Honncher, Erwin: "Fahrten Nach Mond und Sonne," Opeln, Leipzig, 1887.

Faure and Graffigny: "Aventures extraordinaires d'un savant russe sur les planètes," 1889.

Schiaparelli, Giovanni: "Osservazione astronomiche e fisiche sulla topographia e constituzione del pianeta marte fatte nella specola reale in milano coll' equitoriale merz-repsold durante l'opposizione del 1890," 1890. Reale Accad. dei Lincei, Atti, Mem. della classe di Scienze fisiche, etc., Roma, 1912, serie 5, vol. 8, pp. 103–156.

Lasswitz, Karl Theodor Victor Kurd: "Auf zwei Planeten," Leipzig, 1897.

Wells, H. G.: "War of the Worlds," W. Heinemann, London, 1898.

————: "First Men in the Moon," G. Newnes, London, 1901.

Schiaparelli, Giovanni: "Di alcune macchia osservate in Mercurio dal Signor Jarry Desloges in Mattina del 19 Agosto, 1907," G. U. Cassone, Torino, 1909.

Krijanowsky: "The Death of a Planet," 1910. (In Russian.)

Krasnogorsky: "On the Ether Waves," 1913. (In Russian.)

Goddard, Robert Hutchings: "A Method of Reaching Extreme Altitudes," Smithsonian Institution, Washington, D.C., 1919.

Burgel, Bruno: "Der Stern von Afrika," 1920.

Oberth, Hermann: "Die Rakete zu den Planetenraümen," R. Oldenbourg-Verlag, Munich, 1923.

Rynin, Nikolai: "In the Celestial Ocean," 1924. (In Russian.)

Hohmann, Walter: "Die Erreichbarkeit der Himmelskörper," R. Oldenbourg-Verlag, Munich, 1925.

Joulaski, G.: "The Conqueror," 1925. (Author was a Pole, work was published in Russia.)

Gail, Otto Willi: "Mit Raketenkraft ins Weltenall," K. Thienemann, Stuttgart, 1928.

Ley, Willy: "Die Möglichkeit der Weltraumfahrt," Hachmeister & Thal, Leipzig, 1928.

Scherschewsky, Alexander B.: "Die Rakete für Fahrt und Flug," C.J.E. Volckmann, Berlin, 1928.

Esnault-Pelterie, Robert: "L'Exploration par fusées de la tres haute atmosphère et la possibilité des voyages interplanétaires," Societé Astronomique de France, 1928.

Oberth, Hermann: "Wege zur Raumschiffahrt," R. Oldenbourg-Verlag, Munich, 1929. A revised and enlarged edition of "Die Rakete zu den Planetenraümen."

Noordung, Hermann: "Das Problem der Bafahrung des Weltraums," R. C. Schmidt, Berlin, 1929.

Esnault-Pelterie, Robert: "L'Astronautique," Imprimerie A. Lahure, Paris, 1930.

Biermann, Gerd: "Weltraumschiffahrt," Leuwer, Bremen, 1931.

Lasser, David: "The Conquest of Space," Penguin Press, London, 1931.

Mandl, Vladimir: "Das Weltraum-Recht," J. Bensheimer, Mannheim, 1932.

Brügel, Werner: "Männer der Rakete," Hachmeister & Thal, Leipzig, 1933.

Ananoff, Alexandre: "Le Problème des voyages interplanétaires," Société Astronautique de France, 1934.

Esnault-Pelterie, Robert: "L'Astronautique" (complément), Imprimerie A. Lahure, Paris, 1935.

Ananoff, Alexandre: "La Navigation interplanétaire," Société Astronomique de France, 1935.

Damblanc, Louis: "Les Fusées autopropulsives à explosives," Office Nationale des Recherches Scientifiques et Industrielles et des Inventions, Paris, 1935.

Cleator, Philip Ellaby: "Rockets through Space," Simon and Schuster, Inc., New York, 1936; Allen & Unwin, London, 1936.

Philp, G.: "Stratosphere and Rocket Flight," Sir Isaac Pitman & Sons, Ltd., London, 1937. (1st ed., 1935.)

Northrup, E. F.: "Zero to Eighty," Scientific Publishing Company, Princeton, N.J., 1937.

Ananoff, Alexandre: "Navigation Interplanétaire," Editions Elzévir, Paris, 1946.

McLuquer, Juan J.: "A la conquista del espacio," Editorial Seix-Barral, Barcelona, 1946.

Harper, Harry: "Dawn of the Space Age," Sampson & Low Marston & Co., Ltd., London, 1946.

Wilcox, Arthur: "Moon Rocket," Nelson, London, 1946.

Ducrocq, Albert: "L'Humanité devant la navigation interplanétaire," Calmann-Levy Editeurs, Paris, 1947.

Richard-Foy, Robert: "Voyages interplanétaires et énergie atomique," Editions Albin Michel, Paris, 1947.

Gail, Otto Willi: "Physik der Weltraumfahrt," Hanne Reich Verlag, Munich, 1948.

Nicolson, Marjorie: "Voyages to the Moon," The Macmillan Company, New York, 1948. A scholarly study of the origin and development of the idea of space flight, as reflected by flights to the moon during the seventeenth and eighteenth centuries, traced from antiquity.

Schaub, Werner: "Weltraumflug," Dummlers Verlag, Bonn, 1949.

Laming, Lionel: "L'Astronautique," Press Universitaires de France, Paris, 1949.

Ley, Willy: "The Conquest of Space," The Viking Press, Inc., New York, 1949.

Proell and Bowmann: "A Handbook of Space Flight," Perastadion Press, Chicago, 1950.

Ananoff, Alexandre: "L'Astronautique," Librairie Arthème Fayard, Paris, 1950.

Clarke, Arthur C.: "Interplanetary Flight," Temple Press, Ltd., London, 1950.

————: "The Exploration of Space," Temple Press, Ltd., London, 1951.

"The Artificial Satellite," proceedings of the Second Congress of the International Astronautical Federation, British Interplanetary Society, London, 1951.

Margarger, John P., ed.: "Space Medicine," University of Illinois Press, Urbana, Ill., 1951. "The human factor in flights beyond the atmosphere."

Gartmann, Heinz: "Raumfahrtforschung," R. Oldenbourg-Verlag, Munich, 1952.

Koelle, H. H., ed.: "Probleme aus der Astronautischen Grundlagenforschung," Stuttgart, 1952.

Linke, Felix: "Rakentenflug ins Weltall," Franzis Verlag, Munich, 1952.

Bergaust, Erik, and Berndt Balchen: "Reisen til Manen," published in Norway, 1952.

Tilton, George, ed.: "The Mystery of Other Worlds Revealed," Fawcett Publications, Greenwich, Conn., 1952. An interesting but somewhat treacherous survey in pictorial fashion of the present status of space flight: flying-saucer nonsense, miscellaneous photographic dredgings from movies, and artists' conceptions. Also, some good material detectable mainly by the expert.

Coggins and Pratt: "By Space Ship to the Moon," Random House, Inc., New York, 1952. Nicely conceived and reasonably accurate; good for the young reader.

Ryan, Cornelius, ed.: "Across the Space Frontier," The Viking Press, Inc., New York, 1952. A symposium, largely on the space station of von Braun, who contributes with J. Kaplan, Heinz Haber, Willy Ley, Oscar Schacter, and F. Whipple.

Firsoff, V. A.: "Our Neighbour Worlds," Hutchinson's Scientific and Technical Publications, London, 1952.

"L'Astronautique," Science et vie; hors de serie, Paris, 1952. Written in the same general theme as "Mystery of Other Worlds Revealed," but incomparably better. A gold mine for those who can read French.

Cleator, Philip Ellaby: "Into Space," George Allen & Unwin, Ltd., London, 1953.

Haber, Heinz: "Man in Space," Sidgwick & Jackson, Ltd., London. The Bobbs-Merrill Company, Inc., Indianapolis, 1953. A book for the layman on the space-medical aspects of space travel.

Errebo-Knudsen, Hansen, and Hansen: "Verdens-rummets Erobring," Hans Reitzels Forlag, Copenhagen, 1953. In Danish, and probably done largely by the senior author.

Thompson, G. V. E.: "The Adventure of Space Travel," Dennis Dobson, Ltd., London, 1953.

Leonard, Johnathan Norton: "Flight into Space," Random House, Inc., New York, 1953.

Von Braun, Wernher, et al., (C. Ryan, ed.): "Conquest of the Moon," The Viking Press, Inc., New York, 1953.

————: "The Mars Project," University of Illinois Press, Urbana, Ill., 1953.

Gatland, K. W., and A. M. Kunesch: "Space Travel," Allan Wingate, London, 1953. A good introduction, in one volume, for the adult layman; gives the full sweep of the present astronautical vista.

Clarke, Arthur C.: "Going into Space," Harper & Brothers, New York, 1954. For the young reader.

"Space Flight Problems/Probleme der Weltraumforschung/Problèmes d'astronautique," Laubscher & Cie., Druck und Verlag, Biel-Bienne, Switzerland, 1954. Proceedings of the Fourth Congress of the International Astronautical Federation.

Logan, Jeffrey, ed.: "The Complete Book of Outer Space," Maco Magazine Corp., New York, 1954. Contributions by Ley, von Braun, Gernsback, etc. Much better than "Mystery of Other Worlds Revealed," but still far short of "L'Astronautique," Science et vie.

Buedeler, Werner: "To Other Worlds," Burke, London, 1954. A translation of "Telescope, Raketen, Gestirne."

Goodwin, Harold L.: "Science Book of Space Travel," Watts, New York, 1954. General-level book on astronautics.

Haber, Heinz: "The Physical Environment of the Flyer," Air University, 1954. Good source book on aviation, space medicine, high-altitude physics.

Koelle, Hermann, and Hans Kaeppeler: "Literature Index of Astronautics," Pustet, Tittmoning, 1954. Includes lists of books, papers, articles on space flight, rocketry, and related sciences and fields of interest, which are prepared according to the Sänger classification system.

Heuer, Kenneth: "Men of Other Planets," The Viking Press, Inc., New York, 1954. Reminiscent of the old book by Bernard de Fontenelle, but with an informed Cook's Tour of astronomy. The novice should be cautious with this book; it is honest, but the legitimate fantasy sneaks up on the reader somewhat. The initiated student of astronomy will find some useful information and some thought-provoking ideas.

Sternfeld, Arny: "Le Vol dans l'espace cosmique," Les Editeurs Français Réunis, Paris, 1954. Translated from the Russian by Paul Kolodkine. This new edition contains, oddly, less information than the first, with practically no reference to Western achievements, and it includes frequent excursions into dialectical materialism. No new ideas.

Smith, Ralph A., and Arthur C. Clarke: "Exploration of the Moon," Frederick Muller, Ltd., London, 1954. Text by Clarke, pictures by Smith, who is also a competent structures engineer for Hawkers, England. A pleasing gallery of astronautical pictures.

Caidin, Martin: "Worlds in Space," Henry Holt and Company, Inc., New York, 1954. Many illustrations by Fred Wolff, adapted largely from Smith and Von Braun. Interesting variety of angle of view; good pictorial array.

————: "Rockets beyond the Earth," McBride, New York, 1954. Similar to "Worlds in Space" and published somewhat before it. (Pictures there also by Fred Wolff.)

Oberth, Hermann: "Menschen in Weltraum," Econ Verlag, Düsseldorf, 1954. New thoughts on astronautics and astronautical devices by the father of astronautics.

Partel, Glauco: "A Technical Dictionary of Rockets and Astronautics," Associazione Italiana Razzi, Rome, 1955. Offers translations of terms in French, Italian, English, and German.

Hecht, Friedrich, ed.: "Bericht über den V. Internationalen Astronautischen Kongress," 1955. Editor is also editor of *Astronautica Acta,* a learned and scholarly journal on astronautics published in Germany. Format resembles that of the *Acta.*

Tabanera, Teofilo: "La Exploración del espacio," Editorial Sol, Buenos

Aires, 1955. A good survey in Spanish of astronautics by the Vice President of the International Astronautical Federation.

Ley, Willy, and Wernher von Braun: "The Exploration of Mars," The Viking Press, Inc., New York, 1956. Pictures of great skill and artistry by Chesley Bonestell. A new book in the fine tradition of Willy Ley's "The Conquest of Space." A skillful popularization, in part, of Von Braun's "Mars Project." Contains revised designs for the Martian expeditionary spaceship fleet, and a wealth of much-needed data on Mars itself.

Levitt, I. M.: "A Space Traveler's Guide to Mars," Henry Holt and Company, New York, 1956. Mars, its atmosphere, possibility of life on, etc. Appendices on beginning of life and the "Martian Clock."

"Orbital and Satellite Vehicles," published course notes of the Massachusetts Institute of Technology summer session on satellites (not for sale), 1956.

Mayer, Ernest: "Astronáutica," Editorial Universitaria, Buenos Aires, 1956. A general book on space flights; in Spanish.

Gaul, Albro: "The Complete Book of Space Travel," World Book Company, Yonkers, 1956. Large, popular-style picture book of astronautics and its science-fiction background.

Krieger, F. J.: "A Case Book on Astronautics," 1956, 1957. A Rand Corporation report on the background of Soviet astronautics. Included are many translations of Russian articles from journals and the press. (Two volumes.)

"Earth Satellites as Research Vehicles," 1956, proceedings of a satellite symposium held in 1956 at the Franklin Institute, in Philadelphia. Includes papers on moon rockets, satellites, and recovery of data from satellites.

Moore, Patrick: "Earth Satellites," W. W. Norton & Company, Inc., New York, 1956. Popular book on satellites, with emphasis on Project Vanguard.

Gartman, Heinz: "The Men behind the Space Rockets," David McKay Company, New York, 1956. Discusses the men of space flight.

"Specialized Books on Space Flight," bibliography, General Astronautics Corporation, 1956 (rev. ed., 1958).

Van Allen, James A., ed.: "Scientific Uses of Earth Satellites," University of Michigan Press, Ann Arbor, Mich., 1956. Collection of papers presented at the Tenth Anniversary Meeting of the Upper Atmosphere Rocket Research Panel.

"International Geophysical Year," 1956, special report published by the National Academy of Sciences on the over-all IGY program.

Bergaust, Erik, and William Beller: "Satellite!" Hanover House, New York, 1956. Offers background on Vanguard, Big Brother, Project Orbiter, and Russian satellites and other related information.

Caiden, Martin: "Vanguard," E. P. Dutton & Co., Inc., New York, 1957. Survey of the current Earth Satellite Vehicle Program.

Clarke, Arthur C.: "The Making of a Moon," Harper & Brothers, New York, 1957. On the Vanguard & Earth Satellite Vehicle Program.

Oberth, Hermann: "Man into Space," Harper & Brothers, New York, 1957. This book, by the famous rocket-astronautical pioneer, gives some of his latest ideas on satellites, space stations, moon cars, etc.

Carter, L. J., ed.: "Realities of Space Travel," Putnam & Co., Ltd., London, 1957. Collection of key papers published by the British Interplanetary Society.

Mueller, Wolfgang: "Man among the Stars," a translation of "Du Wirst die Erde sehn als Stern," Criterion Books, New York, 1957.

Coombs, Charles: "Rockets, Missiles and Moons," William Morrow & Company, Inc., New York, 1957. Broad survey of current rocket and satellite work.

Burgess, Eric: "Guided Weapons," The Macmillan Company, New York, 1957. Classification of missiles.

Buedeler, Werner: "Operation Vanguard," Burke, London, 1957.

Bates, D. R., ed.: "Space Research and Exploration," Eyre & Spottiswoode, London, 1957.

Bizony, Th. T., ed.: "Space Encyclopedia," Artemis Press, London; Dutton, New York, 1957.

Burgess, Eric: "Satellites and Spaceflight," Macmillan, New York, 1957.

Beard, R. B., and A. C. Rotherham: "Space Flight and Satellite Vehicles," George Newnes, Ltd., London, 1957.

Benecke, T., et al.: "History of German Guided Missiles Development," Appelhans & Co., Brunswick, 1957.

Gatland, K. W., ed.: "Project Satellite," The Macmillan Company, New York, 1958.

2
The Rocket

Background

Uncertain rumors in the literature place the first rockets in China between 3000 and 2000 B.C., but there seems to be no real reason for believing them. A reaction device, the first one with reasonable bibliographic support, is the "wooden dove" of Archytas,[1] a device propelled by steam and capable of semiflight from the end of a tether. It was probably not a free-flying object, or the historians of aeronautics would long since have claimed it as the first true airplane. The conventional source for this "dove" is the "Noctes atticae," of Aulus Gellius, who gives the time and place as 360 B.C. and the town of Tarentum, a Greek colony in southern Italy at the present site of Taranto, 40 miles west of Brindisi.

About 50 B.C., Hero of Alexandria constructed a machine called an aeolipile.[2] It consisted of a boiler, two vertical pipes bent in at the top to form an axle for a hollow sphere, and a tangential vent mounted in the sphere's vertical equator. Fire under the boiler created steam, and the steam was forced by pressure up through the pipes, into the sphere, and out through the vent. This caused the aeolipile to spin, for much the same reason that the modern rotary garden sprinkler spins. The machine could conceivably have been put to some useful work, but the economics of the day favored the extreme cheapness of slave labor. Dampier

[1] G. Sarton, "A History of Science," p. 440, Harvard University Press, Cambridge, Mass., 1952.

[2] W. Dampier, "A History of Science," p. 48, Cambridge University Press, London, 1948.

described the aeolipile as the forerunner of the modern jet-propelled airplane. The notion of using steam for reaction power cropped up repeatedly in the later history of the rocket, but not, it should be noticed, until after Newton propounded the laws of reaction.

Rockets, as rockets, made their appearance in China in about A.D. 1040, probably as an accidental discovery. Most adults can recall imperfect firecrackers that acted like miniature rockets instead of exploding. There is a reasonable chance that the Chinese were making bombs (which in those days would simply have been very large firecrackers) for attachment to arrows. The arrows would then have much the same effect as modern rifle grenades, but were probably somewhat cumbersome.

The discovery that imperfect bombs had a propulsive effect may have led eventually to some experimentation and the discovery of how to make the bombs do this "on purpose." This added to the range of the arrows and allowed the smoldering carcass to set fires at the target. It was only a matter of time before the fire arrows became bigger (rocket lances are reported) and independent of any launching apparatus except a stand or rack to give them direction.

The Chinese book "Wu Ching Tsung Yao" indicates that black-powder rockets were used during the Sung Dynasty, and there is some possibility that they were used as early as A.D. 900, although the 1040 date is more generally accepted. One type of rocket, called San Kung Chuang Tzu Nu, probably an earlier type, was fired from crossbows. Mongolian cavalry was beaten back by such rockets, with heavy losses, at the battle of Peking, in 1230.

Gunpowder was apparently introduced into Europe by the Saracens. An Arab writer, in the Escorial collection, mentions rockets as being used for warfare in 1249, and others refer to them as Alsichem Alkhatai (Chinese arrows).

Rockets found their way to Italy by 1260, and in the following years were adapted by the Italians into ingenious pyrotechnic devices. Fireworks displays eventually took Europe by storm; no celebration would have been considered complete without them. Rockets thus assumed a commercial importance, and their manufacture was guarded with fanatical secrecy by the rocket guilds of the time. Powder recipes were written in cipher [3] in such books as "De mirabilis mundi," of Albert the Great, and "Epistola," of Bacon.

During the Renaissance, the free-flying rocket continued to develop, but a number of devices operating on land and water also made their appearance. Hassan er-Rammah, writing about 1280, reports a "self-moving and combusting egg" which was evidently discus-shaped and perhaps a foot in diameter. Its use was not described but it was evidently intended to slither across solid ground (and possibly water) and explode. Joanes de Fontana, in Italy, proposed rocket-propelled cars and marine torpedoes, in about 1420. Rockets for carrying messages along wire or ropes strung between buildings under siege were also proposed. "Bellifortis," by Konrad von Eichstadt, 1405, mentions aerial, floating, and wire-running rockets.

The story of Wan Hu is now a favorite legend among rocket men. It springs from that hazy borderline between history and legend but is, like an Aesop fable, worth retelling even if totally mythical. Tradition has it that Wan Hu was a local Chinese official of somewhat the same rank as Confucius had been at the start of his career. Wan Hu lived about the time of Christopher Columbus, and it is conceivable that a little of Western dynamism had begun to trickle into China.

In any event, Wan Hu constructed a rocket-propelled flying machine whose exact appearance is confused by a welter of conflicting descriptions. The only points of agreement are that Wan Hu caused to be built a device consisting of a chair (or saddle), two kites, and forty-seven rockets. Coolies with torches closed in at a signal from Wan Hu, when he was seated, and lighted the rockets. There was a tremendous flash and Wan Hu was never seen again.

Either of two things could have happened: The machine could have vanished to a distant point with high acceleration and deposited Wan Hu in a lake, or the flash could simply have been the flash of an explosion. In either case it amounted to a novel variety of suicide.

[3] Willy Ley, "Rockets, Missiles and Space Travel," p. 54, The Viking Press, Inc., New York, 1957.

In 1610, the Count of Nassau (of England) described a floating rocket which would dive under water and explode. The rocket's mysterious ability to burn under water, in addition to all its other odd properties, helps to account for the semimystical terminology widely used in describing rockets. Sulfur was called the "life," saltpeter the "soule," and charcoal the "coales of the body."

Rockets and their manufacture were rather simple in that period. A paper tube reinforced by a steel sleeve was placed over a spindle-shaped "thorn" and gunpowder was pounded into it. The sleeve and thorn were removed from the tube, one end of the tube was closed off, and the finished object was bound to a guiding stick. Crude as this may seem, it was rather successful, and rockets up to 132 lb in weight were fired near Berlin, in 1668.

Steam reaction came back into the picture momentarily with the invention in 1721, by Willem Gravesande, of Leyden, Holland, of a vehicle resembling a metal retort mounted snout rearward on a stagecoach chassis. It is likely that only a classroom model was made; an actual full-sized working model would have been simply too spectacular to escape wide chronicling, even if it failed to work well. This modification of an experiment by Hero of Alexandria had to wait until scientists had had a chance to digest the implications of Sir Isaac Newton's third law of motion, propounded in 1687.

During the eighteenth century, pyrotechnics reached the state of a fine art, and expert Italian fireworks exhibitors roamed Europe, enthralling kings and commoners alike. A performance staged by the Ruggieri brothers, in 1749, in London for King George II used over 30,000 rockets, fire pots, cascades, fountains, and other devices, punctuated by orchestral music and cannon fire. It is doubtful whether the world had seen anything like it before, or has since.

Wherever they went the Italians left their word *rocchetta* in some form. The Germans were left with the word *rakete;* the Swedes, with *racket;* the Russians, with *rakyeta;* and the English, with *rocket.* There were variations. The French term *roquette* has since been displaced, in some applications, by *fusée.* The Spanish word, of unknown origin, is *cohete.* The Portuguese *fougete* is detectably similar. The Dutch *vuurpijl,* being literally, like the Chinese, "fire arrow," is a mystifying throwback, unless one takes into account the Dutch colonial contacts in the Far East. The Arabic *sarukh* awaits the explanations of scholars. The Turkish *fizek* is fairly close to the French *fusée* and can possibly be explained by a study of the cultural ties between the two countries.

Between the introduction of the rocket into Europe and the middle of the eighteenth century, military engineers performed experiments in various countries. Rockets were used as weapons only at random until 1760. Then matters changed. Prince Hydar Ali, a local ruler in India, added a body of 1,200 rocket troops to his army, and he equipped them with rockets that weighed between 6 and 12 lb and were capable of ranges up to a mile. Using these, he inflicted a blistering defeat on British colonial troops in the battle of Guntur. Spurred by this success, Hydar Ali's son, Tippu Sahib, expanded the rocket corps to 5,000 a decade later, equipped them with very large rockets, and beat the British several times in battles near Seringapatam.

Rockets had plainly become practical weapons again. Concerted studies began in England. A General Desaguliers of the Royal Military Laboratory conducted some experiments between 1785 and 1790; they were inconclusive. William Congreve began private experimentation about 1800 and achieved enough success to enlist the support of the Royal Laboratory at Woolwich. By 1805, a rocket of 2,000 yards was demonstrated to the government, accepted, and authorized for "mass" production. An inconclusive naval attack was made with it on Boulogne the same year. In 1806, however, the British Fleet returned to inflict heavy incendiary damage on the city. In the following year, an avalanche of 25,000 rockets nearly wiped out the city of Copenhagen, in reprisal for the Danish entry into Napoleon's political entity, known as the Continental system.

Rockets soon demonstrated their prowess in land warfare. Rocket troops pounded Napoleon's army at Leipzig and contributed to a defeat that ultimately broke Napoleon's power in Europe. Some of the rockets had 40-in. bodies weighing 7 lb, 16-ft guiding sticks, and ranges of 3,000 yards! Rocket corps sprang up in all the major armies of Europe, but they were not destined to endure. The heavy and inaccurate cannon, with which they had competed successfully (because of their lightness and low price), were suddenly improved about this time by the innovation of rifled barrels, which imparted spin to the projectiles and so reduced dispersion that artillery achieved what amounted, in those days, to pin-point accuracy. The still imperfect rocket could not compete. The Hale rocket, invented by the British around 1850, resembled and spun like a modern artillery shell. The Austrian Army used Hale rockets with apparent success in mountain operations where enemies could not bring artillery. In 1866, however, on flat terrain, Austrian rocket corps were decimated by Prussian artillery. This was the last serious engagement involving rockets until World War II.

In the naval world, rockets were tried as propulsion for torpedoes to sink ships and also as line carriers in the rescue of stranded persons. The latter application was the more successful of the two and earned a noble name for the rocket by rescuing seamen and passengers from foundering ships—but not without difficulty. A number of successful tests were made by Ehrogott Schaefer in Prussia and Henry Trengrouse in England, both in 1807. A mortar was briefly popular for line throwing, but John Dennet finally got an English patent for his line-carrying rocket in 1838. By 1855 these rockets had become recognized, and a system of life-saving stations had been set up. Rocket-propelled torpedoes never overcame one basic difficulty: To be effective they had to strike underwater, but, being rockets, they were constantly becoming more buoyant as they lost weight with the consumption of their propellants.

Meanwhile, the steam reactor had reappeared, and in 1824, James Perkins, of London, produced a rocket consisting of a hollow container, possibly with guiding fins. The rocket was partly filled with water, sealed with a solder plug, and placed in a bonfire. The heat developed steam pressure and eventually melted the plug. The released steam pressure created an imbalance of physical forces, driving the rocket upward. We may thank Mr. Perkins for what is probably history's simplest and neatest illustration of how a rocket works.

What we would now loosely call "high-altitude research" was carried on in a biological vein by Claude Ruggieri. He is reported to have sent mice and rats aloft in rockets during the 1830s, and he developed a large rocket to accommodate a ram or a small human being. A test, planned for Paris, aborted when police prevented Ruggieri's volunteer passenger, Wilfred de Fonvielle, from taking part. It was probably just as well. Although there was provision for descent by parachute, it would not likely have worked.

This was perhaps the first attempt at rocket transportation, an idea which must have been somewhat in the air by the latter half of the nineteenth century. A number of these attempts were mentioned in Chap. 1, and they indicate how the notion of rocket transportation and the fact that rockets characteristically were flying objects eventually got together at the end of the century, when it became evident that man was due to make some really practical advances in aeronautics. Forward-thinking scientists, as always, looked ahead, beyond rapid flight and beyond high-altitude flight. They looked toward superlatives in both—flight at tremendous speed through the space that lies beyond the atmosphere.

The limitations of airplanes soon became apparent. Although yet to be proven conclusively, the ability of the rocket to operate in space was widely suspected. Pioneer scientists wrote their treatises, and rocket societies were formed, gradually, as the twentieth century progressed. The underlying aim of all these societies was essentially astronautical, but they fostered practical experimentation in the construction of small rocket engines, test stands, and "air frames." As experimentation was expensive, societies provided a medium where members could pool their resources and accomplish what they could not likely afford as individuals—though reports of scattered lone experimenters cropped up from time to time.

Among experimenters there have been two technical schools since the turn of the century: the proponents of solid propellants (gunpowder, resins, etc.) and those of liquid propellants (hydrogen peroxide or one of any number of two-liquid combinations, such as nitric acid and gasoline). There have also been two philosophical schools: space-flight proponents (Ziolkowski, Oberth, and von Braun) and "down-to-earth" rocketeers (Congreve, Tiling, Goddard, Hickman, and Rosen). Adherents of both schools privately admit strong points on the other side; there is no hard and fast line between the two.

Generally speaking, the first quarter of the twentieth century was a rather quiet one for rocket development. Just before this, in 1895,

Paulet, of Lima, Peru, claims to have successfully run a small liquid-propellant rocket engine weighing 5 lb, which developed 198 lb of thrust on gasoline and nitrogen peroxide. It was not reported until 1927 in the newspaper *El Commercio*[4] and is generally doubted because of the very long time the inventor took in making his achievement known. Such a motor, in 1895, would have shaken rocketry to its foundations.

Some experimentation was done in France and the United States during World War I, chiefly with solid-propellant rockets. This was mainly because solid-propellant rockets, because of their small size, convenience, storability, and low weight, recommended themselves for weapons and other uses where short burning times were required. Durations for more than a very few seconds, on the other hand, developed intense heat which soon destroyed cases, throats, and nozzles (usually made of metals never intended to encounter such high temperatures). Liquid-propellant engines which could produce long durations met with an exasperating series of failures.

Thus the rockets of World War I were solid-propelled. Special French Nieuports, called *les Fuséens,* discharged stick-stabilized rockets that were rather primitive, but destroyed enough captive observation balloons to "obsolete" them immediately. Anti-aircraft rockets, launched from moving railroad cars, were credited with shooting down at least one German zeppelin. In America, Dr. C. N. Hickman worked on aircraft rockets and Dr. Robert H. Goddard on what is now understood to be the grandparent of the bazooka, but no American rocket ordnance saw any noticeable service during that war. After the armistice, both men returned to private life and quietly set about their own studies. These gentlemen were of the "practical" school and worked in what amounted to secrecy. Their contributions—Hickman in solid rockets and Goddard in liquid rockets—were basic but have received relatively little publicity.

Dr. Hickman has been the guiding force in solid-rocket development, particularly in the field of ordnance rockets. He is regarded by many as the man who set the solid-rocket development program

[4] A. B. Scherschewsky, "The Rocket for Transport and Flight," C. J. E. Volckmann, Berlin, 1929; also *Mech. Eng.,* vol. 69, pp. 457–464, 1947, a discussion by the late James Wyld.

in motion in the World War II period, of which more will be mentioned later.

Dr. Goddard was teaching in the years immediately following World War I but found time for extensive private experimentation on rockets in the basement of a building at Clark University. He was exacting, cautious, and thorough. Although he had been interested in interplanetary flight since 1897, he was nearly silent on his astronautical views. He had published, in 1919, a paper entitled "A Method of Reaching Extreme Altitudes," in which he championed the usefulness of rockets for high-altitude research. The study met with the approval of the Smithsonian Institution, which granted him limited funds to continue his studies. He assembled a small team about him as the years went by. A private flight, in 1926, by his fragile, nose-driven, liquid-propelled rocket vehicle marked the first flight of the type in America. It attained only a few hundred feet but it changed Goddard's thinking about propulsion. More rocket vehicles were made and flown. In 1929, a refined liquid-propelled rocket was sent aloft with a camera and instruments. Daniel Guggenheim gave Goddard larger amounts of money in 1930, and Goddard moved to Mescalero Ranch, New Mexico, not far from where White Sands Proving Ground now is. Within two years he was firing large rockets 11 ft long—highly developed vehicles with engines in the rear. The German and American rocket-society experimenters, still using nose-driven contraptions and uncooled motors, were at least five years behind him. Goddard was already working on regeneratively cooled motors (Chap. 3), gyroscopic stabilization, and steering vanes. Altitudes achieved were never impressive, because Goddard was mainly interested in reliability. He was practicing what many a rocket engineer preaches: "Improve what you have and don't try to build the ideal vehicle, or you will never finish."

Superficially it would seem that Goddard had made the rocket societies look foolish. Not at all. Rheinhold Tiling, of Germany, made highly finished aluminum rockets operating on solid propellants. If the German society was embarrassed, it should not have been. The importance of the rocket societies was and is that they provided a focal point of popular interest and were directly responsible not only for informing the public on rocketry and space flight but also for providing industry with competent engineers whom they had interested in rocket problems.

At first there was no such industry. The societies generated the industry, and since then they have provided men for it in the sense of acting as a channel of interest. The great rocket development station at Peenemünde was organized around Dr. Wernher von Braun, of the German Rocket Society; and Reaction Motors, the first rocket-engine company in the United States, was founded by several members of what is now the American Rocket Society: John Shesta, James Wyld, Franklin Pierce, and Lovell Lawrence.

Rocket societies were active in the Soviet Union in the early thirties, probably assisted by the government. A "stratosphere committee" rocket reportedly achieved an altitude of 30 miles in one flight during upper-atmosphere researches. This is a little hard to believe in view of the general state of the art in those days, but is apparently true. The British Interplanetary Society, formed about the same time, was able to perform a few actual rocket experiments before the authorities enforced a rather antique law about explosives, and thus stopped the programs. In France, an astronautics section to the Société Astronomique de France was formed in the late 1930s, but did not last long. (After the war, A. Ananoff organized astronautical sections to various aviation clubs, one of which, the Groupement Astronautique Français, sponsored the world's first astronautical congress, in 1950. A few years later it also collapsed, because of some rather subtle technicalities of French academic protocol.[5] In 1955, an independent Société Française d'Astronautique was established, headed by leading scientists, and a new *Bulletin d'astronautique* is being published.) Robert Esnault-Pelterie, famed rocket-astronautical pioneer, worked in government laboratories from 1934 on, and Louis Damblanc performed some

[5] It is important to know the history of the activities of these and other societies. Aside from the human drama and the unfolding of ideas, it is probably the best way for the interested layman to get the "feel" of rocketry. For the German society, read W. Ley, *op. cit.*, chaps. 5–8. For the American Rocket Society, read G. E. Pendray, "The Coming Age of Rocket Power." The story of the society runs through the whole book, but is chiefly in pp. 35–42, 118–130. The story of British-society development appears in Burgess, "Rocket Propulsion," pp. 225–228, while an account of French activities is found in A. Ananoff "L'Astronautique: Science Internationale," Université de Paris, 1953.

very useful solid-propellant research as an individual. In Italy, Prof. Gaetano Crocco and Dr. Ricardo Corelli worked on liquid-propellant rocket engines, and some systematic private researches on propellants were conducted by Joseph Stemmer in Switzerland.

The German society (Verein für Raumschiffahrt) [6] was formed in Breslau, in 1927, by Johannes Winkler and other rocket enthusiasts. In 1930, the society leased a tract of land which they called Raketenflugplatz (rocket proving ground). A series of tests of liquid-propellant rocket engines called Miraks,[7] which had begun elsewhere, were continued here. After a number of burnouts and explosions, some good flights were made with nose-driven *repulsors,* the name having been chosen from Lasswitz's novel to distinguish the rockets from the pyrotechnic type. Regeneratively cooled rocket engines were eventually made, but before the general trend of rocket experiments could assume much stature, the German Army took over the records and personnel of the society in order to organize a rocket research program which culminated in the great development station of Peenemünde.

Whereas the German society favored liquid oxygen and alcohol, the American Interplanetary Society (later the American Rocket Society) preferred gasoline as the fuel propellant. Rocket No. 1, made by H. Pierce and G. Edward Pendray, developed a 60-lb thrust in November, 1932. The second enjoyed a powered flight of 2 sec before the oxygen tank exploded, but it did fly. A third was ground-tested, and the fourth, a multinozzle design, was flown in September, 1934, reaching an altitude of 382 ft and a velocity of 700 mph, breaking the speed record of 500 mph set by Goddard in New Mexico.

Seven solid-propellant rockets, fired during 1937, reached altitudes up to 1,500 ft, and the following year James Wyld produced a regeneratively cooled engine that solved the same problems of burnouts and explosions as those which had plagued the German society. The Cleveland and California rocket societies also carried on experiments, and, as in Europe, back-yard experimenters continued. This all stopped somewhat abruptly with the war, and there has been little society or private experimentation since.

[6] Literally, space travel club. The word "club" has more dignity in Europe.
[7] *Minimum Raketen.*

The Rocket Matures

By 1930 the basic facts about rockets and space flight were generally known, though perhaps not as a unified package by any one person or group. Those who knew their astronautics found themselves handicapped by lack of money to experiment with the rocket. Those who somehow got the money and improved the rocket were more interested in the rocket as a machine than as a vehicle of space flight. This odd dichotomy is still with us to a certain extent today and seems to be the inevitable result of a civilization steeped in the tradition of the anthropocentric universe. Here and there were exceptions—men who not only knew rockets intimately but were also astronautically minded. Such men are Eugen Sänger, Wernher von Braun, Robert Esnault-Pelterie, and, to a lesser extent, Dr. Robert Goddard. In terms of influence, von Braun has been the most important. Goddard left a heavy imprint on American rocketry, but his unfortunate passing and the achievement of the huge and expertly engineered V-2 has catapulted von Braun to the top.

The V-2 was designed as a sort of superheavy artillery of tremendous range and had its original roots in the German Rocket Society, from which the government hired Dr. von Braun. The Army Weapons Department in Berlin had embarked on a research program on somewhat the same grand scale as the American atomic-bomb program and in what amounted to a long "crash" program. Compared with the later Viking program in America, engines and missiles were expended at a frightening rate.

A series of A vehicles was produced rapidly. The A-1 was a missile with an engine developing 660 lb of thrust on liquid oxygen and alcohol. An improved model, the A-2, attained an altitude of 6,500 ft. The A-3 was a much larger rocket, 25 ft long, which weighed 1,650 lb and reached an altitude of 7½ miles.

The program was outgrowing the Berlin establishment by this time, and the project was gradually moved to Peenemünde, a location on the Baltic Sea, near Stettin. Here the A-4 came into being, later to be called the V-2 ("Vengeance Weapon No. 2") for propaganda reasons.

By conventional rocket standards, the V-2 was colossal. It

weighed over 14 tons, stood over 47 ft high, and developed a thrust of 56,000 lb. Produced by the thousands in underground plants at Nordhausen and elsewhere, in the face of shortages of materials and trained workers, this rocket was fired at London and Antwerp in enough numbers to worry the Allies deeply. It was estimated that the Germans, given another 6 months of production time with these rockets, could have turned the tide of war. A high number of the slow jet-propelled "buzz bombs" had been shot down; the V-2s, although a number went wide of the mark, traveled at 3,600 mph and not one was intercepted.

The A-4b was a winged version of the V-2; two of these were built, and one was successfully flown. The object was increase of range by gliding. The A-5 was an air-launched test vehicle about the size of the A-3. A-6, A-7, and A-8 were research designations, as were A-9 and A-10. These last two have assumed considerable importance (even though they were never built) because of their astronautical implications.

The A-10 was designed to weigh 76 tons and develop about 220 tons of thrust; it was to act as first stage (booster) for a V-2–sized vehicle with delta wings. The effective mass ratio (Chap. 3) was over 10:1, and the expected range of the second stage was a spectacular 3,105 miles. With this weapon the Germans planned to bomb New York; the A-10 was the forerunner of what we call today the intercontinental ballistic missile (ICBM).

Dr. Eugen Sänger proposed a somewhat similar idea, the "antipodal bomber," which was to achieve its initial altitude by launch from a large rocket sled and then level off to skim across the top of the atmosphere better than halfway around the world. The developed thrust was to be about 112 tons and flight was to be prolonged by rebounding into space and returning to the air canopy by a long succession of smaller and smaller leaps. With a firing time of just under 500 sec, the plane would achieve a maximum velocity of 13,000 mph and a maximum range (with a little luck) of 25,000 miles.

It is not hard to see that increases in range inevitably lead to higher altitudes, and that, when intercontinental missiles of enough range have been perfected, the step to space, the realm in which the missiles operate for most of their flight, is almost perfunctory.

The A-9 and A-10, as well as the antipodal bomber, represented a combination of ballistic and aerodynamic missiles. Other intercontinental missiles are purely ballistic and, to achieve long range, must first climb to even higher altitudes than the weapons just mentioned. At their extreme ranges they very nearly attain altitudes at which they can orbit (see Chap. 4, on artificial satellites).

In addition to the V-2, the Germans evolved a lavish arsenal of guided missiles, devices which represented a refinement of early attempts at expendable pilotless bombers that were made as early as World War I. The Rheinbote (Rhine Messenger), a three-stage (plus booster) solid-propellant rocket, saw action against the Allies. Antiaircraft missiles were the most numerous, for the Allied air forces, by 1944, were beginning to make heavy inroads on German industry. The missiles included the Enzian (Gentian), Hecht (Pike), Feuerlilie (Fire Lily), Schmetterling (Butterfly), Rheintochter (Rhine Maiden), Taifun (Typhoon) and Wasserfall (Waterfall). Notable about the Taifun was its fantastic terminal acceleration of 45 g. Wasserfall was a very fine missile, 25 ft long, but it never quite became operational—luckily for Allied bombers.

A number of air-to-surface missiles were developed by Henschel and Rheinmetall-Borsig. Air-to-air rockets took a heavy toll of B-17s, but the fighters launching them suffered serious air drag created by the launching racks and became easy prey for the unencumbered Allied fighters. A vertically launched airplane, Natter (Viper), was not successful, but a tailless rocket interceptor (rising from the ground), the Messerschmitt Me-163, did score some kills. For sheer magnitude and variety, the German program perhaps outclassed all the programs of the rest of the world combined. But important things were going on elsewhere, if one knew where to look.

Solid-propellant research had been going on in England since 1936 under the direction of the Research Department of the Royal Laboratory at Woolwich. A number of small, reliable rockets (chiefly antiaircraft) were developed. Research was momentarily suspended during the early part of the war but later was resumed on a larger scale. The most famous of the Royal Laboratory's weapons was the so-called Z-Gun, which fired barrages of rockets at the Luftwaffe.

The British, immediately after World War II, made a few V-2

firings from Cuxhaven in North Germany, and then apparently went into a deep slumber. In the late forties and early fifties a series of rocket, motor, control, ramjet, and general-purpose test vehicles were evolved, many featuring a wrap-around booster technique.

The first operational air-to-air missile is the Fireflash, while the second is the infrared-guided Firestreak. Vickers Armstrong's Red Dean, recently announced, is the third major air-to-air missile known to exist in Great Britain. In the surface-to-air field, the Bloodhound (a semiactive homer) leads the field, though there are several other entries, including the Seaslug of the Royal Navy, and RAF's Thunderbird. A number of surface-to-surface missiles are under development, including long-range rockets by Rolls-Royce, Armstrong-Whitworth, and A. V. Roe. Both the Royal Air Force and the Royal Navy are supposed to be developing air-to-surface missiles. A rather large air-to-surface missile has been rumored to tie in with the V bombers, perhaps something like the Rascal.

English rocket and missile work is still very secret today. Flight tests are made at the Guided Weapons Trials Department, in Aberporth, South Wales, and from a new range in the Hebrides, off Scotland, at South Uist. Long-range tests are generally conducted at Woomera, Australia. This range has a corridor nearly 3,000 miles long, and well over 700 rockets of various sizes have been fired there in the last 5 years. Although little is announced, the basis of England's defense strategy suggests emphasis on air-to-air, antiaircraft, and medium-range (800- to 1,500-mile) missiles.

For high-altitude research Britain's Ministry of Supply has developed the 25-ft-long Skylark, a solid-propelled vehicle. This rocket can reach from 90 to possibly 130 miles and offers a payload capacity of 65 lb. In addition to scientific experimentations, it can carry telemetry, Doppler, and beacon-tracking equipment. During the International Geophysical Year the United Kingdom may also fire balloon rockets to a height of 60 miles. Rockets from Antarctica are being launched to test electric charges in the atmosphere in south-polar regions. A full line of high-altitude-research experiments will be carried out under the direction of government and private institutions. It includes the following: grenade experiments to determine winds and temperatures, mass spectrometry for ion sampling, ionospheric conductivity, concentration studies, electron densities, relative intensities of spectral lines of molecular oxygen, sodium- and potassium-emission studies, and solar-radiation and ultraviolet measurements.

Russia, as always, is a question mark. Practically no information about specific missiles has come out of that country, though delegates to the October, 1957, IGY rocket and satellite conference in Washington surprised Western attenders by being specific on a research rocket, dubbed Meteo. During the war, Russians fired Katiusha (Swish) rockets from Stalin Organ launchers. Germany had a solid respect for the Soviet rocket-firing Stormoviks and rocket-propelled bombs. The Russians overran Peenemünde in 1945 and, by agreement with the Allies, took over the underground V-2 factory at Nordhausen. Plausible reports have since been received that the Russians have improved the V-2 for both high-altitude research and bombardment applications. They claim that rocket-power fighters have reached 1,700 mph and single-stage sounding (high-altitude) rockets have reached 240 miles.

By deduction it may be believed that the Russians have made pronounced improvements in the German designs they inherited when they overran Peenemünde, including, conceivably, the A-9/A-10 missile. Naval vessels armed with guided missiles and medium-range (1,500-mile) surface-to-surface missiles are believed to exist now on an operational basis. A two-stage 1,850-mile model M-103 (T-2) is probable, and there is some chance that the Russians have resurrected an old German idea, the underwater-to-surface rocket: a V-2 fired from a pod towed into position by a submarine, upended, surfaced, used, and discarded.

In a nutshell, we find the Russians today with a fairly good series of surface-to-surface missiles, including antitank (T-5A, 25-KGM, barrage, close support, artillery (including the 7-A), and tactical. A series of J cruise missiles exists, similar to the German V-1, Matador, and Regulus. The 4-A cruise missile may be like the *Snark*. A three-stage T-3 ICBM is known to exist, a rocket which also goes under the M-104 designation. It presumably launched their satellite, long under development, and will probably be the carrier vehicle for yet more ambitious projects than Sputnik. Next to nothing is known about air-to-air or air-to-surface rockets, though a few surface-to-air missiles are known. At least three manned rocket planes are presumed to exist, including the I-1 research plane and the La-17 and Yak-21 military planes.

A healthy crop of Russian research rockets is in existence, including meteorological and geophysical models. Scientists Poloskov and Mirtov of the Russian Academy have reported (*Jet Propulsion,* February, 1957; *J. Brit. Interplanet. Soc.,* April–June, 1957; and *Fusées et recherche aéronaut.,* March, 1957.) extensive high-altitude research work, including the sending and recovering of dogs. The Russians are making thorough studies of the upper atmosphere, cosmic radiation, the solar ultraviolet spectrum, and meteorites during the International Geophysical Year.

France today emerges from an apparent long inactivity with a variety of missiles. Notable among these is the Veronique, largest sounding rocket developed in Europe since the war. The French have made significant progress in the application of rocket power to airplanes and have developed several promising guided missiles.

In the air-to-air field, the AA-20, M/04, R-051, 1524, and 5103 are all respectable missiles, most of which are in production. Like the British, the French are planning a rather large air-to-surface missile and in the meantime are content with the SNCASE (now Sud-Aviation) model 1522. Maruca and Masalca Naval surface-to-air missiles are under development, while the Army has its Parca, SE-4300, and SE-4100. Surface-to-surface missiles center around bazooka types (BTZ-411-01), antitank rockets like ENTAC, SS-10, and SS-11 (now the SS-22). The latter two are considered among the most accurate in the world, are wire-guided, and incorporate a hollow charge.

France has a number of target drones, the outstanding ones being the CT-10 and CT-20. In the test field are the ECA-20 and -26 and the parachute-recoverable OPD-320. The French have some excellent rocket-powered airplanes, including the SNCASO (Sud-Aviation) 2026 and 9000, the Durandel, Espadon, Griffon, Harpon, Mirage, and MD-550. The famed Trident 2 broke world speed records and the French altitude record (it is powered by an SEPR rocket and two Viper wing-tip jets). For upper-atmosphere research, other than the Veronique, there is the ATEF-14 Monica, available in four models for altitudes from 25 to 60 miles. It is being used during the IGY period to supplant the large Veronique.

In Switzerland, Oerlikon has produced an ingenious model which shifts its center of lift with the changing center of gravity as propellants are consumed. Missile programs of one sort or another are known to be underway in Italy, Sweden, Canada ($24,000,000 spent on Velvet Glove before cancellation), Argentina, Australia, and Japan. The first three countries have small military-missile developments underway, though in the case of Canada her Velvet Glove did not turn out so well. Australia has an excellent target drone, and is cooperating with Britain on IGY research rocketry. Sweden has a $2,500,000 research and development and procurement missile budget for 1958 and has air-to-air, surface-to-air, surface-to-surface, and underwater-to-air types under development. Argentina has one small tactical rocket, the A-3F. Japan, for its part, has a very active rocket research program, with a series of Baby, Pencil, Sigma, and Kappa rockets firing regularly. Japan will fire 30 balloon rockets and 50 additional types in support of the IGY. Flights have already taken place from the Ryofu Maru missile-launching ship. Successful flights of two-stage Kappa 3 rockets have taken place, according to dispatches from the *Yomiuri Japan News*. Militarily, Japan will buy Swiss Oerlikon-56 and Italian Airone Orione until her own industry picks up. The October, 1957, issue of *Missiles and Rockets* has an excellent roundup of foreign missile developments, including Russian.

The United States began experimentation in the field of ordnance rockets as early as 1932, but no organized programs were sustained. Colonel Leslie Skinner of the Army Ordnance Corps began private studies, as a lieutenant, which eventually led to the weapon we know as the bazooka. The term refers to the launching tube's resemblance to a primitive yard of light plumbing used by the late comedian Bob Burns to produce a sound resembling music. Dr. C. N. Hickman, who had been working on solid rockets since World War I, persuaded the United States government to set up a program in 1940. A rocket laboratory was established in 1941 at Indianhead, Maryland, about 20 miles southwest of Washington, D.C., on the Potomac River, where the Navy had its powder factory. Research contracts were let by both the Army and Navy. Some of the items developed there were Minnie Mouse, an antisubmarine rocket depth charge, an antisubmarine "retro-rocket" (vertically falling rocket bomb), a variety of famous armament rockets such as the HVAR, Super 4.5, and the Tiny Tim, some chemical-warfare rockets, and JATO units.

During this time, Goddard was continuing, under Guggenheim grants, work begun under the sponsorship of the Smithsonian Institution. In 1936, the Guggenheim Aeronautical Laboratory of the California Institute of Technology (GALCIT) was organized under the direction of Dr. Theodore von Karman, who was, even then, a scientist of imposing caliber. Among the pioneer leaders of this group were such men as Dr. Frank J. Malina, Dr. A. M. O. Smith, and Dr. H. S. Tsien. During World War II the emphasis was somewhat on solid-propellant rockets and the production of finned and spinning artillery-barrage rockets which converted airplanes and landing barges into miniature battleships. Liquid-propellant research at GALCIT led to the later development of such sounding rockets as the Private A, WAC-Corporal, and Aerobee-Hi, the first two under ORDCIT Project.[8]

GALCIT was responsible for the development of JATO in the United States. In response to a Navy requirement for jet-assisted take-off units (to enable large aircraft to rise from restricted waters or overloaded aircraft to rise from normal runs), a program of solid-propellant research was begun at GALCIT. Units developing 100 lb of thrust were produced at first, followed by larger and larger ones delivering up to 1,000 lb. The Aerojet Engineering Corporation was organized to manufacture these units, and since then the company has produced hundreds of thousands of them. The company, now the Aerojet-General Corporation, has grown rapidly and has just established a new Astronautics Research Laboratory with propulsion, astrophysical, and materials sections to study very high-energy fuels, including plasma propulsion systems; magneto-hydrodynamics; and high- and low-temperature materials for space flight.

At the U.S. Naval Engineering Experiment Station at Annapolis, Commander Robert C. Truax, Ray C. Stiff, Jr., and John R.

---

[8] ORDCIT Project, of course, was an Army Ordnance undertaking by GALCIT. The WAC-Corporal was essentially the concept of Dr. Malina. It was 16 ft long, weighed 665 lb and delivered 1,500 lb of thrust with a liquid-propellant motor. It was first flight-tested in 1945.

Youngquist worked on liquid-propellant JATO units for Navy flying boats. History repeated itself on the East Coast. Reaction Motors, Inc., an infant company in 1941, undertook development of a 3,000-lb liquid-propellant JATO unit, and in succeeding years produced a distinguished series of liquid-propellant rocket engines which have established nearly every speed and altitude record ever made by rocket power. Reaction Motors power plants include those for the Lark, Gorgon, Viking, and Titan missiles and propulsion for the Douglas Skyrocket, Bell X-1, and the forthcoming North American X-15 supersonic research airplanes.

Despite the lively rocket and JATO programs underway during World War II, no organized guided-missile program was started. There were not even any missiles on the drawing boards. American consternation at the advent of the V-2 was more than military embarrassment upon learning that Germany had sprung a new weapon on us. The significance was that Germany had beaten us into a totally new era of weapons engineering, not with a mere improvisation, but with a huge, deadly, fully engineered rocket. Luckily for the Allies, it had come too late.

America heeded the implied lesson and took special pains to capture a hundred V-2 rockets and a large number of German scientists in an effort known as Project Paperclips. An Upper Atmosphere Research Panel was organized in 1946 and sent men and rockets to White Sands Proving Grounds, near Alamogordo, New Mexico, to learn about large missiles and how to train men in their maintenance and use. The V-2, because of its size, was also converted to a high-altitude research rocket. The General Electric Company, acting as the main coordinator, fired about 70 of the converted rockets at White Sands and elsewhere, achieving altitudes up to 132 miles. The V-2s gathered a treasury of scientific data.

But the V-2 did more than gather data. Because of its unprecedented size, it permitted an experiment which engineers must have dreamed of for decades. The V-2 was modified to act as the first of two stages in a multiple rocket aimed at extreme altitudes. According to theory, step rockets obtain high performance because they add velocity rather than range or altitude. The V-2 and WAC-Corporal were capable of separate altitudes of 114 and 19 miles, respectively, or a total of 133 miles. If the step principle based on velocity were as valid as it seemed to be, a WAC-Corporal, properly launched from a V-2, should be able to climb to well over 200 miles. It did. On February 24, 1949, the two-stage Bumper missile achieved an altitude of 244 miles over the Long Range Proving Ground, in Florida.

It was obvious that the V-2s would not last indefinitely. The tasks at hand were to combine what had been learned from America's own wartime experimentation with the new knowledge gained from the V-2 firings and apply the complete information to the tasks ahead. These were the development of research rockets of greater altitude and instrument-carrying capacities and the perfection of guided missiles of greater range and controllability. The two projects were somewhat kindred in the nature of the work required to produce them, but they were utterly opposite in the effects they were to produce themselves.

First among the new high-altitude rockets was the Aerobee, which has reached altitudes of about 80 miles since 1948 in a multitude of flights with instruments and biological specimens, including mice and monkeys. An improved version, the Aerobee-Hi, was early able to carry 230 lb of instruments to 120 miles, while subsequent flights soared to 164 miles and later (1957) to 193 miles. Work on a very large sounding rocket, the Viking, began shortly after that on the Aerobee and grew out of planning at the Naval Research Laboratory by Milton W. Rosen, D. E. Kreuse, and C. Smith. The Martin Company was awarded the airframe contract and Reaction Motors a contract for the development of an engine that could create 20,000 lb of thrust on alcohol and liquid oxygen. Twelve regular firings, begun May 3, 1949, and concluded February 4, 1955, allowed one to reach 136 miles with the original design and 158 miles with a redesigned body. Vikings 13 and 14 reached 125 and 120 miles, respectively, as part of the Vanguard testing program in late 1956 and 1957.

The Nike-Cajun and DAN (Deacon-and-Nike) are essentially the same rocket, though the former is somewhat improved and is being used extensively during the International Geophysical Year for research in the 70- to 90-mile region. Iris and Arcon are research rockets developed by the Atlantic Research Corporation, while Terrapin is a Republic Aircraft—University of Maryland two-stage rocket designed for the 80-mile region. Rockoons are balloon-launched vehicles, and Rockaires are launched from airplanes. Both are used extensively during the International Geophysical Year. ASPs (atmospheric sounding projectiles) and HASPs (high-altitude sounding projectiles) are also used. For day-to-day gathering of weather data, low-cost solid rockets proposed by the Stanford Research Institute would take a parachute *sonde* up to 150,000 ft for release. Meteorological data would be telemetered to Earth. All in all, some 200 vehicles will be fired to determine pressures, densities, composition, and temperatures of the upper atmosphere, perform cosmic-ray studies, aurora and air-glow investigations, magnetic-field determinations, and so forth. Little by

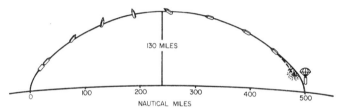

FIG. 2-1. Trajectory of a troop-carrying missile. (*U.S. Army.*)

little, small, solid rockets are handling more and more of the upperatmosphere research largely because of their ease of handling and lower cost and because the philosophy of "one rocket to one experiment" seems to be gaining favor.

Almost immediately after World War II the "cold war" began. The United States, like the Soviet Union, embarked on a lavish guided-missile research and development program. We have now produced, or have still in development, about 50 guided missiles and modifications. Some of the best known are the Matador, Regulus, Nike, Bomarc, Hawk, Terrier, Corporal, Falcon, Sidewinder, Sparrow, Redstone, Jupiter, Atlas, and Honest John. Tables 2-1 and 2-2 summarize the chief types of guided missiles of the United States.

Surface-to-air and air-to-air missiles are designed to overcome the speed and maneuver of enemy aircraft. Air-to-surface missiles

TABLE 2-1 *Current and Major Surface-to-surface Missiles*

	Designation	Cognizant agency	Contractor	Power plant	Power-plant manufacturer
Army:					
Corporal	SSM-A-17	Army Ord	Firestone Tire	Liquid rocket	Aerojet, Ryan
Dart	SSM-A-23	Army Ord	Aerophysics Utica-Bend	Solid rocket	Grand Central
Honest John	M31	Army Ord	Douglas A/C	Solid rocket	Hercules Powder
Jupiter		Army Ord	Chrysler	Liquid rocket	North American
Lacrosse	XSSM-A-12	Army Ord	Cornell Aero. Martin Co.	Solid rocket	Thiokol
Little John	XM-47	Army Ord	Douglas Emerson	Solid rocket	Hercules Powder
Redstone	SSM-A-14	Army Ord	Chrysler	Liquid rocket	North American
Sergeant		Army Ord	J. P. L. Sperry	Solid rocket	Thiokol
Navy:					
Polaris		Navy Bu Ord	Lockheed	Solid rocket	Aerojet
Regulus I	SSM-N-8	Navy Bu Aer	Chance Vought	Turbojet	Allison
Regulus II	SSM-N-9	Navy Bu Aer	Chance Vought	Turbojet	General Electric
Triton	XSSM-N-2	Navy Bur Ord	McDonnell	Ramjet	McDonnell
Air Force:					
Atlas	WS-107-A (SM-65)	AFBMD	Convair	Liquid rocket	North American
Matador A	TM-61A	USAF	Martin	Turbojet	Allison
Matador B (Mace)	TM-76	USAF	Martin	Turbojet	Allison
Navaho	XSM-64	USAF	North American	Ramjet	Curtiss-Wright
Snark	SM-62	USAF	Northrop	Turbojet	Pratt Whitney
Thor	WS-135A (SM-75)	AFBMD	Douglas	Liquid rocket	North American
Titan	WS-107B (SM-68)	AFBMD	Martin	Liquid rocket	Aerojet, Reaction Motors

58

Thrust, lb	Length, ft	Diam, in.	Loaded wt, lb	Range, miles	Velocity	Remarks
20,000	40	30	12,000	75–125	Mach 3	Hundreds fired; in full Army service; guided; atomic warhead
	5	8		5	650 mph	Wire-guided, anti-tank type; in production
	27	30	6,000	15–30		Unguided, free-flight; in service U.S.A., Japan, Europe
150,000	60	90	100,000	1,500	Mach 15	First U.S. IRBM; many successful firings after two failures
	20	20.5		10–20		Tactical, close-support, guided; in production
	12	12.5	1,000			First fired June, 1956
82,000	62	72	40,000	250	Mach 5	In service with 217th Missile Battalion; air-transportable
60,000	30	36	30,000	100		Has one of largest proven solid-rocket motors existent
	30	100	30,000	1,000–1,500	Mach 15	Navy to spend $68,000,000 in 1958; may be underwater-launched
4,600	32	54	14,500	300–500	Mach 0.9	Can be recovered on test flights; often sub-launched
12,000	57	72	25,000	800–1,000	Mach 1.5–2	Can carry atomic charge; costs twice Model I
	45	60	20,000	1,500	Mach 3.5	Solid-boosted; inertial guidance (program canceled)
200,000 150,000	70	100	240,000	5,000	Mach 15	Successfully test-fired; top of trajectory approx 800 miles
4,600	39.5	54	12,000	620	Mach 1	Solid-rocket booster; in squadron and wing use
4,600	45.8	54	14,000	650	Mach 1	Higher-altitude capability, improved guidance
20,000			300,000	5,000	Mach 5.5	Rocket-boosted (400,000-lb-thrust NAA liquid engine). Program canceled
11,000	74	54	50,000	5,000	Mach 1	In production; solid-rocket–boosted; celestial inertial guidance
150,000	60	100	100,000	1,500	Mach 15	Numerous failures before final successes
300,000 60,000	100	100	240,000	5,000	Mach 15	$358,000,000 allotted to its development; two-stage

TABLE 2-2 *Other Current United States Military Missiles*

	Bomber-defense missiles	Diamondback	Falcon
Air-to-air:			
Contractor	Cornell Aeronautics Laboratory	Naval Ordnance Test Station	Hughes
Agency	USAF	Navy	USAF
Remarks	Nasty, Goose, Duck, and WS-126A and WS-132A are also associated with this concept; B-52s will probably use one type or another	Will probably succeed the sidewinder	Four models are radar-guided, one infrared-guided; 5-mile range; solid propellant

	Antimissile	Bomarc	Hawk	Loki
Surface-to-air:				
Contractor	Various	Boeing	Raytheon	East Coast, Bendix
Agency	USAF, Army	USAF	Army	Army
Remarks	Preliminary studies going on; Nike-Zeus and Wizard are best known	Long-range ramjet rocket	Designed to destroy low-flying attack airplanes	Barrage rocket, now converted to upper-air research use

	Bullpup	Corvus	Crossbow	Dove
Air-to-surface:				
Contractor	Martin	Temco	Radioplane	Kodak
Agency	Navy	Navy	USAF	Navy
Remarks	Solid propellant, in production; for use against small tactical targets	For use on carrier-based airplanes	No details of importance available	For underwater targets

Genie (MB-1)	Mighty Mouse	Sidewinder	Sparrow	Zuni
Douglas	Aerojet, etc.	Philco	Sperry	Naval Ordnance Test Station
USAF	Navy, USAF	Navy	Navy	Navy
World's first atomic-warhead AAM, first fired in summer of 1957	Standard unguided aircraft rocket, costs $65	Infrared-guided very accurate; fleet-operational	Models 2, 3, and 4 also exist; standard service weapon	New HVAR replacement, unguided, fast; also for air-surface use

Nike-Ajax	Nike-Hercules	Nike-Zeus	Talos	Tartar	Terrier
Douglas, Western Electric	Douglas, Bell Telephone	Douglas, Bell Telephone	Bendix	Convair	Convair
Army	Army	Army	Navy	Navy	Navy
Standard air-defense weapon with 30-mile range; a Nike battery consists of 12 launchers	Faster, longer range model with 75-mile range, atomic warhead	No details available; an AICBM type	Mach 3–4 long-range air-defense ramjet missile; solid-rocket-boosted	Radar-guided, homing head; smaller than Terrier; in development	Two models: I is in service, has 20-mile range; II is in research and development

Green Quail	Petrel	Rascal	Hound Dog	Miscellaneous
McDonnell	Fairchild	Bell Aircraft	USAF	Various
Navy	Navy	USAF	Navy	Navy, USAF
No details available; may be GAM-72 rocket	Essentially a guided torpedo with aerodynamic surfaces; program now canceled (1957)	Liquid rocket, 100-mile range, supersonic guided bomb (*Note:* A new North American post-Rascal missile is being developed)	GAM-77, 40-ft long jet-powered B-52 weapon	A variety of unguided rocket ordnance missiles, like the 5-in. HVAR, are widely used

TABLE 2-3   *United States Research Rockets*

Rocket	Altitude, miles	Agency	Contractor	Average payload, in lb	Length, ft	Diam, in inches	Gross weight in lb	Engine
Farside	4,000	USAF	Aeronutronics	35	23	15	1,900	Solid
Spaceobee (proposed)	350		Aerojet	40	7.7		481	Liquid
Iris (design)	200	Navy	Atlantic Research	100	14.8	12	1,000	Solid
Aerobee-Hi	193	Navy, Army, USAF	Aerojet	150	23.5	15	1,200–1,500	Liquid
Viking (8–12 series)	158	Navy	Martin	1,000	41.6	45	14,400	Liquid
Viking (1–7 series)	135	Navy	Martin	500	48.6	32	10,700	Liquid
V-2 (research-adapted)	132	Army		2,000	46.5	65	28,500	Liquid
Nike-Cajun	95	USAF		50	13	6.25	1,550	Solid
Aerobee	90	Navy, Army, USAF	Aerojet	150	18.8	15	1,070	Liquid
Terrapin	80	Navy	Republic Aviation	6–9	5.6	6.25	224	Solid
Dan	75	USAF	Univ. of Michigan	20–50	13	6.25	1,540	Liquid
Arcon (design)	70	Navy	Atlantic Research	40	11	6	250	Solid
Rockoon	70	Navy, USAF	Douglas	25	12.3	6.6	218	Solid
Deacon	50	Navy		20	12	6.25	184	Solid
WAC-Corporal	44	Army	Calif. Tech.	25	6	12	691	Solid
Rockaire	40 (AF)	Navy, USAF		40 USAF / 6.5 Navy	8.8 USAF / 4 Navy	8 USAF / 2.5 Navy	181.4 USAF / 18.1 Navy	Solid
Asp	40	Navy	Cooper Development	25	12	6.5	245	Solid
Wasp	25	Navy	Cooper Development	5–10	3.3	1	24	Solid
Hasp	20	Navy			8.6	5		Solid

TABLE 2-4 *Rocket-airplane Records*

Plane	Record
X-1	Mach 1
D-558-2	Mach 2
X-1A	Mach 2.5
X-2	Mach 3

TABLE 2-5 *The X Missiles*

Number	Engine	Velocity	Purpose	Manufacturer	Remarks
7	Ramjet	Mach 3.5	Ramjet test vehicle	Lockheed	Recoverable by parachute
10	Turbojet	Mach 1	Navaho test vehicle	North American	Lands after use; guidance test bed
17	Rocket	9,000 mph	Reentry test	Lockheed	Three-stage, 700-mile range, 600-mile altitude attained

TABLE 2-6 *The X Planes*

Number	Engine	Manufacturer	Agency	Velocity, mph	Altitude record
X-1	RMI rocket	Bell Aircraft	USAF, NACA	967	
X-1A	RMI rocket	Bell Aircraft	USAF, NACA	1,650	90,000 ft
X-2	RMI rocket	Bell Aircraft	USAF, NACA	2,200	126,000 ft
X-15	RMI rocket	North American	Navy	Mach 6 design	100 miles (design)

seek to reduce the vulnerability of our aircraft to enemy antiaircraft artillery and missiles. Surface-to-surface and intercontinental missiles are, generally, a means for delivering atomic and hydrogen bombs as a sort of "interception-proof" air weapon. These latter types are of particular interest to space travel and consequently will be covered in more detail than air-to-air, surface-to-air, and air-to-surface missiles. There seems little doubt that extrapolations of our current crop of surface-to-surface intermediate and intercontinental ballistic missiles will be tomorrow's space rockets.

Both upper-atmosphere research and aerodynamic and hypersonic research rockets are important in their relations to space flight; key American types are listed in Table 2-3. Rocket airplanes (Table 2-6), which are rapidly becoming spaceships (the X-15 is designed for 100 miles), represent another road to space flight, and it may be that an eventual combination of the X-15 and the Atlas could, in effect, put a man into deep space. The use of aerodynamic descent techniques could permit his return.

The development of the guided missile's speed, altitude, and maneuvering capabilities has a direct bearing on astronautical engineering, more so than supersonic aircraft, which to date have sought merely to explore turbulence and aerodynamic heating in terrestrial flight. The provisions necessary to protect the pilot, however—the realm of aviation medicine—have important implications regarding the well-being of man in space. They are treated in Chap. 10.

BIBLIOGRAPHY

Fiock, F., and C. Halpern: "Bibliography of Books and Published Reports on Gas Turbines, Jet Propulsion, and Rocket Power Plants," *Natl. Bur. Standards Circ.* 509, 1951; supplement: January, 1950 to December, 1953.

Bonney, E. A., et al.: "Aerodynamics, Propulsion, Structures," Principles of Guided Missile Design Series, D. Van Nostrand Company, Inc., Princeton, N.J., 1956.

Bolster, C. M.: "The Assisted Take-off of Aircraft," The Norwich University, J. J. Cabot Fund Publication No. 9, Northfield, Vt., 1950.

Kooy, J. M. J., and J. W. H. Uytenbogaart: "Ballistics of the Future," McGraw-Hill Book Company, Inc., New York, 1946.

Pendray, G. E.: "The Coming Age of Rocket Power," Harper & Brothers, New York, 1947.

Gatland, K. W.: "Development of the Guided Missile," Philosophical Library, Inc., New York (Iliffe and Sons, London), 1954.

Ley, W.: "Die Fahrt ins Weltall," Verlag Hachmeister und Thal, Leipzig, 1929.

Burgess, E.: "Frontier to Space," Chapman & Hall, Ltd., London (The Macmillan Company, New York), 1955.

General Electric Company, "Final Report, Project Hermes V-2 Missile," TUL-2000A, Report No. R52A0510, 1952.

Locke, A. S., et al.: "Guidance," Principles of Guided Missile Design Series, D. Van Nostrand Company, Inc., Princeton, N.J., 1955.

Ross, F., Jr.: "Guided Missiles," Lothrop, Lee & Shepard Co., New York, 1951.

Weyl, A. R.: "Guided Missiles," Temple Press, Ltd., London, 1952.

Parson, N. A., Jr.: "Guided Missiles in War and Peace," Harvard University Press, Cambridge, Mass., 1956.

Bowman, N. J.: "Handbook of Rockets and Guided Missiles," Perastadion, Chicago, 1957.

Newell, H. E., Jr.: "High Altitude Rocket Research," Academic Press, Inc., New York, 1953.

Kaiser, H. K.: "Kleine Raketenkunde," Mundus Verlag, Stuttgart, 1949. Translation: "Les Fusées," Amiot Dumont, Paris, 1954.

Mallan, L.: "Men, Rockets and Space Rats," Julian Messner, Inc., Publishers, New York, 1955.

Merrill, G., et al.: "Operations Research, Armament, Launching," Principles of Guided Missile Design Series, D. Van Nostrand Company, Inc., Princeton, N.J., 1956.

Valier, M.: "Raketenfahrt," R. Oldenbourg-Verlag, Munich, 1930.

Nebel, R.: "Raketenflug," Raketenflugverlag, Berlin-Reinickendorf, 1932.

Goddard, R. H.: "Rockets," American Rocket Society, New York, 1946.

de la Ferté, P. J.: "Rocket," Hutchinson & Co. (Publishers), Ltd., London, 1957.

Boyd, R. L. F., and M. J. Seaton, eds.: "Rocket Exploration of the Upper Atmosphere," Interscience Publishers, Inc., New York (Pergamon Press, Ltd., London), 1954.

Humphries, J.: "Rockets and Guided Missiles," The Macmillan Company, New York, 1956.

Goddard, R. H.: "Rocket Development," Prentice-Hall, Inc., Englewood Cliffs, N.J., 1948.

Sänger, E., and I. Bredt: "Rocket Drive for Long Range Bombers," reproduced by R. Cornog, Whittier, California. (Original issue date was 1944.)

Burchard, J. E.: "Rockets, Guns and Targets," Little, Brown & Company, Boston, 1948.

Ley, W.: "Rockets, Missiles, and Space Travel," The Viking Press, Inc., New York (Chapman & Hall, London), 1957.

Williams, B., and S. Epstein: "The Rocket Pioneers," Julian Messner, Inc., Publishers, New York, 1955.

Buedeler, W.: "To Other Worlds," Burke, London, 1954.

Gartmann, H.: "Traümer Forscher Konstrukteure," Econ Verlag, Düsseldorf, 1955.

Vaeth, J. G.: "200 Miles Up," The Ronald Press Company, New York, 1955.

Dornberger, W.: "V-2," The Viking Press, Inc., New York, 1954.

Rosen, M.: "The Viking Rocket Story," Harper & Brothers, New York, 1955.

The following journals contain valuable information on the history and development of rocketry:

Fusées et Recherche Aéronautique

Jet Propulsion (formerly *Bulletin of the American Interplanetary Society, Astronautics,* and *Journal of the American Rocket Society.* In July, 1957, *Astronautics* was reborn and henceforth appeared regularly.)

Journal of the British Interplanetary Society and *Spaceflight*

Missile Engineering

Missiles and Rockets

Ordnance

Seisan-Kenkyu, Journal of the Institute of Industrial Science, University of Tokyo

Weltraumfahrt (Earlier German journals included *Das Neuefahrzeug, Ad Astra, Rocket Flight Post, Die Rakete, Mitteilungsblatt, Raketenflug,* and *Weltraum.*)

Raketentechnik und Raumfahrtforschung

Voprosy Raketnoi Tekniki

Astronautica Acta

3

Basic Theory of Rocket Propulsion

Fundamentals

The chief purpose of the rocket engine is to deliver thrust in a given direction for a given period of time. The thrust is obtained from the ejection of microscopic particles generated completely from substances carried within the system itself. The rocket thus differs from other types of jet propulsion in that it does not require any outside material, such as air. Characteristics of rocket propulsion include the following: constant—or nearly constant—thrust, high thrust per unit area, a self-contained system, relatively simple construction, high thermal efficiency, high propellant consumption, and no recoil (in a closed mechanical system all forces balance).

The reaction principle may most easily be visualized by considering a chamber in which pressurized gas is stored. Pressure is exerted equally in all directions. Once an opening is made, however, pressure forces no longer balance. The gas rushes out, unhindered, through the opening, while on the opposite side the gas pressure still pushes against the obstructing wall, and the chamber moves in the direction of the push. This push is called thrust and is measured in pounds.

To sustain the thrust of a rocket engine, propellants are burned in the combustion chamber and are exhausted through a convergent-divergent (De Laval type) nozzle which serves to direct and control the exhaust and, at the same time, increase the thrust by 20 per cent or more. The maximum velocity of a rocket is obtained at the end of powered flight. It is thus unlike the cannon shell, the propulsive force of which is applied only while the shell

67

remains in the barrel. Also unlike the cannon shell, the rocket steadily decreases in mass until all its propellants are exhausted. Since thrust is constant, the rocket continues to accelerate. This property of the rocket permits low-g take-off and slow ascent through dense, friction-producing layers of the atmosphere—an important consideration in astronautics.

The laws of mechanics show that the action of a force on an object is equivalent to the rate of change in the object's momentum in the direction of the force. Momentum is the mathematical product of the velocity and the mass of an object. Newton's third law of motion ("to every action there is an equal and opposite reaction") comes into play here, as the reaction of the rocket is equal to the rate of change in the momentum of the exhaust, which is made up of microscopic gas particles.

It becomes apparent that high thrusts (reaction forces) will be realized if the exhaust velocity is high and the jet flow—the quantity of particles consumed in the chamber in a unit time—is great. For this, the greatest possible quantity of thermal energy, for later conversion into kinetic energy of directed motion, must be imparted to the matter ejected.

Today rockets rely on energy liberated from chemical reactions in combustion chambers to obtain the desired thermal energy. Conversion from thermal to kinetic energy is accomplished by expanding gaseous reaction products from a high chamber pressure to ambient (outside) conditions, and the efficiency of operation depends partly on the so-called expansion ratio—that is, the ratio between the pressure in the combustion chamber and the ambient pressure. If ambient pressures are zero (i.e., the rocket is in space), improved operation can be expected. Gases expanding from the nozzle throat lose heat energy through conversion into kinetic energy of directed motion (velocity). Thrust is thus produced not only in the combustion chamber, but in the nozzle expansion area.

Key items to be considered when evaluating the amount of propellants burned and ejected per unit time are the expansion ratio, the pressure under which propellants are injected into the chamber, and the nozzle throat area. Propellant feed pressure is always higher than chamber pressure, permitting continual supply to the combustion area.

It can be appreciated that rocket engines require a tremendous liberation of energy, high operating pressures, temperatures measured in thousands of degrees, and unusual propellant flow rates (all of which impose difficult problems on the designer). The development of materials resistant to high temperatures and corrosion, accurate sensing equipment, reliable propellant valves, adequate heat-transfer methods, and efficient injector-assembly operation are typical areas where near perfection is a necessity. The net efficiency of a system consisting of parts whose individual efficiencies are 99 per cent each can be as low as 35 per cent when there is a large number of parts.

Rocket-engine Calculations

The rocket is very much like a continually firing machine gun, except that the bullets of the rocket are not lead, but minute particles. If a machine gun were mounted on a rail car and allowed to fire for a period of time, it would be a primitive sort of rocket. The more bullets fired and the faster they left the gun the faster the machine-gun vehicle would move. Newton's third law shows that every action force has an equal (and opposite) reaction force. This may be written as

$$MV = mv \qquad (3\text{-}1)$$

where M and m are the masses and V and v the velocities involved. From Eq. (3-1) it becomes apparent that the velocities in any

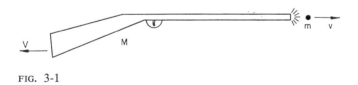

FIG. 3-1

given case will be inversely proportional to the respective masses; that is, if M is larger than m, then V will be less than v. In the case of a rocket, we are continually disposing of a part of the reaction force. The rocket designer wants to keep the over-all mass at a minimum, while assuring exhaust velocities as high as possible.

Exhaust velocity may be denoted by c and the jet flow per unit time (rate of discharge) by dm/dt. To determine the *thrust* F of any rocket engine, i.e., the thrust developed by the jet exhaust, merely find the product of the jet flow and the exhaust velocity, or

$$F = c \frac{dm}{dt} \qquad (3\text{-}2)$$

A minus sign can be inserted to indicate that the thrust and jet exhaust are opposed to each other in direction, or

$$F = -c \frac{dm}{dt} \qquad (3\text{-}3)$$

The over-all performance of a rocket engine is normally referred to by the *specific impulse* I_{sp} and may be defined as the number of pounds of thrust obtained for each pound of propellant during one second. It depends on both propellant characteristics and operating conditions, will normally rise with the expansion ratio and chamber temperature, and will decrease with increasing molecular weight of exhaust particles. It is thus evident that what we desire is a low molecular weight of combustion products and a high heat of combustion.

$$I_{sp} = \frac{F}{W_p} \qquad (3\text{-}4)$$

where W_p = weight of propellants consumed, lb/sec
       F = measured thrust, lb

The *effective exhaust velocity,* in rocket terminology, denotes the speed of exhaust-gas discharge through a De Laval nozzle. It is a term useful in describing the over-all performance of a rocket using a particular propellant or propellant combination and is directly related to performance in the combustion chamber and expansion through the nozzle. The effective exhaust velocity c is equal to the thrust coefficient of the propellent C_f multiplied by the characteristic velocity C^*, whence

$$c = C_f C^* \qquad (3\text{-}5)$$

c can also be defined as $c = F_g/W_p$, where g is the gravitational acceleration, 32 ft/sec^2.

The *thrust coefficient* is unitless and describes the amplification of thrust resulting from the expansion of gases in the divergent (expansion) section of the nozzle. To obtain C_f measured data from the test stand and design data are used.

$$C_f = \frac{F}{P_{ch}A_t} \tag{3-6}$$

where P_{ch} = chamber pressure, lb/sq in. abs
A_t = throat area of nozzle, sq in.

The second term in the effective-exhaust-velocity equation (3-5) is the *characteristic velocity* of the propellant C^*. This expresses the performance of a propellant or propellant system under given chamber operating pressures. Calculated from test data, it is associated with chemical combustion properties of the selected propellant combination.

$$C^* = \frac{P_{ch}A_t g}{W_p} \tag{3-7}$$

where P_{ch}, A_t, g, and W_p are as defined above. The units for C^* are feet per second.

Specific impulse can be related to the effective exhaust velocity by

$$I_{sp} = \frac{c}{g} \tag{3-8}$$

and it can also be calculated from C^* and C_f by

$$I_{sp} = \frac{C^* C_f}{g} \tag{3-9}$$

Specific fuel consumption W_s is measured as the number of pounds of propellant consumed per second to produce a pound of thrust and is the reciprocal of specific impulse. That is,

$$W_s = \frac{W_p}{F} \tag{3-10}$$

An inspection of Eqs. (3-2) to (3-10) shows us that we can obtain thrust by knowing the chamber pressure P_{ch}, the area of the nozzle throat A_t, and the thrust coefficient C_f.

$$F = P_{ch} A_t C_f \tag{3-11}$$

The characteristic velocity can be determined similarly:

$$C^* = \frac{g P_{ch} A_t}{W_p} = \frac{c}{C_f} \tag{3-12}$$

A rocket in a planetary gravitational field must fight attraction constantly, and the initial weight must be less than the initial thrust if the rocket is to rise. Commonly, large missiles take off at accelerations of fractions of g. (If thrust F and weight of rocket W_r are related as $F = 2W_r$, 1-g acceleration results.) If A_c is the effective upward acceleration of a rocket from any center of attraction,

$$A_c = \frac{F}{W_r} - 1 \tag{3-13}$$

It must not be forgotten, however, that gravity is not the only retarding force acting on a rocket. Atmospheric-drag resistance must be taken into account; it will vary according to the velocity of the rocket, the density of the atmosphere, and the configuration of the hull.

$$D = C_d A \tfrac{1}{2}\rho V^2 \tag{3-14}$$

where D = drag
C_d = drag coefficient
A = frontal cross-sectional area upon which C_d is based
ρ = atmospheric density
V = velocity

If, on the other hand, we suppose that the rocket is in a complete vacuum and not subject to any gravitational force, rocket acceleration becomes directly related to thrust, according to the law that force equals mass multiplied by acceleration. The rocket's equation of motion becomes, therefore,

$$c = \frac{dm}{dt} = m \frac{dv}{dt} \tag{3-15}$$

where dm/dt indicates the rate of matter discharge and dv/dt the rocket's acceleration. The instantaneous mass of the rocket is m.

Recalling the relation between the effective exhaust velocity and thrust, we have

$$F = \frac{W_p c}{g} \tag{3-16}$$

Assuming the propellant flow rate to be constant, thrust can be obtained by

$$F = \frac{m_p}{t_p} c \tag{3-17}$$

where m_p = propellant mass (initial) flow rate, lb-sec/ft
t_p = powered time until cutoff, sec

Rocket-vehicle Calculations

It is often convenient to express the instantaneous mass of the rocket m as a function of the loaded rocket m_o and the instantaneous time t. This can be done by

$$m = m_o \left(1 - \frac{m_p t}{m_o t_p} \right) \tag{3-18}$$

The term m_p/m_o is called the *mass ratio* of a rocket and relates to the ratio of the propellant mass to the over-all mass; the term t_p is the powered time. When mass ratio is expressed in this way, the figure for Viking 12, fired in February, 1955, is approximately 0.80, meaning that only 20 per cent of the over-all weight was allotted to air frame, motor, and payload.

Often the mass ratio is looked at from another angle, that is, as a ratio of the mass of a rocket before the propellants are burned and after they are completely expended. This compares the mass of a loaded rocket to its empty mass, or m_o/m_1. It has been calculated that, no matter what the propellant, the mass ratio required to propel a rocket at its own exhaust velocity is 2.72:1 (a 27-ton loaded rocket would thus have an empty weight of 10 tons). Put this way, the Viking 12 would have a mass ratio of better than 4½, a big improvement over Viking 1 (3½) or typical V-2s.

Using v as the rocket's forward velocity and c as the effective exhaust velocity, one sees that Vikings should do considerably better than equal their own exhaust speed ($v = c$), at least in theory, ignoring both gravity and air drag. The mass ratio for this simple equation is 2.72, and equals the familiar e.[1] To determine rapidly what the mass-ratio requirements would be for various forward rocket velocities, we can use

$$\frac{m_o}{m_1} = e^{\frac{v}{c}} \tag{3-19}$$

If we desire our rocket to go twice c, a mass ratio of approximately 7.4 is needed, while for $3c$ we need 20.1! At the present time our best mass ratios for large missiles lie below 7. Just how much better we can do will depend largely upon the structural engineer, but figures above 9 seem out of the question today. When we come to the problem of escape from the earth by rocket, the importance of high mass ratios, as well as high values of c, will become apparent. Meanwhile, having introduced the notions of mass ratio and e, we can now relate them to v from the equation of motion

$$v = c \log_e \frac{m_o}{m_1} \tag{3-20}$$

The restrictions which mass ratio places on final rocket velocities now become apparent: Suppose we assume one of the best propellant combinations known, liquid hydrogen and liquid oxygen (theoretical I_{sp} about 345). In a free, frictionless field, a mass-ratio-2.7 missile traveling at its exhaust's velocity would move at some 11,000 mph. To go twice as fast (all conditions still ideal) a mass ratio of 7.4 would have to be realized. And even assuming that, such a rocket would still not be able to attain the velocity of 25,000 mph required to escape from the attraction of the earth. These notions will be discussed in Chap. 7 but are introduced here to provide a logical basis for the consideration of step rockets.

In February, 1949, we recall, the multistage (or multistep)

[1] e is the base of natural logarithms (ln). The series $\log_{10}a = (\log_e a) / (\log_e 10)$ is the exponetial series, and takes us to e.

$$1 + x + \frac{x^2}{2!} + \frac{x^3}{3!} + \frac{x^4}{4!} + \frac{x^5}{5!} + \frac{x^6}{6!} + \cdots$$

Taking x to be 1, the value becomes e.

$$e = 1 + 1 + \frac{1}{2!} + \frac{1}{3!} + \frac{1}{4!} + \frac{1}{5!} + \frac{1}{6!} + \cdots$$

No matter how many terms we consider, e gets no larger than 2.7182818285 (to ten places).

rocket Bumper broke all previous altitude records. A V-2 rocket took off from the White Sands Proving Ground with a small WAC-Corporal, as its payload, fitted on the nose cone. At the moment of motor cutoff in the V-2, the WAC-Corporal began firing and added its own velocity to that of the first-stage missile. As noted in Chap. 2, it reached an altitude of 244 miles and a velocity of 5,150 mph. The V-2 used in the experiment weighed 28,297 lb and reached a maximum altitude of 63 miles. The WAC-Corporal weighed only 621 lb; it was given a boost velocity by the V-2 of 2,615 mph. It is important to note that a step rocket adds *velocities* and *not* the individual altitudes when fired at sea level. It increases the *effective mass ratio* of a missile.

One can look at the effective mass ratio in terms of the mass ratio of a single-stage vehicle that would give the desired terminal velocity. Defined for a multistage missile system, it is the mass ratio of each component raised to a power determined by the total number of steps used. The effective mass ratio of the three-stage missile, each of whose components has a mass ratio of 4, would be 4^3, or 64. Compare this attainable figure with the limitations mentioned earlier.

To calculate the final velocity of a multistage missile, assuming that, immediately upon motor cutoff of one step, the next one fires, we may use

$$V_f = Nc \log_e [\sigma(1 - \lambda) + \lambda] - gt_p \qquad (3\text{-}21)$$

where $V_f =$ final vehicle velocity (of last or top step)

$\quad N =$ number of steps

$\quad c =$ effective exhaust velocity

$\quad \sigma = m_1/m_o$

$\quad \lambda =$ payload ratio (ratio of payload, including all steps above, to weight of particular step being considered)

$\quad g =$ acceleration due to gravity

$\quad t_p =$ total time of motor firing

It is assumed that σ does not vary from step to step.

Solid-propellant Rockets

The most simple type of rocket engine, and by far the oldest, uses a solid propellant. A "solid" rocket engine, consisting of a propellant charge placed inside a combustion chamber, has no moving parts, can be easily stored, presents no particular handling and firing problems, and once ignited burns completely. The solid-propellant rocket cannot be turned off,[2] and is generally used where short firing times are desired.

Solid propellants are combinations of fuel and oxidizer. When a propellant is termed *homogeneous,* it means that the oxygen is contained in the same individual molecules as the fuel; when a propellant is termed *heterogeneous,* it means that the oxygen is contained in a substance separate from the fuel. In preparing the latter type, the constituents must be mechanically mixed, the fuel normally acting as the binding agent. Such a composite propellant is generally prepared in the liquid form and extruded into the mold selected.

Typical applications of solid-propellant rockets are jet-assisted take-off (JATO) units, ordnance rockets (where rapid burning and high specific impulses count heavily), and boosters for many types of missiles. The thrust provided by solid engines can be constant or can increase or decrease during the burning time. Constant-thrust rockets are those characterized by "neutral" burning, while "progressive" burning and "regressive" burning refer, respectively, to cases where the thrust increases and decreases during the operating time. Neutral burners and regressive burners are by far the most common types.

This introduces the matter of grain configuration. A neutral-burning rocket will require grains that provide a constant burning area. Typical grain configurations are known as tubular, internal burning, star, multigrain, cruciform, rod-and-cylinder, octaform, and multiperforated.

Some applications demand what is known as restricted-burning charges. If the rocket designer wishes to prolong the burning time of the solid propellant for a specific purpose, he will use a propellant charge partially coated with an inhibitor, thereby allowing the burning to take place in certain areas only. An unrestricted-burning

---

[2] This problem has been at least partially solved by venting the combustion chamber when shutdown is required. The idea is to lower P_{ch} to a value low enough to cause combustion to stop.

propellant has all surfaces ignited except the ends. High burning rates are obvious here.

Common oxidizers include potassium perchlorate, $KClO_4$; ammonium perchlorate, NH_4ClO_4; and ammonium nitrate, NH_4NO_3. Ballistite, a well-known propellant, is composed largely of plasticized nitrocellulose and nitroglycerine. The oldest propellants were the black powders, made of saltpeter (KNO_3), sulfur, and carbon. Composite propellants usually provide a good deal of smoke, but those prepared with *ammonium* nitrate are smokeless, as are the majority of homogeneous types. Smokeless powders are typically extruded and belong to the unrestricted-burning category.

Solid propellants are normally ignited by some sort of pyrotechnic device. A successful igniter must provide enough gas to raise the chamber pressure to a value where steady operation can be initiated. At the same time it must give enough heat to ignite the exposed burning surfaces of the propellant.

Obtaining the required thrust depends, as we have seen, on the burning surface exposed. A large burning area means a large mass flow and hence a high thrust. Low thrusts imply restricted burning areas and longer firing times. To produce the correct durations and thrusts is one of the solid-rocket engineer's tricks of the trade, and he does it largely by juggling the geometrical distribution of the charge in the chamber.

Modern solid propellants operate in the specific-impulse region up to 210 to 240 lb-sec/lb. Experts see no way of getting beyond 265 in the immediate years ahead, and 300 seems the top. Stable solid-chemical systems contain just so much energy and no more. Higher values may be forthcoming, but what we would have then would be a very *unstable* system. With a given propellant system we can raise the specific impulse somewhat by raising the temperature and pressure operating conditions, but this immediately brings us face to face with heavier, stronger materials and attendant problems.

Up to a few years ago there were no long-burning solid propellants; today they exist. The Phillips Petroleum Company has led research in this area, and when successful production units are ready, the position of the solid rocket in terms of space flight will become stronger. The Aerojet solid motor being developed for the Navy Polaris IRBM is coming along nicely, and Thiokol is making good progress also. Already some scientists and engineers have made space-flight proposals based on solid rockets. Companies like Reaction Motors and Curtiss-Wright, long solely interested in liquid engines, have now entered the solid field as well. This is indicative of the greatly increased attention being paid to solids.

Whatever the advantages and disadvantages of solid rockets, there are many areas where they will almost definitely be used in space flight, though these are manifestly subsidiary uses. Solid propellants are simple, reliable, and compare favorably with liquids in price. They can be stored readily, and since the combustion chamber is at the same time the propellant container, storage-space requirements are modest. For all purposes where small propulsive devices are required, such as moving men and materials between spaceships, aiding crews repairing vehicles, and constructing satellites, we may possibly find solid rockets used. Solid-propellant powerpacks may be used in various emergencies, when main power sources fail, or when no other sources are available. Space-ferry rockets may be solid-propelled; and when landings on planets and satellites are made, solid missiles may be used for a variety of exploration purposes. The French astronomer G. de Vaucouleurs, at a 1957 space-flight symposium at Harvard University, visualized small meteorological rockets fired into Mars's atmosphere from a satellite to make density, pressure, and other measurements.

Liquid-propellant Rockets

Liquid propellants are used where high specific impulse, longer firing time, and on-off operation are desired. As is not true of solids, liquid propellants are stored outside the combustion chamber, to which they are supplied by a variety of methods.[3] The liquid propellants are injected into the chamber by injector assemblies, atomized, and mixed to obtain a physical diffusion which achieves the greatest possible liberation of energy. Liquid-propellant rocket engines call for intense liberation of the available chemical energy —a fact that leads to rather high operating feed and combustion

[3] Some work is now being done to develop rockets in which liquid propellants can be more or less permanently stored.

pressures, temperatures, and flow rates. These, in turn, bring up a variety of material problems relating to melting point, strength, corrosion resistance, and manufacturing tolerances. Heat transfer is often critical and must be successfully worked out. The use of liquid engines, furthermore, imposes a myriad of developmental problems on the engineer, who must design special valves, turbines, pumps, and pressure-sensing devices.

Two classes of liquid propellants are used: monopropellants and bipropellants. A *monopropellant* is generally unstable and delivers energy through its own decomposition, which is generally induced by a catalytic agent such as potassium permanganate (with hydrogen peroxide). A reaction verging on explosion produces hot decomposition products that supply the reactive energy to the rocket missile. The *bipropellant* system, on the other hand, operates by ignition, whether spontaneous or applied, and involves the formation of combustion products by combination, rather than by decomposition.

In rocket terminology the propellants are referred to separately as *fuel* and *oxidizer*. Except in cases where simplicity is paramount and relatively low heats of combustion are acceptable, rocket engineers will invariably utilize the bipropellant system. Here the released energy is great and specific impulses are better, as a rule. The following combinations, listed in order of increasing specific impulse, should be noted:

Hydrogen peroxide, with self
Ethylene oxide, with self
Furfuryl alcohol–white fuming nitric acid
Hydrazine hydrate–white fuming nitric acid
Hydrazine–hydrogen peroxide
Kerosene–liquid oxygen
Hydrazine–liquid oxygen
Hydrazine–liquid ozone
Hydrazine–liquid fluorine
Hydrogen–liquid fluorine
Hydrogen–liquid ozone

An inspection of this ascending order of specific impulses I_{sp} shows the relative capabilities of various fuels and oxidizers. Thus, hydrogen peroxide used with hydrazine does better than hydrogen peroxide used alone (i.e., as a monopropellant). Hydrazine performs better with liquid oxygen than with the peroxide and further improves with liquid ozone and liquid fluorine.

Comparing the nitric acid combinations, we can see the place of the acid in terms of other oxidizers and, at the same time, compare the performance of the two fuels used with it. We can see at a glance that ozone and fluorine look particularly attractive as oxidizers, while hydrogen appears to be the best fuel. Because of its low molecular weight, it is not surprising that hydrogen should be an ideal fuel from a performance standpoint, yet its practical application in missiles has been retarded by its low density and the large propellant tanks that would be required for its use.

Ideally, propellants should not only have great propulsive efficiency, but also be stable and easy to handle, transport, and utilize. They should be nontoxic and noncorrosive and have low vapor pressures. Freezing points, boiling points, viscosity, ignition characteristics, availability, logistics, and price are a few other factors that must be taken into account before a choice of propellants is made. Unfortunately, the ideal has not been achieved, and the engineer must, in effect, choose the least of a number of evils.

The list of fuels and oxidizers that have been tested under laboratory conditions is imposing; its inclusions range from tetranitromethane and ethylene diamine to hydrocyanic acid, butyl mercaptans, and acetylene. Despite the length of the list, only a relatively few propellants find common use. Among these are liquid oxygen and ethyl alcohol (a combination exhaustively studied and used by the Germans), hydrogen peroxide, hydrazine, ammonia, nitric acid, aniline, and gasoline. These and many other liquid propellants give the rocket engineer approximately the performance he needs for missile and other applications.

Liquids are like solids in that thermodynamic calculations show us that there are definite performance limits and that these limits are not too much higher than specific-impulse values we are now accustomed to. For example, a 1957–1958 liquid-propellant rocket may use a system giving an I_{sp} of 250 lb-sec/lb. And we know that we shall not get above 400, a theoretical value for the best-known system at an elevated chamber pressure. Laboratory tests show liquid oxygen and hydrazine producing 280 lb-sec/lb at a chamber pressure of 500 lb/sq in. abs, and under like conditions fluorine and hydrogen would give 373. To assess properly any system we must know something about its types of reaction product, stability, heat content, vapor pressure, molecular weight, chamber operating conditions, and so forth. It is never possible to extract all of the available energy, since combustion losses, heat losses through the walls, residual kinetic energy, and unavailable thermal jet energy all have to be considered.

Rocket engineers, with an eye to space flight, know that, by lowering the propellant molecular weight, specific impulses will go up. They also know that lowering the ratio of specific heats (molar specific heat at constant pressure divided by molar specific heat at constant volume, in Btu per mole per degree Fahrenheit) helps also, as do high temperatures and pressures. To improve fuels light metals such as lithium, boron, and beryllium are being added, and names such as lithium borohydride are becoming common. Amine fuels are likewise the objects of careful research.

We see, then, that, in so far as stable molecular liquid systems are concerned, the energy content is higher, in general, than with solids, but limits are there. Apparently we can do nothing about altering bond energies, molecular weight, or molecular dissociation, and if we accepted the present situation as final, the road to true space travel might be so difficult as to frustrate any sustained effort.

Yet, despite the energy and controllability advantages inherent in liquids, the problems are many. Long, tedious fueling and readying periods before launching are required. Toxic fumes, acid burns, and accidental combustion of the chemical elements involved are bothersome and dangerous. Many propellants are dangerous explosives, and utmost care must be exercised in their transport and use. Others are corrosive, or have abnormally high, or inconveniently low, boiling or freezing points, or possess other physical characteristics that reduce their desirability.

Liquid-propellant Supply Systems

As a rule of thumb, it can be said that short firing times indicate a preference for solid rockets; medium durations, for pressure-fed liquid rockets; and long durations, for pump-fed liquid rockets. The reason for this is primarily weight. The more propellants carried (for greater duration), the greater the weight. Solid rockets burn at exceedingly high temperatures, so that the longer propellants burn the more resistant the chamber walls must be. This means heavier walls and more weight. In the case of pressurized liquids, heavy propellant and pressurizing fluid tanks are mandatory. For long durations the turbopump system requiring lower pressures and lighter tankage is available. An advantage of the turbopump assembly is that it does not necessarily have to increase in weight merely because it must furnish more propellants to the chamber.

A liquid-bipropellant rocket operates by burning a fuel in the presence of an oxidizer, both of which are stored in suitable tanks in quantities necessary for the mission of the vehicle. In a pressurized system, high-pressure gas, such as nitrogen or helium, is stored in a heavily constructed vessel. Upon command, this gas pressurizes the propellant tanks, forcing their contents to flow through the vehicle manifolding and injector assemblies and into the combustion chamber.

If we employ turbopumps, it is only necessary to apply a small amount of pressure to assure a constant flow into the pumps, which pick up the fuel and oxidizer and furnish them to the combustion chamber. The pumps can be driven by a turbine itself driven by the decomposition products of hydrogen peroxide, flowing out of a gas generator. These gases impinge on the blades of the turbine, which is directly coupled to the oxidizer and fuel pumps. The turbine does not have to be powered by the exhaust from a gas generator, however, but may withdraw a small percentage of the energy produced in the main combustion chamber. The advantage of the latter method lies in the fact that the auxiliary propellant (H_2O_2), the catalyst, and the gas generator can all be dispensed with, resulting in important weight savings. Disadvantages are that some energy is withdrawn, the gases may have to be diluted so that turbine-blade burnout does not result, and, furthermore, the method has not yet been subjected to exhaustive tests in actual applications.

In the *topping turbine* arrangement, the turbine wheel is immersed in the exhaust gases in the nozzle throat area of the combustion chamber. When the turbine is located in the exhaust at the mouth of the nozzle, it is termed a *blast turbine*. If gases are bled from the chamber and conducted to the turbine wheel, the device is called a *bleed turbine*. Each method has its advantages and disadvantages; in each case high temperatures and exhaust velocities must be handled, often only inches away from valves conducting liquid oxygen, whose boiling point is −298°F. Incredibly large flow rates must often be handled by lightweight pumps.

In the rocket, everything must work—every valve, switch, and control. A single failure often means the destruction of a complete missile, costing hundreds of thousands of dollars. Thus the reliability factor of each part must be fantastically high.

In a typical large rocket missile, such as the Viking, the following sequence of operation takes place: Upon command, nitrogen gas pressurizes the hydrogen peroxide–auxiliary-turbine-drive fuel tank, causing flow into the gas generator. Upon entering the generator, the hydrogen peroxide comes into contact with a permanganate catalyst and is induced to decompose rapidly. The decomposition products are then so conducted that they impinge on a turbine wheel, which drives two directly coupled pumps.

Meanwhile, the fuel and oxidizer, under slight pressure from the nitrogen-gas sphere, flow into their respective pumps, from which they are furnished directly (in the case of the oxidizer) or indirectly (in the case of the fuel) to the injector assembly and combustion chamber. Fuel is routed through a cooling jacket surrounding the combustion chamber prior to its injection and mixture with atomized liquid oxygen. A solid-propellant squib igniter is often used for igniting the mixture of oxidizer and fuel.

Exotic Propellants

During recent months the terms "exotic propellants," "Zipfuels," and "Hi-Cals" have come into the pages of the trade and technical literature of rocketry. These generally embrace efforts outside strictly conventional lines to develop high-energy power sources but do, on occasion, include merely high-energy types of liquids and solids. An unusual concept is that of using atomic oxygen found at high altitude; upon catalyzing it, following intake, great energies of recombination (into molecular form) would result. No information on the catalyst has been released.

Among the more unusual types are the hybrid-propellant systems, wherein a liquid fuel and a solid oxidizer or a solid oxidizer and a liquid fuel are employed. Army Ordnance has backed research in this field; one program involves a hypergolic hydrogen peroxide oxidizer–polyethylene fuel combination that offers a high average density and 228 lb-sec/lb specific impulses obtained at 300 lb/sq in. chamber pressure. The operation is controllable, and the system offers many advantages of the monopropellant with higher general performance.

Work has also been carried on with jelly and related propellants, sometimes affectionately known as "gunk." Under specified conditions, substances will jelly, an example being gasoline into which metallic soaps have been introduced. Jellies are very temperature-sensitive and need stronger pumping arrangements than do liquids

Free radicals are perhaps the ultimate in what might be called "conventional exotics," i.e., propellant schemes not relying on nuclear energy. They derive their attractiveness from the fact that the energy required to dissociate a substance is found stored within its radicals. What has to be done is to break the propellant into its radicals; upon controlled reassociation, the desired energy will be released. Specific impulses may range from 400 to 700 lb-sec/lb or more, an interesting increase over the solids and liquids discussed earlier.

Free-radical research is being undertaken today, notably at the National Bureau of Standards, Aerojet, and Phillips Petroleum. Many universities work on the program under Air Force contract. The problems are many, the greatest being stability and the controlled release of energy. High temperatures associated with free-radical reactions pose formidable problems, as do storage techniques. Many techniques, such as supercooling and magnetic suppression, have been tried in efforts to solve this latter problem.

We shall defer to a later chapter propulsion systems in which the energy source and the exhaust-gas source are not the same. A typical example will be found to be the ion drive.

So far, only a capsule account of some fundamentals of solid and liquid rocketry has been given. Space and emphasis have not allowed more. Tank construction, ignition techniques, turbopump design—all have to be brushed over in this rapid account. What is needed is only basic familiarity with the rocket and a comprehension of the problems facing the rocket scientist. With these appreciations, the position, importance, and weakness of the rocket in the realm of astronautics are somewhat clarified. A more accurate assessment of where we are today and how we shall reach our astronautical objectives can now be made.

BIBLIOGRAPHY

Bonney, E. A., et al.: "Aerodynamics, Propulsion, Structures," Principles of Guided Missile Design Series, D. Van Nostrand Company, Inc., Princeton, N.J., 1956.

Kooy, J. M. J., and J. W. H. Uytenbogaart: "Ballistics of the Future," McGraw-Hill Book Company, Inc., New York (Technical Publishing Company, Haarlem, Holland), 1946.

McShane, E. J., J. L. Kelley, and T. V. Reno: "Exterior Ballistics," University of Denver Press, Denver, 1953.

Wimpress, R. N.: "Internal Ballistics of Solid Fuel Rockets," McGraw-Hill Book Company, Inc., New York, 1950.

Rosser, J. B., R. R. Newton, and G. L. Gross: "Mathematical Theory of Rocket Flight," McGraw-Hill Book Company, Inc., New York, 1947.

Zucrow, M. J.: "Principles of Jet Propulsion and Gas Turbines," John Wiley & Sons, Inc., New York (Chapman & Hall, Ltd., London), 1948.

Sänger, E.: "Raketenflugtecknik," R. Oldenbourg-Verlag, Munich, 1933.

Stemmer, J.: "Raketenantriebe," Schweizerdruck und Verlagshaus, Zurich, 1952.

Goddard, R. H.: "Rocket Development," Prentice-Hall, Inc., Englewood Cliffs, N.J., 1948.

Humphries, J.: "Rockets and Guided Missiles," The Macmillan Company, New York, 1956.

Burchard, J. E., ed.: "Rockets, Guns and Targets," Little, Brown & Company, Boston, 1948.

Burgess, E.: "Rocket Propulsion," Chapman & Hall, Ltd., London (The Macmillan Company, New York), 1954.

Sutton, G. P.: "Rocket Propulsion Elements," John Wiley & Sons, Inc., New York (Chapman & Hall, Ltd., London), 1956.

Zaehlinger, A. J.: "Solid Propellant Rockets," American Rocket Company, Mich., 1955.

Mullins, B. P.: "Spontaneous Ignition of Liquid Fuels," Butterworth & Co. (Publishers), Ltd., London, 1955.

There are a number of journals where articles on rocket propulsion can be found; they include the following:

Jet Propulsion (American Rocket Society)
Astronautics (American Rocket Society)
Missile Design and Development
Missiles and Rockets
Missile Engineering
Journal of the British Interplanetary Society
Astronautica Acta
Raketentechnik und Raumfahrtforschung (German Society for Rocketry and Space Travel, DGRR)
Weltraumfahrt
Fusées et recherche aéronautique

In addition, articles on rocketry are often found in the *Aeronautical Engineering Review, Interavia, Journal of the Royal Aeronautical Society, Aviation Week, Aviation Age, Ordnance, Flight, Engineer, Aeroplane,* and the publications of such societies as the Institute of Radio Engineers, American Society of Mechanical Engineers, and American Physical Society.

A classic paper entitled The Physics of Rockets, by Seifert, Mills, and Summerfield, was published in vol. 15 nos 1–3 (January–June 1947) of the *American Journal of Physics.*

4

Satellites and Space Stations

The Nature of Orbits

Broadly speaking, everything in the universe is a satellite, is part of one, or is held to one by gravity. Tiny atoms, like frantically spinning solar systems, have electrons spinning around their nuclei. These nuclei are electrically stable, except for those of radioactive elements, but are probably vibrating slightly because of infinitely small imperfections in the physical balance of the electrons in their orbits. Atoms as part of molecules, simple or complex, are part of astronomical entities such as the earth, part of objects attached to such entities by gravity, or, if above the atmosphere, travel around them in orbits—of which more presently.

Everything in the solar system travels in some sort of orbit around the sun, for example, planets, asteroids, comets and meteors, or around the planets, for example, our moon and other planetary moons. These are the archetype of satellites because they are of the same order of magnitude as man in this context, as compared with atoms and galaxies. Ice particles, gas, and dust not orbiting around some planet do so around the sun. The whole solar system is probably orbiting around the center of our galaxy.

The universe is believed to be expanding radially, but it could conceivably be spinning itself while so doing; since everything else is spinning, there may be some ground for thinking that this general tendency imparts an over-all gyration. Bodies pursuing parabolic or hyperbolic paths are regarded as nonsatellitic with respect

87

to the body of focus, but to say that they are totally nonsatellitic presumes more than we know.

Conversely, it may be said that a free body is incapable of traveling in a perfectly straight line. Every other free body it passes pulls it aside, be it ever so slightly, and is pulled aside by it. The result is a hyperbola at the very least. A slow pass may result in a pronounced pull and a sharp change in direction. A still slower pass results in capture. "Fast" and "slow" in this sense depend on the masses of the bodies in question. The relationship may be shown by Fig. 4-1: a traveling body of fixed mass approaching bodies of progressively larger mass in both distant and near passes.

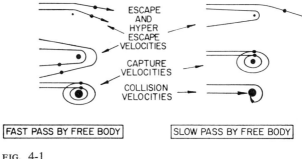

FIG. 4-1

In a given frame of reference, then, hyperbolic speed is high, parabolic speed is moderate, and elliptical speed is slow. That this depends on mass can be shown by the fact that orbital speed is based on the local value of gravity. In Newtonian terms this is stated as: Every particle of matter in the universe attracts every other particle with a force that varies as a product of their masses and inversely as the square of the distance between them.

$$F = \frac{Gm_1m_2}{r^2} \qquad (4\text{-}1)$$

where F is the force, m_1 and m_2 are the two particles, and r is the distance between them. G is the constant of gravitation; when both m_1 and m_2 equal one gram and are one centimeter apart, G equals F.

This constant is truly universal, and even more implacable than the speed of light, which can be slowed by intervening mediums. Gravity is totally unaffected by intervening matter. The constant works out to 6.673×10^{-8}, or an attraction of one fifteen-millionth of a dyne. The *Gaussian constant* (acceleration caused by the sun at one astronomical unit [1]) is more convenient in astronomical work.

When the bodies are of comparable mass, the relative acceleration of the two varies as the sum of their masses. Such bodies will be drawn together and collide if they are motionless with respect to each other, unless they are both in the same orbit around a third body, in which case tidal forces exerted by that third body will slowly separate them. The bodies in a given orbit, whatever their number, will be evenly distributed along the orbit, given enough time.

Orbits of any type always lie in a plane. Any deviation of velocity not inherent in the mechanics of the orbit changes the orbit. Slowing down reduces the size, and speeding up increases the size. Any departure from the plane changes the orbit, which is then said to be inclined to its former plane. If a satellite is in an orbit not that of the planetary equator or the solar ecliptic, it is said to be inclined by so much from these planes. With respect to the body's equator, Fig. 4-2a is inclined by 90°; orbit (b), which is on the equator, is 0°; and (c), viewed here edge on, is at 45° to the equator.

Whereas an equatorial orbit is 0°, as far as the earth is concerned, the earth's equatorial plane is inclined by a little over 23° from the earth's orbital plane (the ecliptic). The ecliptic, since we are of this planet, is taken as a reference plane in determining the orbits of all circumsolar bodies. The orientation of these various planes to each other taxes human conceptual powers and is aggravated by the fact that they are constantly precessing—a phenom-

[1] An *astronomical unit* is about 93 million miles, the earth's mean distance from the sun. It is popular for measurement in the solar system where expression in miles is rather cumbersome. For larger distances the *parsec* (1.92×10^{13} miles, or 206,265 astronomical units and a little over three *light years*) is common. The light year is used when distances become so large that any reference to parallax is no longer meaningful. See T. H. Baker, "Astronomy," 4th ed., pp. 51, 274, D. Van Nostrand Company, Inc., Princeton, N.J., 1946.

enon arising from the fact that most orbits are eccentric (Fig. 4-3) and that orbital speed plus the attraction from a third body in the direction of that third body and the orbital speed minus the pull of that third body in a direction opposite from that third body do not quite cancel out. The result is a gradual regression of the points at which satellites pass through the reference plane, which are termed the *ascending nodes* or *descending nodes,* with respect to a celestial north pole based on the plane in which lies the line con-

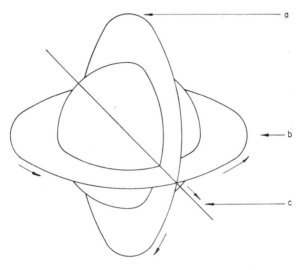

FIG. 4-2

necting the centers of gravities of the two more massive of the three bodies. These disturbances, or pulls, are called *perturbations*.

Before getting into this, we had better start off with a sort of mental development of the mechanics of orbits from simple cases, and, to make it simpler, use closed orbits. Two bodies of perfectly equal mass and shape will revolve about a point halfway between their own centers of gravity. Since they are perfect spheres, the point will be halfway between their centers, as shown in diagram *a*-1 of Fig. 4-3. Since such equality and perfection do not occur in nature, a relation somewhat like *a*-2 would be noted in bodies of near-equal mass. The center around which they revolve is nearer the body of greater mass. Even this, however, is very rare, and the larger body does not seem to move. Although it might seem, at first encounter, that an orbit is naturally like *a*-3, where the large body does not move, it will be realized on reflection that, for the larger body not to move, its mass would have to be infinite (equal to the whole universe) or the mass of the small body equal to zero (equal to nothing material, since even subatomic particles have mass). A combination of the two is meaningless.

Actual orbits are something like Fig. 4-3*b,* although even that diagram is exaggerated. The earth and moon, for example, have ratios of mass to each other of 80:1.[2] This may seem to be a large ratio, but it is rather small compared to other planets and their satellites; the earth-moon system is almost a double planet. Using the rules in Fig. 4-3*a* and *b,* we must look for the center of mass of the *combined system.* This is one-eightieth of the way from the center of the earth to the center of the moon, or only 2,900 miles, and hence well within the earth. An exaggeration of the relationship is shown in Fig. 4-3*b.* It is this systemic center of gravity that pursues the "earth's" orbit around the sun. The same relationship obtains between the center of gravity of the earth-moon system and the sun; the center of mass in that system (governed by a much smaller fraction because of the sun's tremendous relative mass of 332,000:1) is only 280 miles from the center of the sun. The moon makes the earth wobble and the two together make the sun wobble. As there are some forty other satellites and planets (not to mention planetoids, comets, etc.), the wobble in the sun's body is bewilderingly complex, though slight.

Astronomical bodies are normally spherical in general shape. To be precise they are generally oblate spheroids, which means that, in their rotation, they bulge out at the equators because of centrifugal force. Jupiter, which rotates on its axis once every 9 hr, is perceptibly oblate, needing no instruments to detect it. A satellite in an earth equatorial circular orbit would remain at a fixed altitude;

[2] This is not to be confused with the *mass ratios* considered in rocket design; there is no connection whatever.

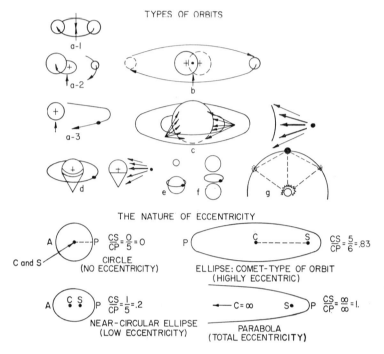

THE NATURE OF ECCENTRICITY

C and S — A — P $\frac{CS}{CP} = \frac{0}{5} = 0$ CIRCLE (NO ECCENTRICITY)

P $\frac{CS}{CP} = \frac{5}{6} = .83$ ELLIPSE: COMET-TYPE OF ORBIT (HIGHLY ECCENTRIC)

A   P $\frac{CS}{CP} = \frac{1}{5} = .2$ NEAR-CIRCULAR ELLIPSE (LOW ECCENTRICITY)

$C = \infty$ S   P $\frac{CS}{CP} = \frac{\infty}{\infty} = 1.$ PARABOLA (TOTAL ECCENTRICITY)

FIG. 4-3.   Fundamental orbit mechanics.

a-1. Two bodies of equal mass; *a*-2, two bodies of near-equal mass; *a*-3, infinite and zero mass.

b. Actual planets and satellites revolve about a common center; both bodies move.

c. Particles stay in equatorial plane in Saturn's rings because of distributed attraction.

d. Improbable planet shape needed for satellite orbit parallel to equator but not in it.

e. How two planets of unequal mass could theoretically maintain non-equatorial orbit for satellite.

f. How two planets of equal mass could accomplish the same general effect.

g. Why Trojan asteroids tend to stay put in the orbit of Jupiter.

Calculating Eccentricity: Circularity is very rare in nature, as it requires unnatural perfection in celestial bodies, both their shapes and motions. Regard the circle as a special case of the ellipse where both axes are

92   *(Continued at foot of facing page)*

a meridianal satellite would vary several miles in vectorial compromise between its own motion and the polar aberration of 13.35 miles (half the total oblateness of the earth). An orbit inclined at 45° would be subject to some complex perturbations.

In any event, looking at Fig. 4-3c, it is seen that whether or not the planet is oblate is immaterial to a satellite in an equatorial orbit. The planet has mass from pole to pole which exerts gravitational attraction, but since the face presented is symmetrical, as viewed from the satellite, the various gradations of attraction balance, and the satellite stays at the equator. To revolve in an orbit other than equatorial, the planet would have to be vertically nonsymmetrical, so that the center of gravity fell above the equator. The imaginary (and ridiculous) planet shown in Fig. 4-3d would be required. Inclined orbits around such a planet would be picturesque indeed.

Now supposing we had a symmetrical planet (and that is what we *are* going to have), could we have a satellite orbit anywhere but in the same plane with the planet's center of gravity? Theoretically, yes, under certain highly special circumstances which are extremely unlikely to occur in nature. Imagine that the earth and the moon were placed, one above the other, as shown in Fig. 4-3e. Disregard the fact they are diagrammatically within Roche's limit.[3] The attraction of the moon would lift the satellite, but not by much, since the gravity of the earth is much stronger than that of the moon. It would revolve around a point *x* between the centers of gravity of the two bodies where their pulls cancel out. Unfortunately, two bodies (especially this close) subject to no other gravi-

---

[3] Roche's limit is a distance from a planet 2.44 times its radius. A smaller body of the same general composition would find the distributed pull of the larger planet more powerful than its own cohesive forces and break up.

---

equal, and regard the sun as major focus of natural ellipses. The eccentricity is the distance from the center to the sun *CS* divided by the distance from the center to perihelion *CP*. In the circle, the sun is the center, and the orbit is concentric or circular. As *CS* becomes a larger part of *CP*, eccentricity increases. When *CS* and *CP* become so long they defy measurement, nothing can be assumed "to close the other end of the orbit." Numerator and denominator become indistinguishable. Infinity over infinity is one.

tational forces would be drawn together promptly, and the satellite would revolve around the center of gravity of the debris that followed the cataclysmic collision. The only way to keep the two apart is to have them do what they do in nature, and what the local earth satellite does in nature—revolve around each other. This could be done, and it would be found that they would revolve around the point x also. As the reader might already suspect, such a theoretical satellite would revolve around the mid-point of two equal bodies, which could also be made to stay apart in this way. Irregularities in the shape of actual bodies and a variety of perturbations abroad in the solar system would break up any real relationship of this type, once established.

This raises an interesting question for some mathematician to solve. Planets are not arranged pole to pole in the solar system, but they do have gravitational pulls, regardless of their orientation. Suppose a satellite were so established in an orbit around the earth that its axis was the earth-moon center line, how far off the orbital plane would the earth's center of gravity be? At the proper distance from the earth, could the moon's attraction hold the satellite in this odd orbit? Could the same thing be done with the earth-sun center line?

There are many other oddities about orbits, but before leaving this question of what the satellites can or cannot do, we should note one more effect which may have important implications in the placement of satellite vehicles in the distant future. This is the matter of *Trojan points*.

Lecompte de Lagrange propounded a hypothesis, in about 1760, to the effect that, if bodies are so placed before and after a planet (Jupiter, for example) that they form a set of two adjacent equilateral triangles, the system is stable. These points, Y and Z in Fig. 4-3g, are now called Trojan points.

Astronomers actually discovered some asteroids in these locations shortly after the turn of this century and began naming them after Homeric heroes of the Iliad—hence the name *Trojan asteroids*. By a superb *faux pas*, the first such asteroid was named not after a Trojan, but after Achilles, a Greek and the archenemy of Troy.

Satellite Mechanics

Before going into detail about what will occur, and is now occurring, with artificial earth satellites, it may be useful to make a quick inventory of the natural satellites in the solar system, partly to see how they behave and partly because they themselves are likely to figure prominently in interplanetary travel.

Most of the planets in the solar system are in rapid rotation. It is possibly a coincidence, but those that are not have no satellites. Mercury has a rotation equal to its short year (88 days). Venus has a rotation the length of which has been estimated to be anywhere from its own year (225 days) to about one terrestrial month. This is not rapid. Pluto, whose rate of revolution is not established but is suspected to be about six days, has no moon, and may not have originally been a planet at all.[4]

All other planets have satellites. Luna, our own moon, may be taken for granted, in the sense of being a basis of comparison. It is larger than average with respect to its parent planet and has a period of 27⅓ days. Since this is one twenty-seventh of the earth's rotational speed, the moon is a decidedly slow satellite. The inner satellite of Mars (Phobos), however, has a period shorter than Mars's rotation. This is the same as saying the Martian month, based on Phobos, is shorter than the day. Phobos is the only such satellite in the solar system, and, needless to say, the Martians, if there are any, use the other moon, Diemos, to construct their calendars.

Jupiter has eleven moons, of which the five innermost ones revolve in small, highly circular, and highly concentric orbits from west to east. Numbers VI, VII, and X also move from west to east, but in large eccentric orbits. VIII, IX, and XI revolve in the opposite direction, east to west, in very eccentric orbits. Whether or not these high eccentricities indicate that the last-named moons were captured has not been answered. It is more likely that their

[4] Demoted Planet, *Time*, Feb. 20, 1956, notes a new theory of G. Kuiper, of the University of Chicago. Pluto, said Kuiper, now appears to be a former satellite of Neptune. Its newly measured rotation of 6½ days is too slow for planets, but is fast enough for satellites, and it acts just like a former satellite of Neptune: It has a high inclination to the ecliptic and has incomparably the most eccentric orbit of any nominal planet.

eccentricity arises from a continual gravitational dispute over them with the sun.

Saturn, in addition to nine satellites, has a set of "meteoritic" rings which, taken as a whole, measure about 10 miles thick and have an outside diameter of 171,000 miles, about twice the diameter of Jupiter. The inner rings revolve faster than the outer one, according to the basic orbital laws, and exhibit gaps at certain diameters due to some subtle resonance effects in the gravitational forces at work in the Saturnian system. The existence of the rings may be explained by the fact that they lie within Roche's limit and hence are either a disrupted former satellite or congealed fragments of former fluids that were located there but which, for the same reasons, were not allowed to assemble into a satellite in the first place.

The satellites of Saturn and Jupiter range from a mere 15 to about 3,550 miles, the largest of Jupiter (and the first discovered) being Io, Europa, Ganymede, and Callisto. The largest satellites of Saturn are Japetus, Rhea, and Titan (the largest moon in the solar system).

The orbits of the five satellites of Uranus are practically circular and are almost in the parent planet's equatorial plane. So far, the structure looks utopian, but Uranus is lying down on his job and moving pole-first along the orbit! Worse than that, the pole is 8° below the orbital plane, or a total tilt of 98° to the ecliptic. Whether these satellites revolve directly or in retrograde depends on how one looks at the situation: if at the 98° angle, they are in direct rotation; but considering the angle complementary to 98°, which is 82°, they are retrograde. The whole planetary system thus travels around the sun like the propeller arc of an imaginary airplane traveling the orbit.

Neptune has two satellites, which are in orbits inclined about 20° to the planet's equator and revolve from west to east. To date no satellite has been discovered for Pluto. This may be due to the great distance of Pluto or, as Kuiper surmises, to Pluto's being a satellite that escaped from Neptune.

Nowhere in the solar system do we notice any examples of satellites having satellites. This may be due to their small size. Small mass generally goes with small size, and any original satellites these bodies may have had could have been lost by capture or perturbation against their feeble gravities. Due also to their small size, their chances of capturing any passing bodies are remote. But there is no physical reason why they could *not* have satellites of their own. The future days of space flight may provide them, but considerable study and planning will be required in the accomplishment.

Other "satellites" abroad in the solar system are asteroids, comets, and meteors. These are covered in detail in Chap. 9, but it may be noted here that they are collections of stone and metal, all possibly originating in a former planet between Mars and Jupiter and now located mainly there, but also—perhaps by the powerful perturbations of Jupiter—thrown around the solar system in a variety of orbits, somewhat according to their size. Many of these small bodies, notably the comets, travel in orbits of fantastic eccentricity which make it hard to believe they are organic members of the solar system. However, we shall discuss this in greater detail later and now return to the earth and examine the environment of earth satellites.

The workings of the orbit can be illustrated by a variation of Ball: [5] Imagine, referring to Fig. 4-4, that you look down at the earth from high above the North Pole, that you see a mountain on the Equator 1,000 miles high with a huge "disappearing gun" aimed eastward, and that the earth is still and airless. If the cannon uses a small charge, the bullet curves down to earth; if magically an airless tunnel appeared ahead of the shell wherever it went, the shell would go down around the center of the earth, back up to where the gun had been, and then continue in the elliptical path *a*. A bigger charge would make the projectile go farther and trace a more "open ellipse" and still come back (Fig. 4-4*b*); a still bigger one would miss the earth entirely (Fig. 4-4*c*). And a still bigger one would cause an ellipse at right angles to the first (Fig. 4-4*d*).

Back, now, to reality. We know a number of things. There is no such mountain, and our planet has an atmosphere. The bullet would burn up on the first two paths; if not, it would strike hard ground in the absence of those mythical tunnels. Moreover, the

[5] R. S. Ball, "Starland," pp. 121–123, Ginn & Company, Boston, 1899.

earth turns. The third path would be acceptable, for it is above the atmosphere where there is no friction of air to slow or burn, while the fourth path would always return to the altitude of start on both sides of the earth. The uneven shape of the earth (such as the mythical mountain and the actual oblateness) and the positions of the sun, moon and planets, comets, meteor swarms, planetoids, and dust clouds make small changes by virtue of their gravitational attractions. Only the sun and moon produce important effects; the effects of the others are probably too small even to measure.

It might seem that the spinning earth would give the bullet all the velocity it needs, but a little reflection shows this to be untrue. If the earth spun that fast, its speed would be nearly enough to throw off the mountain. Since it spins at less than that speed, the mountain (and everything else) is more affected by gravity than by the spin and is pulled toward the center of the earth—which is what we term "down."

Lacking the mountain and cannon, one may use a rocket to do the same things, depending on how long the motor fires. The problem of a satellite, then, is to get a rocket up there and to fire it in the right direction for a certain length of time. Assistance to this rocket in getting to orbit could be given by another rocket, or, better still, two other rockets, in the arrangement called the step rocket (Chap. 3).

Now, although the spin is not enough to start the bullet on its way, it can help. An object must be going at a certain speed at a certain distance from the center of the earth, and whether or not the earth happens to be spinning has a relatively small (but nevertheless important) effect. A rocket taking off from the Equator in an easterly direction would already have some 1,000 mph boost before it took off. Propellants being as precious as they are, we would not make things any harder than necessary by taking off due west, for then we would have to counteract the spin of the earth in addition to the already difficult task of obtaining orbital velocity.

The velocity needed to maintain a body in an orbit around the earth depends first upon the result of the determination of the gravitational pull of the earth generally, and then, specifically, at the earth's surface. Newton's inverse-square law may be applied at the altitude of the satellite, bearing in mind that the altitude is really a radius in addition to the average radius of the earth. It may be calculated by

$$V_s = \sqrt{\frac{gR^2}{r}} \qquad (4\text{-}2)$$

where V_s = orbital velocity of the satellite
     g = pull of gravity at earth's surface, 32 ft/sec^2
     R = average radius of earth
     r = radius of satellite orbit

Average radius of the earth is used because the earth is an oblate spheroid by 26.7 miles. This is slight (the earth is considerably

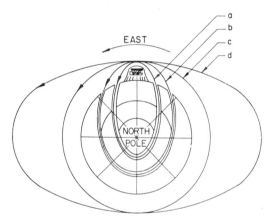

FIG. 4-4

more spherical and smooth, relatively, than a bowling ball [6]) but does have a measurable effect on the satellite if the latter has an orbit inclined to the plane of the earth's Equator.

V_s is actually the velocity of circularity, which is a good deal less than that required for escape. Orbital velocity at the earth's surface (disregarding air friction, earth spin, and the like) is about 4.9 miles/sec; at 1,075 miles, 4.39 miles/sec; at 10,000 miles, 2.3 miles/

[6] R. H. Baker, "Astronomy," 4th ed., p. 41, D. Van Nostrand Company, Inc., Princeton, N.J., 1946.

sec; at 22,300 miles, 1.6 miles/sec; and at 238,000 miles (moon's orbit), 0.613 mile/sec. The period may be simply computed by

$$T_s = 2\pi \frac{r}{V_s} \qquad (4\text{-}3)$$

where T_s is the period in hours per revolution and other values are as defined above. Typical values for the period are:

Altitude, miles	Period, hr
Earth's surface	1.41
167	1.50
350	1.59
1,075	2.01
22,300	24.00
238,000	672.00

These values assume that the earth is stationary. Intermediate values can be determined approximately from the graph in Fig. 5-5. When the earth's spin is included (in the same direction), the altitude needed to produce a given period is very much less. The 2-hr orbit, for example, shrinks from 1,075 to 790 miles. Actually, that is only academic and would be significant only in terms of the time system selected.[7]

It has been stated that escape velocity is to circular velocity as $\sqrt{2}:1$. This also means that the escape velocity needed diminishes with altitude, which, of course, is to be expected, since the pull of the earth's gravity is less. The total escape velocity from the surface of the earth is still 7 miles/sec. The velocity from orbit is simply a fraction of that whole figure. The mechanics of escape are covered in Chap. 7.

Orbital velocity decreases with distance from the parent body, but the velocity required to get to orbit increases. Thus, in estab-

[7] N. V. Petersen, General Characteristics of Satellite Vehicles, *J. Astronautics,* vol. 2, no. 2, p. 43, Summer, 1955. He notes that G. W. Hoover has suggested four time systems:

Time	Purpose
Local	Launching and return
Sidereal	Positioning in the orbit
Orbital	Determination of perigee and apogee
Elapsed	Fuel consumption and return flight

lishing a satellite, a compromise is made between the two. There is a certain minimum, however, since the earth has an atmosphere. Dr. Eugen Sänger has calculated that a 10-ton rocket at 155 miles would not lose even 1 per cent of its altitude in 100 million revolutions. At lower altitudes the air becomes denser and does so at an increasing rate. So massive a rocket would not stay up long at the lower altitudes, and a featherweight satellite vehicle would be even more seriously affected.

There is another matter. Putting a satellite into a circular orbit calls for some very precise maneuvers which must be programmed into the rockets. Unfortunately even the best attainable program will not produce an exactly circular orbit. As we saw, a noncircular orbit is both elliptical and eccentric, meaning that the altitude will vary and, because of varying altitude, the rate of speed in different parts of the orbit will vary. This will not be as dramatic as Halley's comet (which travels at a snail's pace most of the time and then gradually builds up tremendous speed for a careening "pylon turn" around the sun like a racing airplane) but it will be enough to detect, and it must be kept within certain bounds lest its closest approach to the earth during its orbit graze the top of the effective atmosphere.

To know just how long the actual satellite will stay aloft depends on a more intimate knowledge of the atmosphere than is now available, but a guess may be hazarded from the expectation that the orbit will vary between 300 and 800 miles. Data gained from the Russian satellite will assuredly be most valuable here. The atmosphere at lower altitude will be decidedly more dense than the upper one and is the part of the orbit that is of interest. Most of the friction will take place there, and the effect will be to improve the circularity of the orbit, but, unfortunately, the satellite will have been slowed below the minimum velocity necessary to maintain any permanent orbit. The period of such an actual orbit, allowing for the averaging of the fast and slow elements of it, would be about an hour and three-quarters.

Another, the 1,075-mile orbit, is widely looked on with favor because of its 2-hr period, which results not only in an even number of revolutions per day (12), but also, because of this, in a path that will be easy to trace and very convenient for navigation. A 1-hr orbit might be even more convenient—except for the higher theoretical orbital speed and the awkward fact that the orbit (which is

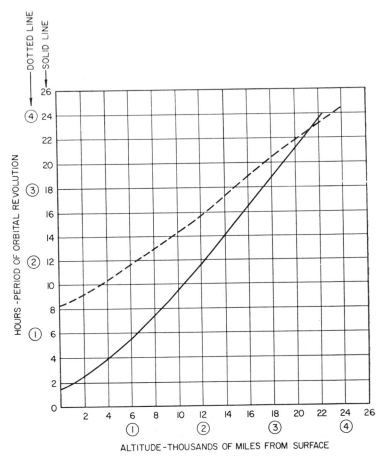

FIG. 4-5. Hours per revolution vs. altitude.

based on radial distance from the earth's nominal *center*) would be hundreds of miles underground!

To place a satellite in orbit around the earth is a highly simplified version of a flight to the moon and far simpler than a flight to Mars, which, in addition, has to reckon with the gravitational attraction of the sun. It may be stated something like this:

1. The satellite orbit must be high enough to avoid most of the denser atmosphere.

2. The orbit must be low enough that propellant consumption will not be too great. (Some economy in propellants may be obtained by higher accelerations, but these are limited by what the rockets and the prospective satellite can survive structurally.)

3. To obtain an orbit the satellite must assume a speed characteristic of the orbit.

4. Earth spin can provide part of the necessary speed with a west-to-east take-off.

5. The difference in speed must be made up by the rocket.

The size of a rocket grows rapidly with required peak altitude, and by the time the desired *average* altitude reaches 500 miles, the entire project becomes a formidable engineering undertaking. The average altitude of Sputnik I was about 400 miles; Vanguard was planned to be somewhat less.

An engineering factor of considerable concern is the fact that the rocket receives no aerodynamic lift from the atmosphere and, in ascending, is lifting dead weight consisting of payload, propellants, and the rocket air frame. The higher the shot the greater the amount of propellants needed and the greater the ratio of propellants to rocket weight. As the rocket carries more propellants, it becomes larger to accommodate them, and hence heavier. The mass of the propellants increases at an even faster rate.[8] This problem of mass ratio, fortunately, has the fairly simple solution of the step rocket.

A single rocket designed for a peak altitude of 500 miles, it will be recalled, would have a mass ratio in the neighborhood of 7:1, based on an exhaust velocity of 8,000 ft/sec. Everything depends on the exhaust velocity obtainable with a given propellant combination, for this is an index to how long a rocket must fire in order to bring itself up to an equal forward velocity under certain condi-

---

[8] As the weight of propellants rises, so also does the weight of the rocket, which must be made structurally stronger to contain the propellants. This greater weight means more propellants to lift the weight. Eventually the rocket reaches ridiculous dimensions.

tions. The length of time (corrected for a number of physical realities of the flight to be made) determines how much propellant will be required, and hence what the mass ratio should be.

A mass ratio of 7:1 (7 tons of propellant to 1 ton of rocket air frame) requires, as we know, more structural strength than can now be built into a rocket. The limit today is considerably better than 5:1. Chief among the obstacles the rocket must overcome is gravity, and the result of having overcome gravity is acceleration. A single rocket overcomes gravity at a slow rate (low acceleration) because of its dead weight.

Obviously a rocket of a certain thrust, not encumbered by unnecessary weight, would do better. The solution then, is to divide the rocket into sections; and three sections, each with an attainable mass ratio of 4:1, produces a theoretical gross mass ratio of 4^3, or 64.

We saw in Chap. 3 the tremendous importance of this whole question of mass ratio. Air friction, we found, was not serious, since the rocket penetrates the densest, friction-producing part of the atmosphere before it attains high speed. Beyond about five miles, the mean free path (interval between molecular collisions) is so long that the molecules are traveling more or less in satellite orbits themselves.

Background to Real Satellites

The idea of a minor earth satellite goes back to Pettit, of France, who stated, in about 1840, that a small moon would revolve at 6,000 miles in a period of 3 hr 15 min. This idea was used by Jules Verne to perturb the cannon-launched projectile into a circumlunar path.[9] The next related idea, already noted in Chap. 1, was the introduction of the station in space, in Lasswitz's "Auf zwei Planeten." In the light of orbital mechanics, it is easy to see why the Martian station needed some agency to suspend the law of gravity. Lasswitz, a German professor of mathematics, was thoroughly aware of this and could well have made the Martian space station a satellite vehicle. His reasoning was that a station over the pole had no motion relative to the earth, simplifying shuttle

[9] P. Moore, "Earth Satellite," p. 68, Eyre and Spottiswoode, London, 1955.

trips to the ground. Since the Martians in the story had already conquered gravity, the addition of orbital speed would have been a dubious advantage.

Professor Hermann Oberth proposed a satellite vehicle, in 1923, intended largely for experimental purposes but also as a location to stock-pile propellants for interplanetary flight. True, a multistage arrangement might fly to the moon and back, but the margin of safety would be appallingly close to zero. The station, then, would be like a mountaineer's camp established at high altitude for an assault on the summit. Velocity obtained in getting to orbit is not lost, and another take-off from there would have a decided advantage.

Austrian Count Guido von Pirquet coined a phrase which translates to something like "astronautical paradox." The paradox was that getting into orbit is the hard part of space flight. From there on, everything is easier. Von Pirquet proposed a novel method of getting to altitude. His was a system of three satellites, one at a 100-min orbit (about 450 miles), one at a 200-min orbit (about 3,000 miles), and a third in an elliptical orbit of 150 min tangent to both. He later abandoned the idea—no doubt because there are too many gravitational forces abroad in the solar system which would break up the system—but it is an interesting approach to the problem.

Hermann Noordung, of Austria, made what amounted to the first "preliminary design proposal" for a space station. There are any number of things we could criticize in it today, but in 1928 it was quite an accomplishment. He had given a great deal of thought to the real necessities of such a station. The structure consisted of three parts connected by flexible tubing and cable. The key part was a *Wohnrad,* or dwelling wheel, the ancestor of the slick modern von Braun design. What tends to conceal this fact is the very large size of the solar mirrors used. Evidently the technological development of the solar-furnace idea was rather primitive, despite ancient theoretical origins, for three mirrors were used in the whole system. The station measured just under 100 ft in diameter and was equipped with various types of room around the tubular area. It was spun at 7½ rpm to provide one earth gravity for the occupants. Counting the large annular mirror, it measured 200 ft across.

Noordung gave details on slip rings for electrical intercontact, air-lock design, solar power plant, and the like. The second part of the station was the observatory, which was cylindrical in shape, about 20 ft in diameter, and about 35 ft long. It received electricity and reprocessed air from the machine house, an unmanned adjunct consisting chiefly of a large solar mirror. Noordung speculated briefly that these might all be combined in one structure.[10]

Prophetic indeed. It remained only for advanced technology and the gifted mind of Dr. von Braun to crystallize the proposition. Making due allowances for the state of the art in those days, it would seem that the chief criticism of the station is that Noordung placed it in a 24-hr equatorial orbit on the Berlin meridian. If the observatory was intended also to observe the earth, he was making it unnecessarily difficult as to distance and seriously lacking in coverage. Only Europe, Africa, and western Asia would be visible, and the prospect would not change. Nevertheless, for its day, it was a commendable effort.

Harry Ross, of England, proposed a smaller (perhaps minimum) version of the manned satellite. In the drawing of R. A. Smith, judging by the apparent size of the earth, it is in the same fantastic orbit as the Noordung station, but it represents quite an improvement. The compact cabin is mounted in back of the 120-ft semitoroidal mirror, which has a parabolic cross section. A latticework boom is provided to allow access to the station. Normally it spins with the station. When occupants want to get out, they don space suits, climb through the inner air lock, seal it, counter-rotate (halt) the boom, and use an outer air lock which then presents a motionless aspect to a visiting spaceship.

The remaining specific manned-satellite proposal of consequence is the von Braun version. In a way it is a visual compromise between the Noordung and Ross stations. It is a wheel, 250 ft in diameter, decidedly toroidal, and much cleaner than its forerunners. The tube is some 30 ft in diameter, and the station has an impressive inside volume, including spokes and hub, of 650,000 cu ft. Entry into the spinning station is by turrets in the axle, an improvement over the Ross boom. The great finesse of the design

[10] H. Noordung, "Das Problem der Befahrung des Weltraums," p. 149, Schmidt and Company, Berlin, 1929.

suggests deep insight and typical Germanic thoroughness; the *esthetique* of the general design has a decidedly American flavor to it.

As a specific proposal, it is very ambitious and far in the future, but it has a basic importance that has somehow escaped general notice: von Braun availed himself of a new concept, called the weapons-system concept, which takes into account every single aspect of a task in one big package. This includes engineering effort, management, logistics of manufacture and operation, training, and maintenance. Put in less warlike terms, it might be called the technological-task-force concept.

Von Braun considered all the things a satellite vehicle might be called upon to do, arrived at a preliminary design, and then continually modified this design to agree with future but reasonable logistical problems. It immediately became apparent that the vehicle would have to be assembled in space, and a system of rockets was built around the realities of this operation. Prefabrication recommended simplicity of hull design, luckily, which also helped to improve appearance, and the erection of the station required a continuing operation of supply, resupply, maintenance, and personnel rotation based on a vehicle system which reused as many parts as possible. Twelve ferry rockets would be required during construction, but only four after the station had been established. One ferry trip every three days would keep the station supplied, though it could conceivably subsist on a Spartan regime for a month at a time.

Space stations of the very distant future could be very large indeed, growing by gradual accretion to perhaps metropolitan dimensions—and no doubt as haphazardly as most of the world's cities. But if, somewhat like Washington, D.C., they were made to grow according to some master plan, such cities would become, in effect, little planets. The bigger they got, the more self-sustaining they could be.

Probably the largest satellite ever seriously conceived was presented in Romick's Meteor concept (manned earth-satellite terminal evolving from earth-to-orbit ferry rockets). The system was prepared in considerable detail for the Seventh Congress of the International Astronautical Federation, held in Rome in September, 1956. Briefly, the ferry rocket is a mammoth three-stage affair with the possibility of glide recovery of the first two stages after use. The third stage goes into orbit, and, after unloading its cargo, can return by aerodynamic descent techniques. Each stage has a multirocket system. The all-up height of the standing three-step rocket is 285 ft. Motors for each booster stage develop some 500,000 lb of thrust.

All internal stringers, ribs, wings, etc. are built-up girder sections, as in airships for which Romick's company, Goodyear Aircraft, is famous. The earth-satellite terminal has an initial tubular section made of the third-stage ferry vehicles. As it is constructed, the base looks like a large cylinder, at one end of which is a rotating wheel in which the crew lives and at the other end of which are docking facilities. After the rocket bodies are joined, a 75-ft-diameter cylindrical section is added, plus the 500-ft-diameter wheel. Still later, a 1,000-ft-diameter, 3,000-ft-long cylinder goes around the whole. Romick feels that step one can be completed in days, step two in weeks, and step three in months or years. It is pointed out that the station is livable from the start, and that it grows "as circumstances dictate." The description of the wheel equipment furnishings is interesting:

The primary purpose of the wheel is to provide comfortable, satisfying, convenient living conditions. Therefore, the furnishings and arrangement of apartment and hotel quarters, offices, stores, etc., should resemble insofar as is practical conventional items. There should also be provided such community items as a gymnasium, stores, theaters, auditoriums, and churches.

A Meteor Jr. tuned-down version was outlined at the eighth congress, in October, 1957.

Here (with the addition of propulsion) is the germ of the "space ark," an interstellar ship designed like a self-sustaining world, so that the occupants could make journeys of tremendous duration. Making the little "worlds" self-sustaining (the province of ecology) and well-protected (engineering) is a problem that applies equally well to spaceships. In this chapter the stress is on the orbital aspect of the space station. A spaceship, in a manner of speaking, is a propelled space station. Discussion of the propulsive aspect of spaceships can be found in Chaps. 3 and 14. Meanwhile, before considering Vanguard, it would be well to trace the events that led up to it.

Orbiter and Other Candidates

Since 1946, the Office of Naval Research has been interested in high-altitude rocket research. By the time the satellite idea had crystallized in the mind of Secretary Forrestal, the proposition of the intercontinental ballistic missile was also coming to the fore. During Forrestal's secretaryship, Project Rand began, under Douglas Aircraft. Several studies were made on satellites, mainly from the viewpoint of propulsion systems necessary to deliver a satellite to orbit. Much useful work was performed, and data gathered during these studies came to fruition in the programs for Titan and Atlas.

By 1948, the High Altitude Panel was organized under Dr. James A. van Allen, of the University of Iowa, for the purpose of exploring the upper atmosphere by means of rockets. Much of the work done and planned to be done was in the nature of exploring our own atmosphere, noting such matters as pressures, densities, temperature gradients, ionospherics, and cosmic rays. The panel is known to have considered a satellite vehicle—a 20- to 75-lb satellite sphere for the purpose of measuring drag. This is not to be confused with the *falling-sphere method,* in which a rocket, near the top of its trajectory, discharges a small sphere which falls to earth and which, by means of a special type of accelerometer, measures the rate of deceleration induced by friction with the atmosphere. This falling sphere has as its purpose measurement of the vertical of atmospheric density, whereas the satellite the panel considered was to travel in an actual orbit, and geodetic measurements taken therefrom would give an indication of the "top" of the entire earth's atmosphere.

On December 29, 1948, the Secretary of Defense, James V. Forrestal, mentioned that a study for the construction of artificial satellites was underway. According to Eric Bergaust, the so-called Forrestal Project soon died. In 1949, A. V. Cleaver, of the British Interplanetary Society, presented a paper which seemed to keynote the thinking of the world's scientists on the matter of artificial satellites. In a nutshell, he said that we might well try for an unmanned satellite first and then, later, work on regular manned satellites, and finally attempt a flight around the moon.

In 1949, Project Bumper made good. This project had as its mission the attainment of extreme altitudes by virtue of the step-rocket configuration. As the history of rocketry has revealed, this principle was long known, but never before had it been attempted on a large rocket with so ambitious an intent. In the early part of that year, a modified V-2 rocket, with a WAC-Corporal mounted in its nose, soared into the air over White Sands Proving Ground, New Mexico. At something over 50 miles, the motor of the giant rocket cut out. At this moment, the WAC-Corporal was discharged from the nose of the larger rocket and, adding its velocity to that of the V-2, attained an altitude of 244 miles. To the layman, who read a report of the flight in the newspaper, it was interesting. But to the scientists engaged in rocket development it was heartening indeed. They recognized it at once as a landmark in the slow and tortuous progress toward space flight.

In 1950, the Second Congress of the International Astronautical Federation convened in London, and the featured topic was that of artificial satellites. Of the many significant papers presented at that congress, one, titled "Minimum Satellite Vehicles," presented jointly by Gatland, Kunesch, and Dixon (all of the British Interplanetary Society), seemed to keynote the mood of the moment. The idea of minimum satellite vehicles had undoubtedly been in the air for a number of years, but this was the first articulate expression of it. The paper was theoretical in nature, being rather an engineering proposal, but the general line of thinking is familiar today. Three models, A, B, and C, were of the classical vertically arranged three-stage configuration. All were intended for a 500-mile orbit. Model A carried no payload at all, but intended the third step itself to assume the orbit. Model B was to carry 100 lb of instruments, and Model C was to carry 100 lb plus guidance equipment. (Needless to say the rockets got larger and larger as the payload increased.) Model D was a bullet-shaped arrangement of three stages, carried one inside the other, which was designed to carry a 220-lb payload. The paper was chiefly a study of vehicles and propulsion. It told, in effect, "how to get the satellite up there," but it gave no design for the satellite itself.

In 1952, the American Rocket Society formed the *ad hoc* Space Flight Committee to assess the state of the art. It worked with Dr. Allan Waterman, of the National Science Foundation, and later became permanent. Members and chairmen of this committee read like the Blue Book of American Rocketry. They include Milton Rosen, Fred C. Durant, Andrew W. Haley, John Youngquist, Kurt Stehling, Sam Hoffman, and Francis van der Wahl.

During this same year, it is reported, Project ARC was conceived at the Aerojet Engineering Corporation, in California. Very little is known about it, except that the propulsion system envisioned the use of fluorine and hydrazine. Whether it was impractical or simply premature is hard to say—at any rate, it was soon abandoned. If it had been officially proposed, it was not bought.

Also in 1952 was proposed the Model T space station. The concept of the von Braun wheel-shaped space station was not yet widely known to the layman, but rocket engineers were aware of it, and this Model T space station was somewhat in the nature of a revolt against what was beginning to be called the "Queen Mary approach." An inspection of parameters, however, reveals that it was not a complete revolt. It assumed a fantastic mass ratio of $9:1$, a specific impulse of 280 lb-sec/sec per stage, and a main power plant of 50,000-lb thrust. In 1952 these were also bold ideas. But for all its boldness, its man-carrying capabilities were modest. It was specified that it should be manned by two 100-lb men. (Kurt Stehling is said to have commented, at a symposium, that two 100-lb *women* were easier to find! He was astonished somewhat later to find himself the target of fan mail from an appreciative fair sex.)

There followed, in 1953, a proposal for a minimum satellite vehicle entitled MOUSE (an abbreviation for minimum orbital unmanned satellite, earth), which went through several stages of concept and was a sort of complement to the proposal of Gatland, Kunesch, and Dixon. Whereas they proposed vehicles but no satellite, directly, the propounder of MOUSE, Dr. S. Fred Singer of the University of Maryland, in effect propounded a satellite but no vehicle. Two of the three designs were spherical in shape, and one was cylindrical. Pictures of the design reveal it to embody compact packaging and reflect the author's intimate acquaintance with the design of instrumentation for rockets. It had certain overtones of the High Altitude Panel, of which Dr. Singer had been a member. The original weight, as Dr. Singer conceived it, was 100 lb, but this later dwindled to 50.

On June 25, 1954, at a meeting which took place in Washington, Commander George Hoover, of ONR, and Alexander Satin, then Chief Engineer of ONR's Air Branch, received a group of distinguished visitors. Present at the meeting were Dr. von Braun; Fred Durant, then president of the International Astronautical Federation; Harvard astronomer Fred L. Whipple; Dr. Fred Singer; and David Young, of Aerojet-General. The object of the meeting was to discuss the best way to set up a research program on satellites.

It was determined that no specific satellite program was underway at that time, but Dr. von Braun is reported, according to Bergaust's and Beller's book "Satellite," to have suggested the possibility of using a combination of the Redstone and Loki missiles. After some discussion, it was concluded that such a program was possible if the Army would be interested in it as an official project. Generalities concerning the nature of the instrumental payload and uses to which such a satellite might be put were discussed.

The candidate satellite was minimal indeed; it was to weigh only 5 lb. It had the virtue of being simple, cheap, and quick of attainment. This, of course, was not the only way the job could have been done, but it was the one which required the minimum amount of modification engineering and the minimum amount of major development.

The Chief of Naval Research was approached on the subject; he became interested and authorized conversations with Redstone Arsenal. On August 3, Navy representatives discussed the matter with Commanding General H. N. Toftoy and Dr. von Braun. General Toftoy agreed in principle, provided that Army participation was concurred in by the Chief of Army Ordnance. The Chief of Ordnance gave his concurrence with the proviso that the effort should not slow down the Army's missile program.

ONR was then contacted and the Chief of Naval Research gave permission to the Air Branch to proceed with preliminary work under Commander Hoover as Project Officer. The effort was entitled Project Orbiter and was classified confidential. The Navy agreed to handle the design, development, and construction of the satellite and to arrange for tracking facilities, logistic support, and the recording and interpreting of the scientific data. The Army agreed to take the responsibility for the over-all design, construction, and launching of the satellite vehicle.

ONR immediately let contracts to the Varo Manufacturing Company, the Alabama Engineering and Tool Company (for the design and development of Loki cluster *mount* and the guidance system), and the Aerophysics Corporation (for the International Business Machines Corporation to handle the communications aspect).

The operation was clearly a global one, and the matter of logistic support (later dramatized in connection with project Vanguard) became immediately evident. At that time, since no one had attempted to launch a satellite before, there were no existing launching sites or tracking stations. The Chief of Naval Operations agreed to handle the transportation aspect of logistics.

On January 20, 1955, a series of contacts were made in the top levels of the government. The matter was submitted to the Assistant Secretary of Defense for research and development, and went up the line until it eventually came to the desk of the President. Project Orbiter held a total of five meetings, the last one of which fell in May. It was decided to attempt an equatorial orbit at first, and later a polar orbit. The Naval Research Laboratory offered its ingenious Minitrack for electronic tracking of the satellite. Meanwhile, in April of 1955, ONR had begun plans for an expedition (two years hence) to establish a launching site which would begin operations in the latter part of that year.

BIBLIOGRAPHY

Ryan, C., ed., with contributions by J. Kaplan, W. von Braun, H. Haber, W. Ley, O. Schachter, and F. L. Whipple: "Across the Space Frontier," The Viking Press, Inc., New York, 1952. This book is probably the best for the beginner, as it covers the space station on a broad canvas of upper-atmosphere physics, space medicine, astronomy, and space law; the problem of getting to orbit; and the space station itself. For these special chapters, see Prelude to Space Travel, by W. von Braun, and A Station in Space, by W. Ley.

Carter, L. J., ed.: "The Artificial Satellite," proceedings of the Second Congress of the International Astronautical Federation, British Interplanetary Society, 1951.

Krieger, F. J.: "A Case Book on Astronautics," Rand Corporation, 1956 (vol. 1), 1957 (vol. 2).

Logan, J., ed.: "The Complete Book of Outer Space," Maco Magazine Corporation, 1953. See part 3, pp. 16–23, A Station in Space, by W. von Braun. Disregard the pictures on pp. 16, 17, 21, and 22.

Moore, P.: "Earth Satellites," W. W. Norton & Company, Inc., New York, 1956.

"Earth Satellites as Research Vehicles," Franklin Institute, Philadelphia, 1956.

Clarke, A. C.: "The Exploration of Space," Temple Press, Ltd., London, 1951. See Stations in Space, chap. 15.

————: "Going into Space," Harper & Brothers, New York, 1954. See Citizens in Space, chap. 6.

————: "Interplanetary Flight," pp. 104–112, Temple Press, Ltd., London, 1950.

————: "The Making of a Moon," Harper & Brothers, New York, 1957.

Ananof, A.: "L'Astronautique" (Science et vie; hors de serie), pp. 134–152, Paris, 1952.

————: "L'Astronautique," chap. 7, part 4, Librarie Arthéme Fayard, Paris, 1950.

"International Geophysical Year," National Academy of Sciences, Washington, D.C., 1956.

Oberth, H.: "Man into Space," Harper & Brothers, New York, 1957.

————: "Menschen in Weltraum," chaps. 2 and 4, Econ Verlag, Düsseldorf, 1954.

"Orbital and Satellite Vehicles," Summer-course notes, Massachusetts Institute of Technology, Cambridge, 1956.

Noordung, H.: "Problem der Befahrung des Weltraums," Schmidt and Company, Berlin, 1929, starting on p. 96 with Eine Warte im leeren Weltraum through Die Erforschung der Sternenwelt, which ends on p. 159.

Valier, M.: "Rakenfahrt," R. Oldenbourg-Verlag, Munich, 1930, section entitled Fahrten in der Nähe der Erde, pp. 20–24. There is an interesting table on p. 23 which examines the consequences of vertical and horizontal launching.

Stemmer, J.: "Raketenantriebe," pp. 493–501 (Der Kunstliche Mond), Schweizerdruck und Verlagshaus, Zurich, 1952.

Carter, L. J., ed.: "Realities of Space Travel," Putnam & Co., Ltd., London, 1957.

Ley, W.: "Rockets, Missiles and Space Travel," The Viking Press, Inc., New York, 1957.

Stemmer, J., ed.: "Space Flight Problems," proceedings of the Fourth Congress of the International Astronautical Federation, Sweizerishe Astronautische Arbeitsgemeinschaft, Zurich, Switzerland, 1954. The following papers presented at the congress are applicable:

> Stehling, K.: Earth Scanning Techniques for a Small Orbital Rocket Vehicle, pp. 63–70.

> Schuette, K.: Die Bahnbestimmung aus dem Vektor der Eigengeschwindigkeit und der Einfluss einer Aenderung derselben auf die Bahnelemente, pp. 89–102.

> Cardozo, A. L.: A General Formula for the Relation between a Field of Forces, and the Orbit of a Body Therein, pp. 103–106.

> Dixon, A. E., K. W. Gatland, and A. M. Kunesch: Fabrication of the Orbital Vehicle, pp. 125–135.

> Singer, S. F.: A Minimum Orbital Instrumented Satellite—Now, pp. 136–139.

Gartmann, H., ed.: "Raumfahrtforschung," R. Oldenbourg-Verlag, Munich, 1952. (Chapter 2, Die Aussenstation, by Rolf Engel, Dr. U. T. Bödewadt, and Kurt Hanisch, and chap. 3, Stationen im Weltraum, which is somewhat parallel to chap. 4 in *"Menschen in Weltraum."*)

Bergaust, E., and W. Beller: "Satellite," Hanover House, New York, 1956.

van Allen, J. A., ed.: "Scientific Uses of Earth Satellites," University of Michigan Press, Ann Arbor, Mich., 1956.

Kunesch, A. M., and K. W. Gatland: "Space Travel," chap. 4 (The Artificial Satellite), Philosophical Library, Inc., New York, 1953.

Canney, H. E., Jr., and F. I. Ordway, III: Uses of the Artificial Satellite. *Astronaut. Acta,* vol. 2, no. 4, 1956; vol. 3, no. 1, 1957.

Caiden, M.: "Vanguard," E. P. Dutton & Co., Inc., New York, 1957.

ARTICLES IN THE *Journal of the British Interplanetary Society*

The Artificial Satellite (editorial), vol. 14, no. 6, p. 297, 1955.

Logie, J.: Effect of Tidal Friction on a Near Satellite, vol. 13, no. 3, p. 170, 1954.

Lawden, D.: Entry into Circular Orbits, vol. 13, no. 1, p. 27, 1954.

Singer, S. F.: Research in the Upper Atmosphere with Sounding Rockets and Earth Satellite Vehicles, vol. 11, no. 2, p. 61, 1952.

Cross, C. S.: The Fundamental Basis of Power Generation in a Satellite Vehicle, vol. 11, no. 3, p. 117, 1952.

Lawden, D.: The Determination of Minimal Orbits, vol. 11, no. 5, p. 216, 1952.

Whipple, F. L.: Astronomy from the Space Station, vol. 12, no. 1, p. 10, 1953.

von Braun, W.: The Early Steps in the Realization of the Space Station, vol. 12, no. 1, p. 23, 1953.

Burgess, E., and C. A. Cross: The Martian Probe, vol. 12, no. 2, p. 72, 1953.

Moore, P.: Has the Earth a Second Moon?, vol. 13, no. 4, p. 202, 1954.

Cross, C. A.: Orbits for an Extraterrestrial Observatory, vol. 13, no. 4, p. 204, 1954.

Extraterrestrial Observatories, Their Purpose and Location, vol. 14, no. 3, p. 137, 1955.

Lawden, D.: The Calculation of Orbits, vol. 14, no. 4, p. 204, 1955.

Gatland, Dixon, and Kunesch: Conception of an Instrument-carrying Orbital Rocket, vol. 10, no. 3, p. 115, 1951.

Gatland, K. W.: Rockets in Circular Orbits, vol. 8, no. 2, p. 52, 1949.

Ross, H. E.: Orbital Bases, vol. 8, no. 1, p. 1, 1949.

Wexler, H.: Observing Weather from a Satellite Vehicle, vol. 13, no. 5, p. 269, 1954.

Anonymous: Power Supplies for an Instrument-carrying Satellite, vol. 13, no. 5, p. 294, 1954.

Power Supplies and Telemetry for an Instrumented Artificial Satellite: Part I, Orbital Considerations, by E. C. White; Part II, Instrumentation and Telemetry, by J. Foley; Part III, Availability of Power, by R. G. Wilkins, vol. 15, no. 14, p. 177, 1956.

Humphries, J.: Observation of Artificial Satellites, vol. 15, no. 6, p. 247, 1956; vol. 16, no. 1, p. 57, 1957.

Lawden, D. K.: The Simulation of Gravity (on a satellite), vol. 16, no. 3, p. 134, 1957.

5
Vanguard, Explorer, and Beyond

But in April of 1955, a curious coincidence took place. According to reports, the National Science Foundation had been conducting a preliminary study on a satellite of its own. Some have said that this was in response to the proposals of the American Rocket Society. In any event, the announcement of this new satellite (Vanguard) came as a complete surprise to ONR. Thus Orbiter, by something of an irony of fate, was forced to give way to a second satellite program which required considerably more development.

The ARS memorandum (which is thought by some to have helped persuade the National Science Foundation, though officials there deny it emphatically) was submitted in 1954 and was entitled "The Utility of an Artificial Unmanned Satellite Vehicle."

From Memos to Satellites

The ARS memo had been prepared by a committee under the chairmanship of Milton W. Rosen. It assessed the state of the art of rocketry and indicated a number of fields in which an artificial satellite could make a significant contribution: astronomy, astrophysics, biology, communications, geodesy, geophysics, and certain experiments made possible by the novelty of the space environment.

Project Orbiter was soon to be completely eclipsed. In retrospect, it never had much of a chance against the massive preparation already underway on an international basis. Project Vanguard began to come into focus in the fall of 1954.

After collaborative studies with other organizations in the International Council of Scientific Unions (ICSU), the special committee for the International Geophysical Year, CSAGI (Comité Spéciale pour l'Annee Géophysique Internationale), with headquarters in Brussels, Belgium, made a formal recommendation that a satellite, and the related problems of instrumentation, telemetering, power supply, and control, be studied. The United States National Committee for the International Geophysical Year did so, concluded the satellite to be important and feasible, and sent a memorandum to this effect to the National Science Foundation and the National Academy of Science on March 14, 1955. By May 6, a preliminary program was submitted to the government. A regional conference of the Western Hemisphere participants in the International Geophysical Year convened in Rio de Janeiro to work out problems of global communication procedures. A representative of the Soviet Union was there and stated that his government would cooperate. On July 29, 1955, the White House, simultaneously with Dr. Marcel Nicollet, of CSAGI, in Brussels, made the historic announcement. Technically, the White House announcement was on behalf of the National Science Foundation and the National Academy of Sciences and said, in substance, "The United States, as part of its contribution to the International Geophysical Year, will launch an unmanned Earth-circling satellite vehicle."

Two phrases in this quotation should be noted carefully. The first phrase, ". . . as a part of its contribution . . ." reminds us that, although the establishment of a satellite is easily the most spectacular effort in the International Geophysical Year, it is by no means the whole effort. The International Geophysical Year is, in a sense, a novelty, but largely so because of its wide scope and participation. Similar undertakings, called Polar Years, which were somewhat geodetic in nature, took place in 1882 and 1932 and were concerned largely with such matters as measuring meridians.

The second phrase to be noted is "will launch." It may be imagined that a number of American scientists have gulped at this categoric statement of technological confidence. The implementation of Vanguard was something more than the improvement of existing systems; it was a bold step into a new age of science. As no one had previously established a satellite in orbit, or had even tried to, this was a firm statement indeed.

Needless to say, the announcement of a satellite vehicle had a tremendous impact on newspaper headlines. Released, as it was, a few days before the Sixth Congress of the International Astronautical Federation was to convene in Copenhagen, Denmark, it bathed the proceedings of that body in a dazzling limelight of publicity. And it came at a particularly fortunate juncture in the development of the organization, which had been struggling since its inception for formal scientific recognition. It had boasted a formidable array of competent scientists and engineers, but acceptance by the international body of scientific men is come by only with the greatest difficulty.

It may be said that the announcement of Project Vanguard vindicated the federation's position. Attendance at the next congress, in Rome, Italy, was, by previous standards, overwhelming. There were perhaps fewer than twenty American delegates and alternates at Copenhagen; in Rome there were over fifty.

The activities of the International Geophysical Year are participated in by practically every educated nation on the face of the earth, which is unprecedented by itself, and they embrace a wide range of studies not only on satellites but high-altitude rocket launchings to gather data on cosmic rays, solar activities, aurora and air glow, ionospherics, and meteorology. These matters are being measured in other ways from the ground and include also surface measurements of geomagnetism, geodetics, gravity, glaciology, seismology, and oceanography.

A significant paper at the Copenhagen Congress was delivered by Krafft Ehricke and dealt with the concept known as the *satelloid*. No pictures which might indicate its physical appearance have been published, but it would perhaps not be too imprudent to visualize it as a delta-winged rocket airplane similar to the third stage of the von Braun satellite rocket. The important feature of the satelloid is that it represents a compromise of a true satellite. Bearing in mind the very heavy requirements for propellants to establish a satellite in a 1,000-mile orbit, the idea of the satelloid is to establish a vehicle at a much lower altitude, possibly in the range of 90 to 100 miles, using 2,400 lb of propellants, applied in short bursts now and then, to overcome air friction and maintain a nominal average speed of 17,400 mph at that altitude for about six days.

With its delta wings, it would become a supersonic glider to re-enter the atmosphere when it could no longer maintain the "orbit."

With the announcement of the American satellite came an immediate news release from the Russians. They, too, would launch a satellite. The same secrecy that astonished Project Orbiter naturally also caught the Soviet Union by surprise. The United States made an important propaganda victory with its announcement, and the Soviet announcement was partly a matter of saving face. Not completely, however. The Russians had long been interested in astronautics, and an examination of the Vanguard orbit revealed that the limits of 40° north and south of the Equator severely limited the visibility of the satellite from within the Soviet Union.

It is also significant that the satellite was included within the International Geophysical Year, an international effort. It was made clear that the information picked up by the satellite would be equally available to all nations. This was in the spirit of the international scientific collaboration, but it was also a disarming gesture to counteract the fact that the satellite, in working its way around the planet, traveled over (and technically trespassed) the national boundaries of nearly every major nation on earth. Unlimited vertical sovereignty is a moot point among the world's lawyers. Arguments, pro and con, have a flavor akin to a discussion of freedom of the seas, but with one crucial exception. A vessel on the high seas cannot perform reconnaissance over other countries or conveniently send missiles into them.

Russia took the announcement about the satellite without a ripple, a curious thing, considering how touchy she is about her borders. The fact was, obviously, that, since she planned to put up a satellite also, she could not object to Vanguard.

The first Russian satellite had a steeply inclined orbit, bringing most of the earth within its view. Knowing the Soviet frame of mind, one may surmise that the USSR, having been "scooped" on the announcement of the satellite, resolved not to be outdone in the satellite itself, and the world saw what happened. Pundits long observed that the Reds would no doubt attempt to have a bigger, heavier, higher satellite, and have it up there first. Since they succeeded, American technological prestige has suffered a shattering blow, particularly in the eyes of the smaller, noncommitted nations of the world.

Earth Satellite Program—Project Vanguard

The organizational structure of Vanguard is rather small, as the bulk of affairs is handled on a day-to-day basis by the scientists and engineers concerned, and by the contractors engaged on the project. The Army and Air Force came into the picture somewhat later, but maintain regular liaison.

The Navy recognizes three requirements. Its satellites, at least one of them, must be established during the International Geophysical Year. Secondly, once established, the Navy must prove the satellite is really "up there"—which is not as simple as it seems, for it is like trying to locate a golf ball traveling at supersonic speed at 60,000 ft. Thirdly, the satellite must vindicate itself; it must in some way aid in the successful prosecution of an experiment of unquestioned value to science. It will probably be able to do this many times over, given time, but it must be able to do it at least once during the program period.

Other responsibilities are as follows: The Air Force, under whose jurisdiction lies the great installation of Patrick Air Force Base—the nesting ground of big missiles—will have the responsibility for the launching of Vanguard and the logistical support connected with launching. The Army has the responsibility for tracking the satellite. Army radars and other tracking devices have reached a startling degree of development, and the Signal Engineering Laboratories, at Fort Monmouth, New Jersey, have charge of this. The competition among the services in connection with missiles is hot, but in the matter of satellites it is a rather friendly one.

It should be noted in Fig. 5-1 that the lines and arrows connecting the various organizations do not represent lines of command; they should more properly be interpreted as lines for the interchange of information and assistance. The government, the military, education, and industry are making important contributions on a more or less equal footing. Since the vehicle used to raise the satellite to orbit is strikingly similar to any large ballistic missile and the military is the only agency making vehicles of this type, the details of the three-stage rocket necessarily are classified.

Thus, while the effort is widely identified with the government, this is not strictly true. The complicated network involves the ICSU, CSAGI, the national IGY committees in each country, and a host of agencies similar to that shown for the United States. In the American setup, we see the National Science Foundation, the National Academy of Sciences, the Bureau of Standards, the Smith-

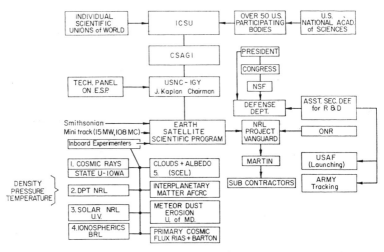

FIG. 5-1.   International Geophysical Year earth-satellite-vehicle program.

sonian Institution, military agencies, industrial firms, universities, scientific associations, amateur satellite-observing teams, and so on. It is complicated just for one country, but each national network is then integrated to a supernetwork which links the entire globe together.

In the immediate sense, however, the hardware may be said to be the affair of the Naval Research Laboratory, under the general direction of Dr. John Hagen. The prime contractor for Vanguard is the Martin Company, which has placed operations under the direction of Elliot Felt. The original contract was for $2,035,033,

but by now has grown to be in the general neighborhood of
$100,000,000.

The total vehicle is about 72 ft high and 45 in. in diameter at
the base, and it weighs approximately 11 tons. Eight or ten of the
vehicles will be launched from Patrick Air Force Base, in Florida,

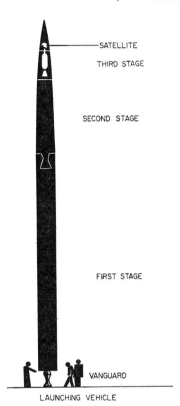

SATELLITE

THIRD STAGE

SECOND STAGE

FIRST STAGE

VANGUARD

LAUNCHING VEHICLE

FIG. 5-2. Vanguard launching
vehicle. (*Martin.*)

during the International Geophysical Year, if possible. Expected
perigee is 200 and the apogee about 800 miles, though some
sources have quoted as high as 1,400.

Martin has subcontracted Vanguard extensively. The major sub-
contractors (those having to do with major or critical components)
are as follows: The first-stage vehicle has been awarded to General
Electric in so far as the engine is concerned. The unit develops

28,000 lb of thrust and has the world wondering how it will adequately lift a gross weight of nearly 22,000 lb with the amount of propellants the vehicle can carry. Prototypes of smaller satellites weighing as little as 10 lb have been developed. In any event, the engine uses a combination of liquid oxygen and kerosene (UMF-1). Hydrogen peroxide powers the turbopumps.

The second stage, which contains controls for both the first and third stages, has the job of maneuvering the rocket progressively into just the right angle of elevation and azimuth for a correct shot into orbit. It is being constructed by the Aerojet-General Corporation, of Azusa, California. It contains the third stage under a nose cone which protects the fragile satellite from incineration by air friction encountered in the ascent through the atmosphere. The engine for the second stage is powered by white fuming nitric acid (RFNA) and unsymmetrical dimethylhydrazine. It burns for about 2 min and builds up 8,000 lb of thrust. Propellants are not pumped, but are delivered by helium pressurization.

Two companies compete for the power plant for the third stage: the Grand Central Rocket Company, of Redlands, California, and the Allegheny Ballistics Laboratory (operated by Hercules Powder Company). The third stage is powered by a solid-propellant rocket producing 2,800 lb thrust over 25 sec burning time. Tiny spinner rockets for the rotation of the third stage (in the fashion of an artillery shell) have been developed by the Atlantic Research Corporation on a contract awarded to them in July, 1956. Magnetic eddy currents, inducted from the general earth field, may slow it down. But no matter, the rocket has already been ejected—and it tags along behind the satellite, inert and probably useless.

The angle of declination of 40° is surveyed in at the launching pad in Patrick Air Force Base, and the cumulative effect of the launching is that of a direction toward the southeast, in the general direction of Johannesburg.

The first stage fires for about 140 sec, achieves perhaps 35 miles altitude and 3,500 mph. At cutoff it has been tilted by the control system to a nose-up angle of about 45°. It "peels off" into a graceful trajectory which presently curves back to earth.

The second stage takes over instantly, to conserve previous velocity, burns for about 130 sec, burns out at 140 miles, but, having achieved 10,000 mph, coasts on up to 300 miles. It remains with the third stage nearly to the altitude of the satellite-orbit entry point. The nose cone has heated to 1000°F but has protected the fragile cargo inside. The second stage is jettisoned and plummets back into the atmosphere after a trajectory resembling, but much larger than, that of the first stage.

The third stage is launched spinning from the second at the proper time; it is now exposed, since the protective nose cone has been dispensed with. It begins firing at about 300 miles, fires for an unknown number of seconds, and attains a velocity of 18,000 mph and a nominal altitude of between 200 and 300 miles. Ten

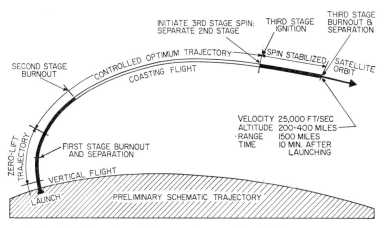

FIG. 5-3. Flight path of Vanguard research vehicle. (*Martin.*)

minutes after launching, the satellite separates from the third stage, in orbit, and about 1,500 miles away from the launching point in Florida. It does not escape, but has an orbital velocity somewhere between that for circularity and escape. The ideal velocity for a circular orbit at 300 miles would be 17,053.2 mph, and not only must the velocity be exact (incredible control of the exact moment of cutoff of the final stage) but the angle must be accurate to a degree that would be hard to duplicate on the ground with such conveniences as transits. Fortunately, this order of precision is not necessary, but neither can much of a compromise with it be tolerated. Velocity must be accurate to within 340 mph and the orbital entry angle accurate to within 2.9°. This is not easy, but it can be done.

The right speed but the wrong angle will cause the orbit to graze the top of the atmosphere and rob the satellite of the last few miles per hour which enable it to stay aloft. If the angle is correct but the velocity too low, the satellite (and the third stage) will arc down to flaming destruction in the atmosphere almost immediately. If the

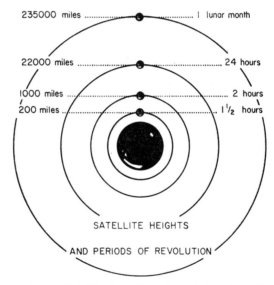

235000 miles .... 1 lunar month

22000 miles .... 24 hours

1000 miles .... 2 hours
200 miles .... 1 1/2 hours

SATELLITE HEIGHTS

AND PERIODS OF REVOLUTION

FIG. 5-4.   Satellite heights and periods of revolution. (*Brooks & Perkins.*)

velocity is too great the satellite will stay aloft but will have such a wide difference between apogee and perigee that it will exhibit pronounced changes in instantaneous velocity and will be hard to track and telemeter. Scientists will hope to err (if they must) on the high side.

Prior to the regular satellite launchings, the program calls for a small, 6.4-in.-diameter satellite weighing 3.5 lb to be launched; it is to contain only a radio transmitter and is intended to provide ground stations with radio-tracking experience. (The small satellite would possibly not be visible to optical tracking teams.) Two attempts to launch such satellites met with complete failure, but by mid-March, 1958, TV-4 had thrown a ball out 2,500 miles for Vanguard's first success.

The satellite proper is a beautiful thing. It is some 20 in. in diameter and is made with a double shell, like a vacuum bottle. It weighs 21.5 lb (with a little latitude) and is manufactured by the Brooks and Perkins Corporation, of Detroit.

The shell is plated with gold on the inside to reduce the natural porosity of metallic magnesium. This is to counter the escape of gas with which the shell will be filled under low pressure. The temperature of the gas will be recorded, and the pressure will be continuously monitored to watch for any sudden drop, which would indicate a puncture by a meteoric fragment from the vast reaches of space. Calculations on the probability of such a puncture are based on the famous Grimminger report; the probability is believed to be very small. A puncture, if one takes place, may be regarded as a coincidence bordering on a miracle.

Now, it is obvious that no satellite, or model of one, could be expected to be instrumented for the conduct of all possible experiments. This would require a gigantic satellite, one needing a formidable vehicle to carry it up to the proposed orbit. To obtain the optimum use of a satellite, the Earth Satellite Vehicle program has a special group, the ESV Technical Panel, which receives and evaluates proposals for experiments to be conducted. Not all can be accepted, and the panel has reluctantly had to reject a number of very interesting and promising ideas. It must keep in mind the tremendous cost of the program as a whole and select those experiments that combine the best chances for success with the maximum production of useful data per experiment. But many groups tried to get their experiments accepted, and competition was healthy.

The present status of the matter—what might be regarded as the top candidates for inclusion—is indicated by Table 5-1. Instruments in the satellite will be many. Among them is the solar cell, a sort of nerve center of the satellite, which resets the memory unit once every time the vehicle completes a circuit of the earth, thus dividing the lifetime of the satellite into discrete segments in which meteoric sampling will have statistical validity. An erosion gauge,

TABLE 5-1   *Accepted On-board Experiments, Earth Satellite Vehicle Program*

Satellite	Description of Experiment	Agency
1	Satellite environmental measurements: pressure, temperature, meteoric incidence, skin erosion	Naval Research Laboratory
	Measurement of solar ultraviolet intensity in the Lyman-alpha region	Naval Research Laboratory
2 *	Cosmic-ray observations	State University of Iowa
	Measurements of interplanetary matter (meteoric-detection experiment)	Air Force Cambridge Research Center
3	Satellite geomagnetic measurements (an inflatable NACA 30-in. subsatellite will be flown with this package)	Naval Research Laboratory
4[a]	Investigation of radiation balance of earth	University of Wisconsin
4[b]	Measurement of the earth's cloud cover and albedo (will probably not be used initially)	Signal Engineering Laboratories

Additional Experiments

	Measurement of ionospheric structure	Ballistic Research Laboratories, Aberdeen
	Measurement of meteoric-dust erosion of a satellite's skin (it is not sure if this will be accepted)	University of Maryland
	Determination of flux of primary cosmic-ray nuclei with atomic number larger than eight (supported by National Science Foundation funds)	Research Institute for Advanced Study, Martin Company; Bartol Research Foundation

* Flown first in Explorer I.

consisting of a nichrome ribbon etched on glass, increases in resistance as (and if) it is pitted by micrometeoric dust. This provides a sort of continuum against which to assess the announcements from the microphone which picks up the collisions by large meteors. This, together with a sudden drop in temperature, indicating puncture by a large (bird shot– to marble-sized) meteor, covers the whole reasonable size spectrum of expectable meteors. Thermistors take the temperature of the shell of the satellite. An ion chamber senses ultraviolet radiation. Narrow-band registration for the chamber records the ionization produced by radiations emanating from flares in the sun, a matter of extreme current interest to astrophysicists. Lyman alpha sensings are stored in cores during each circuit and are triggered into telemetering when the satellite passes over certain designated spots where the coded data are to be picked up.

Minitrack, a sort of lightweight beacon, helps the ground crews to locate the satellite. Printed wiring is used extensively where possible, particularly in the central canister, on stacks of plastic disks which are placed in modular assembly.

Aside from the obvious necessity of knowing where the satellite is at any current or anticipated future time, the progress of the satellite, as such, is of fundamental importance to geodesy. The refinement of the orbit, establishing a nominal "norm," and recording deviations from it enable scientists to measure the oblateness of the earth by triangulation and improve the measurement of distances between continents and the effective height of the atmosphere. The deviations can be caused by two separate phenomena. Deviation from the pure astronomical orbit by the oblateness of the earth is a complex problem in geometry and has to do with the combined action of a number of gravitational forces and anomalies. The location of the effective top of the atmosphere (or lofty filamentary prominences) is a matter of direct physical aerodynamic drag, and this effect must somehow also be taken into account to correct the observations for the purely geodetic observations.

The NRL Minitrack emits a continuous signal of 20 milliwatts of power at 108 megacycles for several weeks and consists of a one-stage crystal oscillator, one transistor, and seven 1.2-volt mercury batteries. The various "layers" in the ionosphere are collectively transparent to 108 megacycles, and the signal can thus reach the ground. At a radiating power of only 20 milliwatts, Minitrack does not enjoy a very high signal-to-noise ratio, as received at the ground. However, special equipment has been arranged for, and no trouble is expected on this account.

The ground receivers are equipped with huge antennas arranged in what is called a Mills cross, a plus-shaped pattern of grids, each of which vaguely resembles a television antenna (not without reason, because of the frequency and nature of the signal). There are eight or twelve of these grids (or "dipoles") in each Mills cross. On a moment's reflection it is seen that the cross can triangulate the satellite as it passes over by a comparison of signal phase—equivalent to a dish-type antenna which is kept constantly aimed at it as it went across the sky—in so far as the end result is concerned. Accuracy of these crosses is reported to be 3′ of arc at low elevations and 20″ of arc near zenith. Unfortunately, these arrays are very expensive, requiring considerable maintenance and several trained technicians to run them. Minitrack II is an alternate system, calling for lower precision, manpower, and maintenance. About a dozen of this model are contemplated for the general line of the 75th meridian, from Maine to Chile.

All this tracking activity calls for some startling coordination and computation. Twenty minutes after the satellite passes over a given meridian where there is a Minitrack receiving station, two bits (elementary data units used in computer technology) of angular data and time measurement are sent to the Vanguard Computing Control Center, in Washington, D.C., operated by the U.S. Navy. IBM 704 computers calculate times of arrival, zenith angle, angular velocity, and location of a favorable acquisition direction for the optical tracking stations.

Now, bearing in mind the nature of Minitrack, which may be thought of as analogous to the "narrow field" aspect of the great 100- and 200-in. telescopes, it is obvious that a system with a broader field of attention is required to acquire the "target." This activity was established under the direction of the Smithsonian Institution, which, among its many activities, conducts astrophysical research. Subdivisions of the Smithsonian Astrophysical Observatory were set up at Harvard College Observatory under Dr. J. Allan Hynek, for precision tracking, and another under Dr. Armand Spitz, the famous producer of planetarium equipment. Dr. Fred L. Whipple has over-all charge of the professional optical tracking program.

Dr. Hynek's group is developing a specialized modified Schmidt camera, based on the Baker-Nunn model. This extraordinary instrument bears something of a resemblance to a large rocket thrust chamber, is delicately mounted on a yoke, and is driven by synchronous motors. The motors enable the camera to traverse the

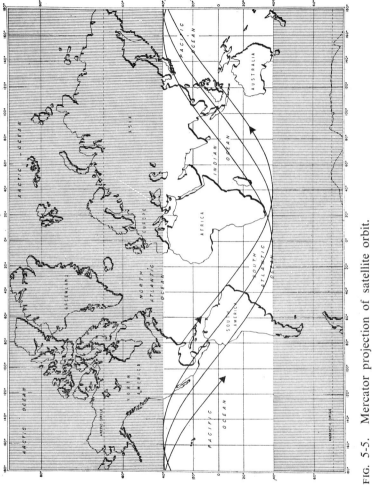

FIG. 5-5. Mercator projection of satellite orbit.

131

dome of the sky at a speed which is equal to that of the traverse of the satellite but is rather fast for astronomical instruments—for the simple reason that no astronomical bodies are close enough to the earth to display such a high angular velocity.

The Baker-Nunn camera has a 20-in. mirror and the startling aperture of $f/1$. It requires that the satellite be already located within 3°, uses a continuous strip of film 55 mm wide and 1 ft long, and has a field of 5 by 30°. Using a film scale of 406″ of arc per millimeter, image diameters down to 30 microns are possible. This is an impressive resolving power. The camera is synchronized with the National Bureau of Standards radio transmitter WWV, whose chief function is to broadcast time signals of incredible accuracy. (It is *the* time standard of the United States.) It does this by means of a crystal clock, accurate to a thousandth of a second, which is "slaved" to WWV. Two quarter-horsepower motors drive the traverse at a possible maximum rate of 5,300″ of arc per second. The satellite cannot be visible to any instrument except during a few hours before dawn and a few hours after dusk. At this time it is expected to be of the fifth photovisual magnitude, which is about the same brightness as the faintest star that, under reasonably good observing conditions, can be seen with the naked eye.

The cameras are a great assistance to Minitrack, but even their field is rather narrow. A trained observer with sharp eyes and a good astronomical sense, if he knew just when and where to look, would have a fighting chance of spotting the satellite with his naked eyes. A fighting chance is not reliable enough for an expensive operation like a satellite program, and, since another stage of backup is needed for the precision optical tracking represented by the cameras, there would not be enough of these experts to go around.

The broad-sweep acquisition is provided by Operation Moonwatch, under the direction of Dr. Spitz, which might be thought of as a comparatively lavishly equipped network analogous to the Ground Observer Corps, which performs aircraft tracking of low-level planes for the Air Force.

The difference is that the Moonwatch teams are looking for something high, tiny, slow, and unfamiliar. At first encounter this sounds like a losing fight. The secret lies in simple equipment and teamwork. Moonwatch teams are organized in various communities, often under the generous sponsorship of local corporations or banks which pay for the equipment and lend moral support to the activity. A myriad of the teams are needed, and they are springing up everywhere, not only in the United States but all over the world within the band 40° north and south of the Equator. Each team monitors a fan-shaped "interception zone" occupying a north-and-south line through the Moonwatch station marker. The marker is a steel, T-shaped mast about 40 ft high.

Five members of a ten-man team are seated at little tables in a line north and south of the mast upright, and each of the five looks through a special telescope (which actually looks more like a microscope) with a field about that of a pair of military field glasses. At the bottom of each miniature telescope stand is a planar front-surface mirror which diverts the axis of vision back upward. When emplaced, either the vertical or the horizontal part of the T mast cuts across the field of each telescope as a sort of hairline. The closer an observer is to the mast, the more vertical is his field of view, and the innermost observers have the horizontal portion of the T mast as their "cross hair." Collectively, they cover a fan of some 45° (22.5° north and south of zenith), and if the satellite is anywhere within their zone, one of the observers is apt to spot the object.

There are two odd hazards here. First, the satellite, which may well wander from the expected path for a number of reasons, may not go through the team's zone at all, and it is at least technically possible that an airplane (equipped with wing lights) may chance through the team's field of vision at just the time the satellite is expected, and a false report may result. The chance of this is small, however, since supplementary observers may be posted to eliminate false register. Also, the station is equipped with a radio receiver tuned to WWV, and the probability that an aircraft will chance across the hairline at the time when the satellite is expected to traverse is small indeed.

The second hazard, a typically human one, is that some members of the team may yield to temptation—once they have gained some familiarity with the antics of the satellite—and observe not the portion of the fan assigned to them but another portion where they feel they might have a better chance of actually seeing it. They may guess wrongly; the satellite may actually traverse the sector they were supposed to monitor and thus be missed in a perfectly legitimate traverse.

We should not worry unduly about these hazards, however. Good discipline will avoid most of these "fluffs," and we can have every confidence that the Moonwatch volunteers are performing yeoman service. Enthusiasm is high, and preparation has been very thorough. Complete alternate teams have even been provided so that no station will go unmanned at a critical time. Teams all over the world have earned the confidence in them during the Sputnik and Explorer tracking endeavors.

Vanguard is an interesting, though minimum, vehicle and a gratifying development in science. Several preliminary test vehicles based on Vikings have been fired, and in late October, 1957, the first Vanguard was fired to 109 miles with dummy second and third stages. In December, 1957, and in February, 1958, complete vehicles completely failed to lift small test satellites into orbit. Vanguard, agonizingly unsuccessful at first, represents a philosophy of approach, not the only one and not necessarily the best one, but a very good one. It does not match Sputnik, but its instrumentation will probably be somewhat more sophisticated. One must be cautious, however, since the Soviets have displayed considerable technical ingenuity in recent years and we may anticipate some novel ideas in their next satellites. The TV-4 must not be overemphasized.

Our current satellite developments are primitive, and later generations will look upon them as crude, yet they are steps outward. One does not get this close to space flight and stop. But neither is the very next step liable to be space flight itself. There will probably be a motley assortment of satellites circling the earth before man makes significant strides toward transporting himself into space.

Explorer and Beyond

The title of this chapter might well have been Explorer, Vanguard and Beyond. Objections have been raised, perhaps justifiably, that the name Vanguard is no longer appropriate, and important segments of informed opinion hold that the whole Navy satellite project should be canceled forthwith. Support is drawn from the fact that the vehicle is at best minimal, that its payload capability is almost ludicrously below that afforded by Russian Sputnik carrier rockets, and that valuable engineering manpower is being spent trying to develop a new, though already outdated, rocket. Why, it is asked, did not the United States use from the beginning existing military hardware rather than attempt to win the race into space with an untried, tailor-made rocket launcher?

Vanguard, it should be quickly pointed out, started out as an advanced, well-designed rocket and eventually will succeed in placing its full satellite into orbit. Like all new rockets it has been plagued with difficulties. It has a role, albeit a minor one, in the Satellite Age; and because it is already so far along, it should be continued. This does not mean, however, that Vanguard ought to have been the first, or only, American satellite project. Missile experts long fought for the use of proven military ballistic-rocket hardware as the backbone of our satellite endeavors, but these voices were not heeded in the highest government circles. History will sooner or later demand to know why.

The United States made a long series of incredibly stupid and costly errors that have resulted in the nation's taking, and at least temporarily accepting, second place among the missile and satellite powers of the world. The intermediate range and intercontinental ballistic missile situation is serious, but an immediate and concerted effort by the United States should rapidly help balance the military dilemma caused by Russian successes. Firings of Thors and Jupiters have passed the dozen mark, and both are in production. The Polaris program is reportedly ahead of schedule. Atlas, after having a few initial failures, proved its design with at least two successful shots. More recent aborts have been discouraging, but the missile should establish itself by 1959. Titan test firings are scheduled for the end of 1958.

The state of the United States short-range ballistic-missile art was sufficiently advanced by late 1955 that it appeared feasible to inaugurate a satellite program based on the Redstone liquid-propellant rocket system. Mated with solid-rocket upper staging, this missile became the Jupiter-C, and by 1956 hurled a payload well over 3,000 miles out into the Atlantic, climbing to over 600 miles along it trajectory. Despite repeated requests from its development team at the Army Ballistic Missile Agency, Huntsville, Alabama, and from high Army and other circles, the Defense Department prohibited any satellite action from taking place. By deliberate, premeditated maneuvers in Washington a key segment of American rocket know-how was smothered, and the nation helplessly sat and watched Russia inaugurate the Space Age.

Washington, stunned by Sputnik successes and Vanguard failures, finally permitted the Army to enter into the arena, and a Jupiter-C carrier vehicle was scheduled to make a satellite attempt in late January. When the Navy failed to launch a Vanguard test vehicle on December 6, 1957, Army hopes that it might launch the first satellite rose, but later it turned out that the Navy would be given another try in late January 1958. If that failed, the Army would be permitted to fire.

TABLE 5-2   *Comparison of Vanguard and Jupiter-C Carrier Rockets*

	Vanguard	Jupiter-C
Length, ft	72	70
Diameter, in.	45	70
Weight, lb	22,600	64,000
Thrust, lb	28,000	82,000
No. stages	3	4
Guidance	Minneapolis-Honeywell inertial system	Ford Instrument inertial system

For a week Vanguard crews attempted to launch their January vehicle, but bad weather and a long series of mechanical difficulties made them finally postpone it indefinitely (they subsequently fired in early February with disastrous results to rocket and satellite alike). The Army then moved onto the stage, and on the last day of January, 1958, Explorer I made its first orbit around the planet Earth.

The Jupiter-C carrier was a four-stage rocket weighing well over 60,000 lb. Standing some 70 ft high, it developed 75,000 lb thrust from its Redstone first-stage liquid oxygen–alcohol engine.[1] The

[1] The use of a hydrazine-type fuel may have boosted thrust up another 10 per cent.

upper staging was quite novel in that the normal tandem technique was not employed; rather the second stage, consisting of 11 scale Sergeant rockets, was "wrapped around" the second stage (containing another ring of three similar solid rockets) which in turn housed the fourth stage. This last stage consisted partially of a single scale Sergeant rocket and partially of the instrumentation package.

Prior to take-off the whole upper-staging package was rotated first to about 560 rpm, and then, at launch, to 750 rpm. This operation not only provided for over-all gyroscopic stabilization of the upper cluster but helped ensure against imbalanced thrust in the event that any of the individual scale Sergeant motors failed to fire.

TABLE 5-3 *Characteristics of Explorers I and III*

	Explorer I	Explorer III
Weight, lb	30.8	31
Dimensions, in.	80 x 6	80 x 6
Shape	Cylindrical	Cylindrical
Payload, instruments, lb	11	11
Maximum altitude, miles	1,590	1,735
Minimum altitude, miles	220	125
Orbit time, min	115	116
Speed, mph	18,000	18,000
Lifetime, approx	5 years	1 month
Angle to equatorial plane, degrees	34	34
Date launched	January 31, 1958	March 26, 1958

The first stage burned over 150 sec and brought the missile up to just over 50 miles and a velocity of approximately 6,800 mph. The upper staging was then separated from the Redstone and coasted to over 200 miles, reached nearly 7 min following launching. Ignited by radio command from the ground, the second stage fired, and in sequence the third and fourth steps fired following motor cutoff of the step just below.

The rocket and satellite making up the Jupiter-C–Explorer I system were designed and developed by scientists at the Army Ballistic Missile Agency and the Jet Propulsion Laboratory of the California Institute of Technology. The Redstone booster missile, a creation of the von Braun team, has been in production for some time at the Chrysler Corporation's plant in Warren, Michigan.

To track the Explorer I satellite, Minitrack and Microlock radio teams and both professional and Moonwatch optical teams went right to work, and preliminary ephermerides were rapidly worked out by the Naval Research Laboratory and the Smithsonian Institution. Whereas the Vanguard satellite is designed to carry only Minitrack radio equipment, Explorer I carries one high- and one low-powered transmitter, the former transmitting on 108.03 megacycles and the latter on 108 megacycles at 0.01 watt. The high-powered 0.06-watt transmitter's life was short (11 days) because of its heavy drain on the batteries. The Microlock's signal was much weaker, and could only be picked up by five (against ten for Minitrack) specially constructed stations located around the world. It was designed to transmit for at least a month and possibly as much as two.

Explorer I's main experiment was the cosmic-ray and micrometeorite package originally designed for the second full Vanguard firing. A Geiger-Müller tube provided the sensing element to count the charged cosmic-ray particles. Each time a hit was made an electrical impulse was recorded, and when 16 such hits were registered, a change in signal tone would take place. In this way detailed, accurate data on cosmic-ray intensity as a function of time and position were accumulated. Preliminary results showed that the intensity was about 12 times that at sea level.

Explorer I carries two types of micrometeorite sensors: one a microphonic device, and the other consisting of a set of 11 gauges encircling the rear portion of the satellite. In the latter experiment each gauge is wire-wrapped, forming a coil, connected in parallel with the other ten. As micrometeorites break the wires, the coil is removed from the circuit and the electrical current is reduced, changing the signal tone.

To monitor temperatures, a number of thermistors are employed. As the environmental temperatures change, electrical resistances change, and it is this resistance that is measured. Again, all changes are reflected by altered radio signal tones, from which scientists at ground recording stations can determine quantitative values. Internal temperatures of between 70 and 80°F. have been reported.

The Army unsuccessfully fired Explorer II in early March, 1958, but a few weeks later orbited Explorer III successfully. Already requests have been made for placing into orbit reconnaissance-type probes weighing 300 and later 700 lb. Just what luck von Braun's team will have in obtaining authority to proceed with such experiments will depend less on already proven technical abilities than on political prowess at the Washington scene. All military branches are maneuvering for key astronautical roles and missions, and only time will tell if the United States can move authoritatively ahead in the Space Age amid the confusion created by excess service rivalry.

Astro (artificial-satellite time and radio orbit) is a proposed system of three satellites, all in orbit at once, in nearly circular, mutually perpendicular paths. Ephemerides would be worked out for the satellites, one of which, since there would be three, would be visible by radar, at a given time, almost anywhere on the face of the globe. The three would be placed in 105-min, 600-mile orbits and be trackable for between 6 and 16 min on any one sighting. (Their orbital speed of 4.5 miles/sec is thought to be adequate for Doppler-type radar.)

Two models of Astro satellite were proposed by Lovell Lawrence of Chrysler. The first, with two dipoles, would keep its axis tangent to the orbit by absorbing the energy of a gyro as it ran down, thus causing the satellite as a whole to behave in a very ungyroscopic fashion. It was realized that this encountered certain problems (such as what to do when the gyro finally gave out) and an alternate design, with eight dipoles, was proposed. This design could disregard the orientation of the satellite. Transmission would be omnidirectional, but for that very reason would require more power. Basic power suggested for the satellite is an atomic pile using strontium 90, delivering 200 watts. The isotope has a half-life of 20 years.

Classical stellar navigation would be performed by taking fixes on the Astro satellite and determining the subastral point. The Doppler would operate at 100 megacycles, and the system as a whole would employ a fast computer which would make a series of approximations and give the correct position distance of the observer from the satellite, as amended for earth motions and other factors.

As the satellite came into view, it would be sensed by an electronic sextant. The altitude angle would be determined. The ephemerides (astronomical almanac) would be consulted, and a great circle—somewhere on which the ship was located—would be determined. As the satellite sensed might not be the polar satellite, the line would not necessarily be a meridian. However, another reading could be taken 2 min later, giving another circle on which the ship was located. Taking due account of passage of time, it would be determined that the ship would fall on two different lines. Where these two lines crossed would be the location of the ship. This procedure is not particularly difficult, but it may be a little hard for the person unfamiliar with navigation to visualize.

Big Brother is an actual satellite project of the Air Force. Since the launching of the Russian satellite, it has become known that it has been renamed Pied Piper and that an accelerated effort has been ordered. A weapons-system number, WS-117-L, has been assigned. It is a reconnaissance satellite equipped with television cameras and radar scanning units which are intended to observe possible Russian preparations to launch intercontinental ballistic missiles at the United States. In this way we could know the instant an ICBM was fired, and this would give us a lead time of somewhat less than a half hour to save one of our cities. Somewhere in the arctic regions, presumably, a large antimissile would leap up to destroy the ICBM. Very few particular data [2] are available on so secret a project, and it may be assumed that Pied Piper, which lacks the benevolent mission of Vanguard, will perhaps not enjoy diplomatic immunity. As a military satellite, it may prompt attempts to shoot it down. This would be no small feat of marksmanship, but the Russians may feel it necessary to try.

There are other satellites, proposed and in development, known and unknown. The Russians are building bigger ones and the French and British are thinking about it. It seems only a matter of time before other countries, possibly Germany and Japan, will take the matter under serious consideration. It is not inconceivable that variations of Project Farside, or Kurt Stehling's proposal Saloon (balloon-launched satellite) may hold the key to economy-type orbiters. As higher and higher orbits become feasible, we will have the prospect of really permanent satellites. A century from now

[2] It is believed to be based on an Atlas carrier rocket, minus warhead. It would carry television and photographic equipment, together with infrared or radar scanning devices.

we might have swarms of them circling the earth, like electrons about an atomic nucleus.

The Matter of Utility

The satellites already launched by the Jupiter-C and also by the Vanguard rockets may not be minimum, but they are close to it. Even the simplest configuration can be put to immediate and good use. The term "simplest" means just that. It could be nothing more than a sphere of metal foil inflated to, say, 15 ft in diameter, by a balloon. It would not matter if the balloon eventually shrank, for there would be no air pressure to crush the inflated foil envelope. Visual observation of it could be made from ground stations, and by development of the data thus obtained, orbital period vs. altitude could be confirmed. Also, the effect of gravity on the vehicle could be verified (and thereby a more precise value of 1 g); any air drag could be measured, especially as the vehicle began to descend; and radio waves could be bounced off it at any time to measure the effects of emission at various angles of elevation.

With a little luck, enough inferred data might be obtained from the orbit to better estimate the shape and dimensions of the earth. If the satellite happened to stay up for a very long period, it might be useful as an aid to the navigation of ships, aircraft, or missiles. This is even "more minimum" than Singer's MOUSE, but note what can be done with it. The list is by no means complete, but it will suffice.

An instrumented satellite, such as Vanguard, which is more properly a vehicle than that just described, can do all these things, and also measure solar and cosmic radiation, the distribution of geomagnetic lines of force, variations of the earth's gravitational pull, and the effective environmental temperature and pressure. In the happy event that the satellite were permanent, it might continue to receive power by means of special solar furnaces powering generators or from solar batteries, which store the sun's energy directly.

Such is the unmanned satellite—perhaps a foil sphere, perhaps a compact ball full of Geiger counters, photocells, telescopes and prisms, gears, sun batteries, and telemetering equipment. Perhaps it is but the last stage of a multistage rocket, packed with even more equipment. It could be a number of things. Whatever it is, it will tell us much that we want to know about our earth, and much that we must know about space hazards to humankind before we go out into space ourselves.

Manned Satellites

A manned satellite will be a formidable project—one whole order of magnitude more difficult. Unlike the robot satellite, it cannot be built in the laboratory and then installed in or on a rocket for delivery to orbit. It must be sent up in sections, which means a number of rockets per satellite. This multiplies the cost, logistics, and engineering. Being manned, such satellites must be more than just vehicles big enough to accommodate a man with room enough to walk around. They must be pressurized, so that a man can take off his space suit, and they must actually be made self-sustaining from the food-air-energy point of view. Structurally, they will be akin to the spaceships discussed in Chap. 7. Physiologically, they will be subject to the human parameters described in the chapter on space medicine.

The increased scope of usefulness of a satellite, when manned, will be breath taking. A manned satellite equipped as an astronomical observatory can obtain a startlingly clear picture of the universe. Above the atmosphere, the shimmer and twinkle produced by air currents will be absent, and the filtering action against a vast spectrum of radiomagnetic signals will have vanished. Here at the surface, we view the cosmos through a spectrographic keyhole, as it were. Our notions of cosmic structure and behavior must necessarily be imperfect. In the free fall (zero gravity of orbit), telescopes (particularly radio telescopes) of fantastic size could be assembled—huge fragile instruments that would immediately collapse under their own weight in normal gravity. There are problems, very serious ones, about designing, transporting, erecting, and using such instruments, but it hardly needs to be pointed out that the new clarity, the increased power of the instruments, and the wider spectra will produce data of staggering impact to astronomy.

Just as unmanned satellites are collecting data permitting the establishment of manned satellites, so the manned satellites, equipped for biological and medical research, will provide a basis for verifying such data and performing experiments which will establish the biological and medical basis for the habitability of spaceships. A number of urgent questions arise for answer. Will cosmic rays kill, or create genetic damage? Will mitosis (cell division) speed up, and possibly bring an evolution of blood cells faster than that of the bodies they sustain? Will they grow large, eventually, and clog the veins? Where would poisons come from? Something not toxic to humans might be toxic to plants on which they depend. What about waste elimination? Can man orient himself in zero gravity? These questions are recognized as important; the U.S. Air Force already has a Department of Space Medicine, at Randolph Field, Texas, which is conducting research on them.

As a laboratory for physical and chemical research, the conditions of zero pressure, temperature, and gravity permit experiments utterly impossible at the earth's surface. There are a number of questions concerning friction, electrical currents, crystalline structures and growth, chemical solubility, molecular structure and size, and perhaps the rate of permissibility of reactions or catalysis. Who knows? We must wait for the true answer.

We live here on the earth, but, strangely, it will be only when we observe it from a manned satellite that we will be able to find out many things we really want to know about it. The geosciences, in a sense, are a specialized kind of astronomy dealing with the earth as a planet, and may be thought to include, broadly, meteorology, geodesy, geology, geophysics, and geomorphology.[3] A number of geoscientific observations can be made with the simplest satellites, as has been shown. A manned station provides the means for an

[3] H. E. Canney, Jr. and F. I. Ordway, III, Uses of Artificial Satellite Vehicles, a paper presented at the Sixth Congress of the International Astronautical Federation, Copenhagen, 1955, and published in *Astronaut. Acta,* vol. 2, no. 4, 1956, and vol. 3, no. 1, 1957. This grouping of geosciences is typical of the congested effect created by the preliminary academic aspects of astronautics. Astronautics, as a science, reveals itself on closer inspection to consist of a great span of sciences, a span so wide that it begins to take on the aspect of all science. This may be merely the first tangible expression that any science really *is* all science, and not just a branch, or it may mean that all the sciences that once stood more or less by themselves are proving fundamentally interdependent and, faced with the first really big task, are evolving into what seems to us now as a sort of superscience.

agency of immediate and transcending importance—a satellitic weather observation station.

In a 4,000-mile (4-hr) orbit, such a station as that proposed by Dr. Harry Wexler of the United States Weather Bureau,[4] could provide a much-needed bird's-eye view of the world. By covering the world in an inclined orbit and by tracking cloud formations and sensing and resolving complexes of reflected light values, a short-range, synoptic, weather picture whose accuracy would be worth countless millions of dollars to the country that maintained the station would be obtained. Observation from such a station also suggests military inspection, iceberg patrol, traffic studies, aerial mapping, and a number of other observational tasks to which great altitudes lend themselves.

The military value of the space station, except as a reconnaissance vehicle, is somewhat uncertain. Whether bombing or space-to-ground missile attacks would be any more effective from such a station has not been established. One small missile of Falcon size could probably destroy almost any space station man can build, if it could be brought within homing distance. As a third stage of a multistage rocket, the attacking missile represents a much cheaper proposition than the much larger third stage of ferry rockets sent up to build and arm the station. It would take ten rockets of 7,000 tons apiece to erect a von Braunian space station; it would take one step rocket grossing perhaps 75 tons to destroy it. Against these economic realities the space station as a weapon would have to demonstrate that it could bombard strategic targets with greater precision and noninterceptability than an ICBM could. As things stand now it does not appear so. As if this were not serious enough, there is one final objection, probably the most damning of all. A satellite vehicle preparing to fire a missile at the ground must wait until it is in the proper position before it can fire with optimum effect; the ICBM may be fired at any time. Furthermore, the use of a space station for military reconnaissance would probably prompt energetic attempts to destroy it. That, of course, would be no easy job until the advent of proven, long-range acquisition and tracking radar and effective anti-ICBM weapon systems. Then

[4] H. Wexler, Observing Weather from the Satellite Vehicle, *J. Brit. Interplanet. Soc.,* vol. 13, no. 5, 1954.

the probability of downing a satellite will depend on how many orbits the defender can tolerate and on what electronic and other countermeasures the attacker might employ.

The satellite vehicle has been widely heralded as an aid to communications. With the advantages of altitude, it could drastically reduce the number of skips or bounces that radio and television waves have to make en route to the receiving sets, and this would improve both the quality and the strength of the signals. Satellites could accomplish this either by reflection or by transpose (receipt and instantaneous amplification and retransmission). Three such stations in a 24-hr orbit, suggested by Arthur C. Clarke, could serve the whole world. Similar stations could relay between earth and a ship in space or, via that ship in space and a satellite vehicle on the other end, to the moon, Mars, or a distant planet.

Finally—and this is what space-flight scientists are coming to regard as the transcending utility of a space station—it may be used as a sort of interplanetary gas station, or permanent "step" in a step-rocket scheme for getting into space. It may be an orderly collection of joined tanks with a snappy platform, cabin, and rows of propellant pumps. More likely it will resemble what the army describes as a fuel dump and will be a collection of tanks bound together by cable and orbiting until used. These space stations would be assembled in the departure orbit, the destination orbit, and probably in the base camp at the destination body.

Perhaps the space station would be set up at the location and orbit of the *probe* [5] and established there to monitor the surface of the destination body long before an expedition arrived, sending back to earth much the same sort of data that were relayed about the vicinity of our own planet by an earth satellite vehicle. The probe is the closest link with actual space flight; it is a sort of unmanned spaceship which has made the journey to the target body. The space station at home prepares man for space flight by telling

[5] This highly apt term originated in a short but significant article of E. Burgess and C. A. Cross, The Martian Probe, *J. Brit. Interplanet. Soc.,* vol. 12, no. 2, p. 72, 1953. A picture of an orbital rocket in the act of surveying Mars, which could be such a probe, is shown in the frontispiece of A. C. Clarke, "The Exploration of Space," Temple Press, Ltd., London, 1951. See also Cross, The Use of Probe Rockets, *J. Brit. Interplanet. Soc.,* vol. 16, no. 3, p. 148, 1957.

him what he needs to know about his own planet, about space, and about himself in space. The probe prepares man for landing on distant bodies where, until more is learned, a manned expedition would be too costly.

Men's notions about space travel have become more cautious through the ages. First (imaginary) trips were by accident, later theoretical trips by ballistic projectiles, then by rockets, multistage rockets, space stations (multistage voyages), and then probes. The more man learns about space the more careful he becomes. If there ever was an enterprise where your first mistake becomes your last one, this is it.

BIBLIOGRAPHY

Stuhlinger, E.: Instrumentation Problems of Unmanned Satellites, American Rocket Society Preprint, 306–56.

Singer, S. F.: Studies of a Minimal Orbital Unmanned Satellite of the Earth (MOUSE): Part II, Orbits and Lifetimes of Minimum Satellites, *Astronaut. Acta,* vol. 2, no. 3, p. 125, 1956.

Wexler, H.: The Satellite and Meteorology, *J. Astronautics,* vol. 4, no. 1, p. 1, 1957.

Rundown on the Vanguard Vehicle, *Astronautics,* vol. 2, no. 1, p. 62, 1957.

Odishaw, H.: The IGY Earth Satellite Program, *ISA Journal,* vol. 3, no. 9, p. 298, 1956.

Hagen, J. P.: The Exploration of Outer Space with an Earth Satellite, *Proc. IRE,* vol. 44, no. 6, p. 744, 1956.

Rosen, M. W.: Placing the Satellite in its Orbit, *Proc. IRE,* vol. 44, no. 6, p. 748, 1956.

Cleaver, A. V.: Progress with Vanguard, *Spaceflight,* vol. 1, no. 2, p. 47, 1957.

International Geophysical Year Earth Satellite Vehicle Program, *Missiles and Rockets,* vol. 1, no. 2, p. 120, 1956.

Morton, D. C.: The Artificial Satellite, *J. Roy. Astron. Soc. Can.,* vol. 50, no. 1, p. 35, 1956.

Kaplan, J.: Rocket and Satellite Studies During the IGY, *Aeronaut. Eng. Rev.,* vol. 15, no. 4, p. 64, 1956.

Gatland, K. W.: The Vanguard Project, *Spaceflight,* vol. 1, no. 1, p. 15, 1956.

Project Vanguard, *Missiles and Rockets,* vol. 2, no. 7, p. 117, 1957.

Furnas, C. C.: The Vanguard Satellite, Ordnance, vol. 41, no. 220, p. 596, 1957.

Odishaw, H.: The Satellite Program for the International Geophysical Year, *Dept. of State Bulletin* 35–894, Aug. 13, 1956.

Clarke, A. C.: Visit to Vanguard, *Spaceflight,* vol. 1, no. 4, p. 127, 1957.

Chubb, T. A., and H. Friedman: Photon Counters for the Far Ultraviolet, *Rev. Sci. Instr.,* vol. 26, no. 5, p. 493, 1955.

Vanguard Instrumentation, *Missiles and Rockets,* vol. 2, no. 1, p. 67, 1957.

Mazur, D. G.: Telemetering and Propagation Problems of Placing the Earth Satellite in its Orbit, *Proc. IRE,* vol. 44, no. 6, p. 752, 1956.

van Allen, J. A.: The Scientific Value of the Earth Satellite Program, *Proc. IRE,* vol. 44, no. 6, p. 764, 1956.

Friedman, H.: Scientific Instrumentation in IGY Satellites, AIEE Paper C.P. 57–213, 1956.

Matthews, W.: Earth Satellite Instrumentation Program, AIEE Paper C.P. 57–323, 1957.

House, C. B., and R. L. van Allen: Commutation and Nondestructive Read-out of Magnetic Memory Cores in Earth Satellite, AIEE Paper C.P. 57–374, 1957.

Matthews, W.: Telemetering in Earth Satellites, AIEE Paper C.P. 57–322, 1957.

Haviland, R. P.: What the Future Holds for the Earth Satellite, *Gen. Elec. Rev.,* September, 1956.

Romick, D.: Meteor, Manned, Earth Satellite Terminal Evolving from Earth-to-Orbit Ferry Rockets, Goodyear Aircraft Corporation, 1956 report. (Presented to Seventh Congress of the International Astronautical Federation, Rome, Italy.)

Expert Charts Future of Big Brother Satellite, *Missiles and Rockets,* p. 32, December, 1956.

Sandorff, P. E., and J. S. Prigge, Jr.: Thermal Control in a Space Vehicle, *J. Astronautics,* vol. 3, no. 1, p. 4, 1956.

Gildenberg, B. C.: An Atmospheric Satellite Station, *Missile Away!,* vol. 4, no. 1, p. 13, 1956.

Ehricke, K.: The Satelloid, *Astronaut. Acta,* vol. 2, no. 2, p. 63, 1956.

Soviets Plan 100-Pound, 20–24-Inch Satellite, *Missile Eng.,* vol. 1, no. 2, p. 28, 1956.

Singer, S. F.: Studies of a Minimum Orbital Unmanned Satellite of the Earth (MOUSE): Part III, Radiation Equilibrium and Temperature, *Astronaut. Acta,* vol. 3, no. 2, p. 110, 1957.

Thomas, I. H.: On Countermeasures for Satellite Vehicles, *Jet Propulsion,* vol. 24, no. 5, p. 321, 1954.

Stecher, L. J., Jr.: The Military Utility of a Space Station, *Missile Away!,* vol. 4, no. 4, p. 8, 1957.

Woolard, E. W.: Satellite Periods and the Gravitational Constant, *Space Journal,* vol. 1, no. 1, p. 32, 1957.

Wilson, R. H., Jr., and J. W. Siry: Theory of Eclipses of a Close Earth Satellite, *Astron. J.,* vol. 62, no. 3, p. 97, 1957.

Soitzer, L.: Effect of Earth's Oblateness on Satellite Period, *Jet Propulsion,* vol. 27, no. 4, p. 405, 1957.

Lawrence, L.: Navigation by Satellites, *Missiles and Rockets,* p. 49, October, 1956.

Henry, I. G.: Lifetimes of Artificial Satellites of the Earth, *Jet Propulsion,* vol. 27, no. 1, p. 21, 1957.

Tousey, R.: The Visibility of an Earth Satellite, *Astronaut. Acta,* vol. 2, no. 2, p. 101, 1956.

Klemperer, W. B., and R. M. Baker, Jr.: Satellite Librations, *Astronaut. Acta,* vol. 3, no. 1, p. 16, 1957.

Sterne, T. E.: A Suggested Analytical Treatment of the Orbit of a Close Satellite, *Astron. J.,* vol. 62, no. 1, p. 33, 1957.

Subotowicz, M.: Satellites for Checking Einstein's Relativity Theory, *Missiles and Rockets,* vol. 2, no. 2, p. 57, 1957.

Robotti, A. C.: Une 'rampe volante' pour le lancement des satellites, *Interavia,* p. 970, December, 1956.

Singer, S. F.: The Effect of Meteoric Particles on a Satellite, *Jet Propulsion,* vol. 26, no. 12, p. 1071, 1956.

Schaefer, D. H.: Magnetic Core Event Counter for Earth Satellite Memory, AIEE Paper C.P. 57–359, 1957.

Rochelle, R. W.: Earth Satellite Telemetry Coding System Using Transistors and Magnetic Cores, AIEE Paper C.P. 57–352, 1957.

Singer, S. F.: "Meteor Erosion Gauge for Earth Satellites," Physics Department, University of Maryland, College Park, Md., 1957.

Friedman, H.: The Vanguard Instrument Package, *Astronautics,* vol. 2, no. 1, p. 66, 1957.

Steier, H. P.: Satellite Tracking Camera Developed, *Missiles and Rockets,* vol. 2, no. 1, p. 64, 1957.

Whipple, F. L., and J. A. Hynek: The Optical Tracking Program for IGY Satellites, *Astron. J.,* vol. 61, no. 4, p. 191, 1956.

Tousey, R.: Optical Problems of the Satellite, *J. Opt. Soc. Am.,* vol. 47, no. 4, p. 261, 1957.

O'Keefe, J. A.: Geodesy Comes of Age with Vanguard, *Astronautics,* vol. 2, no. 1, p. 71, 1957.

Whipple, F. L., and J. A. Hynek: A Research Program Based on the Optical Tracking of Artificial Earth Satellites, *Proc. IRE,* vol. 44, no. 6, p. 760, 1956.

Ordway, F. I., III: The U.S. Satellite Vehicle Program, *Astronaut. Acta,* vol. 2, no. 3, p. 115, 1956.

———: Project Vanguard—Earth Satellite Vehicle Program: Characteristics, Testing, Guidance, Control, and Tracking, *Astronaut. Acta,* vol. 3, no. 1, p. 67, 1957.

Amateurs to Observe Satellites, *Sky and Telescope,* vol. 15, no. 5, p. 203, 1956.

The Artificial Satellite, *Sky and Telescope,* vol. 15, no. 3, p. 112, 1956.

Bulletin for Visual Observers of Satellites, *Sky and Telescope,* vol. 15, no. 9, 1956, to present.

Ehricke, K. A.: Engineering Problems of Manned Space Flight, *Interavia,* vol. 10, no. 7, pp. 506–511, 1955.

Geophysical Satellite, *Sci. American,* vol. 193, no. 3, p. 68, 1955.

Struve, O.: High-Altitude Research Stations, *Sky and Telescope,* vol. 14, no. 10, p. 409, 1955.

Anderson, D. A.: Hypersonic Quest Yields New Techniques, *Aviation Week,* vol. 65, no. 1, p. 46, 1956.

More Satellite Notes, *Sky and Telescope,* vol. 15, no. 6, p. 247, 1956.

Cushman, R.: Next Satellite Problem: Data Descent, *Aviation Week,* vol. 64, no. 20, p. 53, 1956.

Whipple, F. L., and J. A. Hynek: The Optical Tracking Program for IGY Satellites, *Astron. J.,* vol. 61, no. 4, p. 191, 1956.

Plan Missile to Moon, *Sci. News Letter,* p. 262, Apr. 28, 1956.

Satellite Nears Final Design as Scientists Fight Deadline, *Aviation Week,* vol. 64, no. 5, p. 37, 1956.

Newell, H. E.: The Satellite Project, *Sci. American,* vol. 193, no. 6, pp. 29–33, 1955.

Scientists Reveal Vanguard Design Detail, *Aviation Week,* vol. 64, no. 13, pp. 33–34, 1956.

Singer, S. F.: The Artificial Earth Satellite, *Discovery,* vol. 17, no. 4, pp. 140–145, 1956.

————: Design Criteria of Four Minimum Satellites, *Aero Digest,* vol. 72, no. 4, pp. 36–37, 1956.

————: The 'Mouse' Project, *Interavia,* vol. 10, no. 7, pp. 502–504, 1955.

Tabanera, T. M.: El Satellite artificial de la tierra, *Bol. asoc. argentina interplanet.,* vol. 3, no. 10, pp. 17–23, 1956.

Canney, H. E., Jr., and F. I. Ordway, III, The Satellite Vehicle for Communications and Navigation, *Aero Digest,* vol. 71, no. 6, pp. 40–46, 1955.

Haber, H.: Space Satellites, Tools of Earth Research, *Natl. Geographic,* vol. 109, no. 4, pp. 486–509, 1956.

Stehling, K. R.: Aspects of Vanguard Propulsion, *Astronautics,* vol. 3, no. 1, pp. 44–47, 68, 1958.

6

Sputniks, Prelude to Man in Space

The dramatic birth of the Age of Space was manifested tangibly by announcement card no. 1375 from the Harvard College Observatory. It was prepared by scientists of the Astrophysical Observatory of the Smithsonian Institution, Cambridge, Massachusetts, and signed by Prof. Fred L. Whipple. Dated October 15, 1957, it gave the equatorial elements and perturbations for what has come to be known as artificial satellite 1957 α1, popularly known as Sputnik. The announcement referred to the orbiting third-stage rocket of the world's first artificial-satellite vehicle, launched by the Soviet Union on October 4, 1957. The Space Age had opened; the union of astronomy and rocketry officially had brought the infant science of astronautics into existence.

Experts were not surprised that an artificial satellite could be placed into orbit, nor were they unprepared for the accomplishment of the feat by the USSR. What caught some unawares, however, and what astounded laymen the world over, was the date: few people expected an artificial satellite in the fall of 1957.

The successful launching of two Sputniks has precipitated a profound world reaction, one due as much to the authors of the prodigious exploit as to the feat itself. Humanity in general, and the West in particular, simply was not mentally prepared for Sputnik. The political and military overtones were evident even to those with the most meager information on the event.

150

Russian Rocketry

In this chapter we shall first look into the Russian background of rocketry and astronautics and then show that frequent warnings were voiced of far-reaching Soviet progress in these fields prior to Sputnik I. Finally, we shall consider what we know about the artificial satellites and estimate what can be logically expected of Russia in the coming years. Two major conclusions will become evident:

1. There should have been no surprise (and in informed quarters there was little) at the timing and magnitude of the Soviet achievements.

2. The USSR is now engaged in a space-flight program on a scale that evidently exceeds that of the Western World.

Military rockets are not new to the Russians, and interest in them can be traced from at least the 1930s. As we recall from Chap. 2, the Russians were attracted to the small, barrage type during World War II because of the desirable saturation effect and the flat trajectory. Highly mobile launchers which could be emplaced either on the ground or on tanks and trucks were introduced. Best known, the Stalin Organ could handle from 16 to 60 Katiusha rockets, which weighed from 17 to 31 lb, were some 6 ft long, and were effective at from 3 to 6 miles. Calibers of 3¼ in. were first used, but later 5¼- and even 11¾-in. varieties were introduced into action.

Andrei Kostikov, a military engineer, conceived the Katiusha (for which he received a 100,000-ruble Stalin Prize) and, with the assistance of V. Aborenko, I. Gvai, and V. Golkovski (artillery general, engineer, and designer, respectively), developed it into an operational weapon. The fin-stabilized rocket was widely used during the war, notably at the defense of Stalingrad and Kharkov.

Like the British, the Russians experimented with a snare-type antiaircraft rocket which ejected wire at the apogee to foul airplane propellers. In 1943, a 13-lb, 3¼-in.-diameter, rocket-propelled penetration bomb was put into battle, using a 2.2-lb solid rocket to accelerate it to 1,150 mph. Carried by the famed Stormovik, it was 2 ft long and armed its percussion fuse with an airstream propeller. Larger varieties weighing up to 220 lb came to be called Black Death by German tank crews on the Russian front.

Moving into the post-war field, information on Russian missiles has been almost invariably vague and contradictory. Through normal intelligence sources, some data have been picked up, and released German scientists often have provided some valuable insights. Until very recently, pictures of Soviet missiles have not been available, and there has been little reference to specific models. For years the world had to be content with scattered reports, newspaper releases, and speculative articles of a general nature in Soviet publications.

In Chap. 2 we mentioned reports about a geophysical research rocket reaching some 240 miles, two-stage long-range missiles, 1,700-mph rocket airplanes, and missiles launched from underwater platforms. Rumors continually emanated from Russia on animal-carrying rockets capable of attaining more than 100 miles and other interesting achievements ranging from surface-to-air point-defense missiles to moon rockets and interplanetary probes.

For a long time, about all that could be done was to piece together these reports and rumors in the hope of making a coherent picture out of them. There was always a strong lack of certainty on specific details; and this, coupled with the feeling that somehow, across the board, the West must be ahead, gave a false impression of the full scope of Russian progress. It was fairly generally assumed that the Soviets could not advance beyond the state of the art as developed by the West. On the other hand, it was fully appreciated that they had the benefit of a long-time interest in rocketry and astronautics; German techniques, know-how, hardware, and bases (including many captured rocket centers [1]); a growing industrial base; emphasis on heavy industry; a large, skilled, and hard-working population; and a record of solid achievement in such related fields as aviation, jet-engine design, combustion theory, astrophysics, propellant chemistry, and atomic energy. As far back as 1949, they are known to have operated a Central Institute for Guided Missile Development, and a Stratosphere Committee was organized back in the mid-thirties.

[1] Peenemünde, Nordhausen, Rechlin (Air Force Test Center), Heidelager (former German V-2 site in Poland), BMW factory, Walter works, Rabe Rocket Institute, and a rocket-motor facility at Lehesten.

During the 10-year period following the war, it gradually became apparent that the Soviets had put into operational service derivations of many German surface-to-air, air-to-air, and surface-to-surface rocket weapons including Taifuns, Rheintochters, Wasserfalls, R/4ms, V-1s, and V-2s. In addition it was suspected that they had taken the A-9/A-10 ICBM design and put it through at least a preliminary developmental stage, and possibly had applied some of the material found in the Sänger antipodal-bomber report.

Like the United States, the Soviet Union used the German V-2 (Chap. 2) but instead of restricting herself to merely modifying the warhead section to carry out upper-atmosphere sounding, the USSR improved the missile, apparently built it in vast quantities, stock-piled it for possible combat purposes, and trained thousands of troops in ballistic-missile-handling techniques. It is also likely that the Russians used V-2s as test beds for rocket engines, guidance, and component and accessory systems designed for other, more advanced weapons. They probably perfected the V-2 to the point where the sea-level thrust was 77,000 lb, with a range approaching 400 miles. This became the M-101, and later the T-1. Fairly reliable reports were available many years ago that the missile had been fired from Kohlberg to the Isle of Oesel in the Gulf of Riga.

The Russians presumably developed the A-9 concept to the point where it fired over 500 miles, and under the direction of Van Brock and Artakianov, a derivation of the A-10 may have led into the M-103 program. The result was a two-stage rocket whose kerosene–liquid-oxygen first stage may have developed a thrust of up to 260,000 lb. A range figure of 1,850 miles has been fairly often quoted for this IRBM type, whose designation is now given as T-2. Two T-2 motors and a T-1 top stage may be the major ingredients of the T-3 (the former M-104), from which the Sputnik launcher was presumably derived. T-4 type hypersonic, Mach 15 rocket bombers are also apparently under advanced development in the USSR.

There is mounting evidence that Russia is well along the way toward perfecting an operational submarine-launched ballistic missile. The naval publication *Sovetsky Flot* has carried information relating to a 750-mile undersea-launched missile and has suggested that navies would soon be able to engage one another when 600 or more miles apart with their missile armament. Unclassified intelligence information available in December, 1957, suggested that the Soviets had slowed down the building of conventional subs as they shift to the atomic variety, with the capability of handling fleet ballistic missiles.

Russian Astronautics

Turning to astronautics, we know that Russian interest is as traditional as it is profound. In 1873, Konstantin Eduardovitch Ziolkowski made the momentous decision that he would probe into the secrets of space travel, and his pioneering mind was dedicated to the task during the greater part of his long career. Years later he could look back on the "moment when it seemed to me that I had decided this question. . . . I was so excited, even stunned, that I did not sleep the whole night. I strolled around Moscow and continuously thought about the great consequences of my discovery. . . . The thought of space travel never left. . . ." The dream of the conquest of cosmic space was very real to young Konstantin.

Ziolkowski was not a mere dreamer, and he did not neglect the scientist in him. By his early twenties he was a mathematics and physics instructor, and papers on such subjects as the duration of the radiation of a star and the theory of gases began to flow from his pen. Aeronautics soon claimed his attention, and then its obvious (or not-so-obvious, depending on when and where one was born) extension, extra-atmospheric flight, absorbed him completely. His efforts, begun at the end of the nineteenth century (Chap. 1), culminated in the 1903 monograph The Exploration of World Space by Reaction Apparatus. This famous study came out in the *Scientific Survey* (*Nauchnyi Obozrenie*), No. 5, and is recognized as the first scientific treatise dealing with space travel and attendant subjects. At age seventy-five, Ziolkowski was an important hero in the Soviet Union, and in recognition of his achievements the Academy of Sciences established a gold medal in his name.

The great "Mezhplanetnia Sobstchyenia," of Rynin, mentioned previously, still stands as one of the most massive works in the astronautical field: its Volume 8, on the "Theory of Space Travel" ("Teoriya Kosmicheskogo Poleta"), is an example of amazing completeness and foresight, considering the 1928–1932 period in which it appeared.

At about the same time a number of rocket-astronautical societies were founded in Russia, and evidence suggests that more than paper investigations were made. Dispatches from Moscow in 1935 could announce that:

A Soviet stratosphere committee has ordered the construction of a rocket capable of attaining a velocity of 2,200 feet a second and a possible altitude of 34 miles. . . . It is also reported that plans are being studied for a larger rocket designed to ascend several hundred miles.

Then the war came, and astronautics temporarily slid into the background. Following the reestablishment of peace, the Soviet Union embarked on huge programs of science and technology which resulted in such achievements as atomic and nuclear bombs, superb jet aircraft, and large ballistic rockets. The educational base from which the USSR has drawn its highly trained manpower is now probably second to none, and the country currently turns out two to three times more engineers and scientists than the United States.

As far back as 1950, and even earlier, qualified rocket experts were quite aware of the magnitude of Russia's accomplishments and, in the trade and technical literature, were able to report that a vast program was under way in the USSR. An extensive research, development, production, and test network was shown to exist, and Russian missile activities were described with such terms as "immense effort" and "considerable achievement." "The nations of the presently free world, and of this country in particular, cannot afford to let up in their own efforts toward guided missile research and development," a leading United States aviation publication concluded in 1953.

It became known that IRBM-ICBM progress and astronautical progress were far more intimately connected in Russia than in the United States, and during the early 1950s Soviet writers confidently poured forth articles predicting a variety of large satellite and space projects. In an important Western scientific journal it was written in 1954:

To a rocket expert . . . knowledge of a Soviet satellite rocket means that the Russians are in possession of the necessary technical knowledge to put a long-range missile with an atomic warhead on any point of this Earth that they choose.

On August 26, 1957, some six weeks before Sputnik I, information was released officially in Russia that multistage ICBMs had been fired over what was termed "a huge distance." Later, the U.S. Department of Defense revealed that it knew of these ICBMs and that intelligence had detected perhaps five launchings. America was only beginning to awaken. Not only were Russian ICBMs emerging as successful operational weapons, but the West knew that their IRBMs were being produced and fired in quantity and that considerable experience had been gained from a broad upper-atmosphere sounding program with meteorological and geophysical rockets. (The Soviets, incidentally, are firing 125 of these types of missile during the International Geophysical Year.) Thus, it seemed quite clear to some that the USSR had the necessary rocket equipment and know-how to plan ambitious astronautical ventures.

In April, 1955, it was revealed that Academician P. Kapitsa was in charge of a satellite-development group, and several months later, following the announcement of America's Vanguard project, top officials in Russia (including Khrushchev himself) boasted that they were developing a much larger satellite. And in the fall, Prof. Kirill P. Stanyukovich, of the Interplanetary Communications Commission, further underscored the extent of Soviet satellite planning.

More recently (four months prior to the launching of Sputnik I) the Academy of Science's head, Prof. Alexander Nesmeyanov, stated that Russia had "created the rockets and all the instruments and equipment necessary to solve the problems of the artificial Earth satellite."

At the same time Russia reported to International Geophysical Year headquarters in Belgium that it would send a sphere some

20 in. in diameter, *within the next few months,* into a polar orbit. The report carried the signature of I. P. Bardin, vice president of the Academy of Sciences. In *Komsomolskaya Pravda,* Nesmeyanov again stated that the satellite would be launched "within the next few months." This was in June, 1957.

Also in June, an article in the magazine *Radio,* No. 6, offered details on the radio frequencies and trajectories of both Sputniks I and II. Two months later, in the publication *News of the Soviet Academy of Sciences,* No. 8, more data were presented in an article entitled Rockets and Artificial Satellites of the Earth and Research of the Upper Atmosphere, yet the Western World apparently ignored them (or, more probably, never got around to reading the articles).

We can summarize by saying that there was abundant evidence prior to Sputnik I of a far-reaching, well-organized ballistic-missile establishment as well as an ambitious satellite–space-flight program in the USSR. By a judicious combination of their own native ability, background, and hard work, they exploited German contributions, studiously kept informed of Western missile progress, and not only "caught up" with the West, but moved into a strong lead in certain crucial areas of science and technology. Such is the state of affairs in 1958. It can now be properly asked: "What has the Western World learned since the first Sputnik was hurled into orbit?"

Significance of Russian Successes

First, it has been made very clear that an outstanding effort must be made to coordinate *all* scientific activities relating to the missile and astronautical fields. It has also become alarmingly evident that knowledge of important developments in one field are often ignored by workers in another, and that top management and government leaders are frequently poorly informed about the state of the art of the technical elements that feed into the astronautical sciences.

Scientific counseling in the preparation and development of research and military planning has been as noticeably lacking in the United States as it is necessary. One great scientist-administrator put it this way:

Important new technological advances . . . are piling up and are only partially used because our normal planning and decision-making processes cannot respond and make use of them as fast as they become available.

Whether we like it or not, it appears that the world is engaged in a cold-war race for space supremacy, and the mere maintenance of position, let alone of a lead, could well spell the difference between the destruction and survival of the Western World. This race is now predominantly between the science and technology of the great powers, and it seems likely that two factors will contribute heavily to ultimate victory:

1. The building up of the store of basic scientific knowledge

2. Reducing the time period between the "discovery" of this knowledge and the production and application stages

These elements cannot be divorced. The position of rocketry and astronautics today results from a rich past of scientific discovery. Tomorrow's astronautical research tools and military space weapons will rely not only on a continuing harvest from this heritage, but upon *new* insights into the workings of nature.

America in particular is faced with what has been widely called a "crisis in science." Hints that this crisis has long been brewing are found rather easily. In mid-1955, following the Geneva Conference on the Peaceful Uses of Atomic Energy, the Chairman of the U.S. Atomic Energy Commission warned that America was rapidly falling behind in the development of scientists and engineers. It was known then that the number of college graduates qualified to teach mathematics had dropped 51 per cent between 1950 and 1954 and that those able to teach science had declined 56 per cent.

Taking a longer view, we know that, since 1900, the percentage of high school students enrolled in algebra courses has fallen to less than 25 from 56, while the percentage of physics students has plunged from 19 to 4½. In the 1950s, half a million American students studied mathematics under nonqualified teachers. A top official of the U.S. Office of Education remarked, several years before Sputnik, that "the staggering deficiency in scientists and engineers that confronts us will spell disaster to the American People unless we take action at once."

Unfortunately, action was not taken, and a 2-year study of Soviet education released by the Office of Education after Sputnik showed that, whereas the USSR graduates 80,000 engineers a year, the United States must content itself with less than 30,000. Even in the secondary school domain the Russians now have a commanding lead over America and one that is increasing steadily. Trend lines are often treacherous things to play with, but no matter how they are arranged, one conclusion appears inescapable: the United States has been surpassed in education and now finds itself talking not only about how to "catch up" in the missile and satellite fields, but how to regain an educational lead long enjoyed, but now lost.

From the foregoing, it is more than evident that United States and Western missile and space-flight planning must make maximum use of the scientifically and technically trained manpower it now has, and account has to be taken today of what resources we expect to enjoy in future years. That something will be done is indicated by the Eisenhower-backed educational program designed to pour state and federal funds into improving our scientific-educational framework. Heretofore Federal money has gone largely into modernistic, and often fancy, school buildings. Now it may go toward procuring highly qualified teaching talent which, after all, is the essential ingredient of any educational system.

The Sputnik Experiments: Conduct and Data

Now that we have briefly analyzed the rocket-astronautical background of Russian artificial satellites, we can proceed to the experiments themselves. What do we know about Sputnik I, which orbited around our planet until January, 1958? It was launched on October 4, 1957, at an undisclosed location[2] within the Soviet Union, and was given a velocity of approximately 8,000 meters a second (or slightly under 18,000 mph) by the carrier rocket. It described an elliptical orbit of relatively little eccentricity, attracted to within less than 200 miles of the earth at the closest approach and going out to some 550 miles at its apogee, or farthest point. Its orbit was inclined to the equatorial plane at an angle of 65°, and its period was some 96 min.

[2] Probably somewhere north of the Caspian Sea.

What amazed American observers was not the size of the satellite—it was 58 cm (nearly 23 in.) in diameter—but the 83.6-kg weight. This is 184 lb, and when compared with United States Vanguard and Explorer satellites in the 20-lb region, it is heavier by a margin of nine times! Top IGY scientists in this country have labeled the achievement "fantastic," which is admittedly no exaggeration when the magnitude of rocket power and missile complexity required to put such a weight into an orbit is realized. The Soviets have accomplished a technological feat today of considerably greater scope than planned by the United States for tomorrow.

Sputnik I carried two radio transmitters continuously operating at 20.005- and 40.002-megacycle frequencies (respectively, 15- and 7.5-meter wavelengths). The signals of the one frequency were emitted during intervals between the signals of the other (signal pulse was 0.3 sec, followed by a 0.3-sec pause). The *beep-beep-beep* satellite-radio signals were almost immediately picked up by the BBC in London, by RCA in New York, and by other radio and electronic organizations throughout the world. Radio "hams" sent in reports at intervals as the satellite came within range of their equipment. Transmitter power was 1 watt.

It was disclosed that not only the satellite but the protective cone that shielded it en route through the atmosphere and the third stage of the multistep launching rocket entered into orbit. Without doubt the placing of these objects into the planetary frontier has had an enormous impact on the world, and the date October 4, 1957, will long be remembered.

The Soviets have given the length of the radio antennas on Sputnik I as being from 7 ft 10½ in. to 9½ ft. Folded during the ascent phase, the antennas swiveled into position when the satellite was injected into orbit. It soon became apparent that radio signals were being modulated with telemetric information, though at first it was not felt that actual on-board experiments were being carried out. Later it was reported by Moscow that coded signals were emitted by the satellite, yielding temperature, cosmic-ray, meteoric-incidence, density, and possibly other data. Micrometeor impingements were thought to have come particularly from remains of the comet Giacobini-Zinner. According to Moscow dispatches, the satellite's shell was filled, prior to launching, with gaseous nitrogen, which was useful in helping produce temperature equilibrium inside the package.

The satellite was widely observed by radio and optical methods; in the United States, Minitrack stations were hurriedly converted to handle the 20- and 40-megacycle frequencies. Both north- and south-polar stations picked up the satellite and reported frequent variations in signal strength, duration, and pulse rate, presumably partly caused by ionospheric and propagation-path conditions. By the 25th of October, some three weeks after the satellite entered orbit, battery power was exhausted, and then no further radio signals could be heard.

As for visual observations, the simplest object to see was the third-stage rocket, but sightings of the three components (third-stage rocket, protective cone, and satellite) were made all over the world, and data were fed into central computing stations. As of October 11, the carrier rocket's apogee was 483 miles and its perigee 143 miles, with an eccentricity of orbit of 0.05. Precession was slightly above 3° per day, and a complete orbit initially took 96.03 min, but later decayed to 88 min. The rocket fell to destruction on the first day of December, 1957, after completing 886 revolutions of the earth. Its last reported perigee was 107 miles.

Since the satellite, third stage, and nose cone did not assume orbit at exactly the same time, and since they all presented different mass-area ratios, they moved into different paths. The satellite was launched out of the third stage at a speed of about two feet per second, and hence had a slightly faster orbital injection velocity, causing it to move in a somewhat larger orbit. Because of the resulting decreased period, it took longer to make a complete revolution than the carrier rocket, which soon pulled ahead of Sputnik I in its smaller, shorter orbit.

Since the orbital period was much shorter than the earth's rotational period, Sputnik's track (when projected on the planet) did not retrace itself, but had the aspect of a spiral inscribed on a sphere. Traces of the track of both Sputniks, as well as of the United States Vanguard and Explorer, have been frequently published.

The launching rocket was reported to have weighed some 100 tons and to have been three-staged. The first stage brought the velocity up to 4,650 mph, the second to 12,400 mph, and the third to 17,896 mph. The rocket began to tilt into its programmed flight path shortly after it took off, and at first-stage motor cutoff the vehicle was inclined at 45° to the earth's surface. It is believed that the first stage fired 120 sec and that the second stage coasted to 635 miles from the launch site, when the third stage took over. The satellite was injected into orbit at about 300 miles altitude. The following table summarizes what we know about Sputnik I.

Popular name	Sputnik I
Astronomical designation	1957 α
Diameter	22.8 in. (58 cm)
Weight	184 lb (83.6 kg)
Satellite shell	Aluminum
Average altitude (approx)	Less than 400 miles (650 km)
Perigee Y_p	160 miles (258 km)
Apogee Y_a	560 miles (900 km)
Orbit inclination i	65°N–65°S
Semimajor axis a	4,330 miles (6,960 km)
Eccentricity e	0.0462
Mean motion of node (motion of orbit plane)	3.16° west per day
Orbital velocity	
At perigee	19,000 mph
At apogee	17,000 mph
Sidereal period (P)	96.2 min
Lifetime	3 months (approx)

Sputnik II was born a month after Sputnik I, on November 3, 1957. Three things about it were significant.

1. It weighed six times as much as Sputnik I (and, incidentally, some fifty times as much as America's satellites).

2. It was launched close on the heels of the first one.

3. It carried a dog.

Again, one could only speculate on the carrier vehicle, but presumably it relied on IRBM kerosene–liquid oxygen T-2 engines in the first stage. It is possible, however, that higher-energy fuels were employed, containing either lithium or boron additives.

Sputnik II orbited at about 17,810 mph, making 14 circuits a day (Sputnik I made 15), and carried two transmitters which operated on 20- and 40-megacycle frequencies, as did the transmitters of the earlier satellite. The former pulsed at 0.3-sec intervals, but this time the 40-megacycle-frequency transmission was a continuous tone. Experiments carried out involved cosmic radiation, solar X, ultraviolet and corpuscular radiations. Both pressure and temperature studies were conducted.

Three photomultiplier cells spaced at 120° were employed to conduct solar-radiation experiments. Lyman alpha (1216 angstrom units) and X-ray portions of the solar spectrum were isolated by using optical filters, and varying intensities of solar radiation were derived as electrical energy from the photomultiplier tube, amplified, and telemetered to Earth. This experiment was housed at the head of the instrumentation package of Sputnik II.

Behind this, in a spherical capsule hermetically sealed, were located the two radio transmitters, batteries, temperature- and pressure-recording devices, and the heat regulator (excess heat was transmitted to the hull of the rocket by gas circulation).

Two cosmic-ray-detecting devices were carried in Sputnik to determine the distribution and effect of latitude on intensity by essentially simultaneous observations over a wide geographical belt. The axes of the cosmic-ray counters were set mutually perpendicular.

As in the case of Sputnik I, a nose cone (of ceramic, according to some reports) was used to protect the satellite from atmospheric heating during the ascent from the earth. It, too, was discarded in space, and entered into satellite orbit.

The major experiment was, of course, biological, using a Laika dog as the test subject. For one week information on psychological and physiological reactions was gathered, emphasis being on the effects of zero gravity on the animal's circulatory and digestive systems, heart, and lungs. The dog was automatically fed and watered in his sealed environment, pulse beats were read, and data on breathing and blood pressure were transmitted to surface stations. It has been reported that highly active chemical compounds in the chamber provided the necessary oxygen and absorbed the carbon dioxide and noxious vapors.

Sputnik II being nonrecoverable, the dog died in space (about a week after launching). It is believed that the satellite was fitted with a porthole, enabling the dog to be the first earth-born creature to gaze into interplanetary space from outside the atmosphere. This highly significant biological experiment followed a long series of rocket flights in which dogs were flown and successfully recovered. One dog, named Albina, is reported to have made two flights to a peak of 125 miles, parachuting back to earth safely.

During its first day, the period of Sputnik II was 103.7 min, but it shortened at the rate of 1.4 sec a day thereafter. The right ascension of the ascending node initially was found to decrease at 3.1° per day. As of January, 1958, Sputnik II had completed 837 revolutions of the earth (compared with 1,351 for Sputnik I). The following table summarizes what we know about Sputnik II.

Popular name	Sputnik II
Astronomical designation	1957 β
Length	19 ft (approx)
Diameter (max)	4 ft (approx)
Shape	Conical-cylindrical
Weight	1,120.3 lb (508.3 kg)
Average altitude (approx)	575 miles (925 km)
Perigee Y_p	140 miles (225 km)
Apogee Y_a	1,017 miles (1,640 km)
Orbit inclination i	63.4°
Semimajor axis a	1.1463 earth
Eccentricity e	0.0965
Mean motion of node (motion of orbit plane)	3.1° west per day
Orbital velocity	18,000 mph (approx)
Sidereal period P	103.7 min
Lifetime	5 months

Data derived from Sputniks I and II will keep world scientists busy for a long time. Transmitted signals were carefully analyzed so that information relating to extreme-altitude electron density, as well as the thickness of the various ionized layers, could be derived. A periodic "beeping" was discovered to be associated with Sputnik II's steady-tone transmitted signal and has puzzled many investigators. It is possible that this was caused by F-layer turbulence or Faraday rotation.

Signal fading also must be explained, and studies of recordings made are progressing. It was noted that signal fading increased when the satellites moved on the north-south track; possibly this was caused by a shift in signal orientation to the magnetic field of the earth (the satellites crossed the field at right angles from transmitter to antenna in the north, but when coming from the south they were almost parallel to the field).

Atmospheric-density information has benefited greatly from Sputniks, and it is now believed that, at an altitude of 140 miles, the air is five times denser than it was previously considered to be. Science is only beginning to benefit from the first artificial satellites of the earth, fully confirming the predictions of the early, pioneer astronautical thinkers.

Harvard College Observatory announcement cards have been published on both Sputniks. According to a system devised by Prof. Fred L. Whipple, each satellite is named according to the launch year, followed by a Greek letter designating the order. If more than one object enters into orbit at the same time (e.g., a satellite nose cone and last stage of a carrier vehicle), an Arabic number will follow. Decreasing order of brightness will govern the assigning of these numbers. The world, for a while during 1957, had five artificial companions, as seen in the following list:

1957 α1—Third-stage rocket of Sputnik I

1957 α2—Sputnik I

1957 α3—Protective nose cone, Sputnik I

1957 β1—Sputnik II

1957 β2—Protective nose cone, Sputnik II

Figure 6-1 and the nomenclature on the following page will be found useful in interpreting orbital parameters as the artificial satellite becomes a more common research tool.

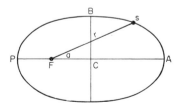

FIG. 6-1

Nomenclature

a	(PC)	Semimajor axis
b	(CB)	Semiminor axis
e	(FC/PC)	Eccentricity of orbit
P		Period (sidereal)
n		Average angular motion (in radians)
r		Radius vector (measured from F to any point S on the orbit)
w		True anomaly
M		Mean anomaly
Ω		Ascending node
$\mho$		Descending node
i		Inclination
ω		Angle in orbital plane between Ω and Y_p
Y_p		Perigee
Y_a		Apogee
F		Earth at focus

Plans for the Post-Sputnik Era

First we looked into the historical background of Soviet astronautics, the progress of rocketry from World War II to the present, and pre-Sputnik warnings of what almost inevitably had to happen. Russia for years had hoped to celebrate the hundredth anniversary of Ziolkowski's birth, (September 17, 1957) with a successful astronautical accomplishment. Sputnik I came less than a month late.

Next we studied both Sputnik I and Sputnik II, outlining as many characteristics as possible of the carrier rockets and satellites themselves, including the respective ephemerides. We saw that these satellites have provided a wealth of scientific information, and that, for months to come, the data derived will continue to be analyzed and fed into the general store of knowledge of the universe. It now becomes appropriate to wonder what will happen next. We surely realize that these Sputniks are just stepping stones to greater things beyond the horizon.

The Russians have shown a marked adeptness at making surprisingly accurate predictions, and there is no reason to expect they will stop making them now. It is more than likely that there is a full-scale moon-rocket effort now under way in the Soviet Union, and some sources suggest early vehicle test firings have already taken place. Informed opinion generally agrees that the USSR will have a minimum moon ship by 1961, though Prof. K. Stanyukovich has recently predicted it could be as early as mid-1959 or 1960. Moscow also reports that manned orbiting vehicles are in development, and in late 1957, Prof. Y. A. Pobendonostev talked of manned space stations as launching platforms for deep-space flight. One of the Russians' top guidance authorities, Y. S. Khebtsevich, has further backed up the 1961 time period for lunar voyages by writing on plans for fully instrumented circumlunar probes, including detailed flight-control methods. 1970 is given as the date of the first Venus and Mars probes, to be developed "as a result of a line of thought on cosmic research originated in the Soviet Union."

There is an abundance of pre-Sputnik astronautical literature that can be profitably studied. It was written at a time sufficiently near the present to reflect modern astronautical research and development accurately, yet back far enough to make manifest that it was not written in definite anticipation of a satellite success in October, 1957.

For example, we find Dr. A. G. Karpenko, reporting on the establishment of the Permanent Interdepartmental Commission on Interplanetary Communications (USSR's phrase for astronautics or space flight), noting that

one of [its] immediate tasks . . . is to organize work concerned with building an automatic laboratory for scientific research in space. . . . Outside the limits of the atmosphere such a cosmic laboratory will revolve around the Earth as its satellite for a long time [observing] phenomena . . . not accessible for investigation under ordinary terrestrial conditions.

Back in 1951, artillery-sciences expert Tikhonlavov felt that a moon voyage could be considered feasible, and that was about the time a 200-ft, 1,000-ton, 20-engine Soviet moon vehicle was first rumored to be under serious study.

All evidence points to the fact that Russia is a nation dedicated to the conquest of space. One of her most honored authorities, Dr. P. L. Kapitsa, made this very clear when he said:

. . . if, in any branch of knowledge, possibilities of penetrating a new virgin field of investigation are opening, then it must be done without fail, because the history of science teaches that, as a rule, it is precisely this penetration of new fields that leads to the discovery of those very important phenomena of nature which most significantly widen the paths of human culture.

The West has begun to realize the near-fatal error of having read only superficially into Soviet scientific literature during the last ten years. Three facts probably contributed to this lamentable situation:

1. Only a very small percentage of Western scientists can read the language.

2. Russian-translating and -abstracting services are notable only by their absence.

3. It was not felt that, in any event, such significant scientific work would come out of a "nation of peasants."

Russia, on the other hand, has an efficient Institute of Scientific Information which abstracts some 8,000 world-wide journals, numbering nearly 1,500 from America and somewhat less than 1,000 from the United Kingdom. The U.S. Library of Congress takes well over 2,000 Soviet journals, but only 30 are normally translated.

Take, for example, the USSR publication *Progress of Physical Sciences,* September, 1957. There, no less than 17 articles appeared on satellites, lunar voyages, and deep-space flight, all by highly qualified experts. According to an outstanding American authority, nothing in the United States has yet appeared comparable to Egorov's Problems of the Dynamics of Flight to the Moon, which incorporated two years of investigation carried out at the Russian Mathematics Institute.

Professor V. V. Dobronravov wrote, in October, 1957, of Russian plans for a 1,700-ton Earth-Mars spaceship, travel time out and back taking about 250 days each way and waiting time on Mars occupying 440 days. V. Kaznevsky, contributing to a special space-flight supplement to *Soviet Aviation,* states that he believes manned interplanetary spaceships will be with us within a few years, and other contributors to the edition feel that solutions to the many problems will be forthcoming.

While most astronautical experts in the Soviet Union hold that space flight is feasible in the fairly immediate future, there are some doubts as to its exact priority. Thus, Prof. K. Sergeyev has said, in effect, that, while it is technically possible now to undertake a moon program, other projects in fact enjoy higher priority, such as permanent space stations and methods of reentry into the earth's atmosphere.

It would be possible to continue for pages to quote assertions, opinions, and predictions of Soviet scientists, engineers, and military experts, but to do so would be lengthy and tedious. Russia has proven what she can do with rockets and artificial satellites, and in these two areas has a substantial lead over her only significant competitor, the United States. From an analysis of hundreds of statements of Soviet experts and abstracts and translations of articles, one comes to the inescapable conclusion that Soviet space-flight developments can only accelerate in the coming years. The position of the West in the face of growing Soviet space supremacy is by no means hopeless, but it is serious. Only a most vigorous and ambitious space program in the United States will prevent the Soviet conquest and complete control of space contiguous to the earth, and eventually of the moon itself. The effect this would have on Western democratic development is not encouraging.

BIBLIOGRAPHY

There are three good sources of Russian rocket and satellite bibliography:

Ley, W., "Rockets, Missiles and Space Travel," pp. 510–512, Viking Press, New York, 1957.
Krieger, F. J.: "A Casebook on Soviet Astronautics":
    Vol. 1, Rand Corp. Rept. No. RM-1760, pp. 21–35, June 21, 1956.
    Vol. 2, Rand Corp. Rept. No. RM-1922, pp. 11–29, June 21, 1957.

Because of their general unavailability, no attempt is made to offer a list of Russian book titles. However, there are available a number of articles about Russian rocketry and astronautics in Western languages.

Soviet Troops Get New Missiles, *Missiles and Rockets,* vol. 2, no. 12, p. 37, 1957.
Poloskov, S. M., and B. A. Mirtov: L'Étude de l'atmosphère supérieure à l'aide des fusées à l'Académie des Sciences de l'U.R.S.S., *Fusées*

et Recherche Aéronautique, vol. 2, no. 1, p. 49, 1957 (see also translation appearing in *J. Brit. Interplanet. Soc.,* vol. 16, no. 2, p. 95, 1957).

Zaehringer, A. F.: Soviet Missile Progress, *Aero Digest,* vol. 71, no. 6, p. 48, 1955.

Dogs and Russian High Altitude Research, *Jet Propulsion,* vol. 27, no. 2, p. 186, 1957.

Tabanera, M. T.: La Cohetería y La Astronáutica en Rusia, *Revista de la Asociación Argentina Interplanetaria,* vol. 4, no. 14, p. 22, 1957.

Sutton, G. P.: Evaluation of Russian Rocket Developments, *J. Brit. Interplanet. Soc.,* vol. 13, no. 5, p. 262, 1954.

————: Rockets Behind the Iron Curtain, *J. Amer. Rocket Soc.,* vol. 23, no. 3, p. 186, 1953.

Missiles of Russia, *Missiles and Rockets,* vol. 2, no. 10, p. 72, 1957.

Zaehringer, A.: A Table of Soviet Missiles, *J. Space Flight,* vol. 8, no. 5, p. 1, 1956.

————: Soviet Astronautics, *Missiles and Rockets,* vol. 2, no. 2, p. 45, 1957.

Vast Missile Program Pushed by Soviets, *Aviation Age,* August, 1953.

Soviet Missile Arsenal, *Missiles and Rockets,* vol. 2, no. 2, p. 36, 1957.

Ordway, F. I., III: Will Russian Scientists Beat us to the Moon?, *American Mercury,* vol. 86, no. 409, p. 20, 1958.

Soviet Missile and Rocket Installations, *Missiles and Rockets,* vol. 2, no. 2, p. 40, 1957.

Rockets and Rubles, *Missiles and Rockets,* vol. 2, no. 2, p. 44, 1957.

Organizational Chart of the Soviet IGY Satellite Program, *Missiles and Rockets,* vol. 2, no. 2, p. 49, 1957.

Parry, A.: What the Russians Tell . . . and Don't Tell (Rockets), *Missiles and Rockets,* vol. 2, no. 2, p. 70, 1957.

Another Russian Satellite, *Sky and Telescope,* vol. 17, no. 2, p. 55, 1957.

The First Man-made Satellites, *Sky and Telescope,* vol. 17, no. 2, p. 56, 1957.

Artificial Satellite No. 1, *Sky and Telescope,* vol. 17, no. 1, p. 11, 1957.

Hersey, I.: The Meaning of "Sputnik," *Astronautics,* vol. 2, no. 4, p. 22, 1957.

"Sputnik": What Are Its Technical Implications?, *Electronic Inds. & Electronic Instrumentation,* vol. 16, no. 11, p. 70, 1957.

Satellite Carriers: Vanguard vs. Sputnik, *Missiles and Rockets,* vol. 2, no. 12, p. 51, 1957.

Koelle, H. H.: Sputnik and Vanguard, A Comparison, *Astronautics,* vol. 2, no. 5, p. 32, 1957.

Sandorff, P. E.: A Study of the Soviet Satellite Program, published at Mass. Inst. Tech., Nov. 25, 1957.

Sputnik II—Cosmic Fact-finder, *U.S.S.R.,* vol. 16, no. 1, p. 4, 1958.

The First Days of Sputnik I, *Spaceflight,* vol. 1, no. 6, p. 198, 1958.

7

Escape

The Problems of Escape

The proposition of escape is a rather forbidding and mathematical one, but an effort should be made to understand it. We saw in Chap. 4 that the rocket is ideally equipped to defeat the retarding forces of the atmosphere and gravity. Today, a rapidly growing body of serious engineers and scientists have come to the inescapable conclusion that the state of the art of rocketry is sufficiently advanced to make the first steps toward the exploration of the moon and closer planets.

There are two fundamental problems which have to be solved. The first (and least troublesome) is the problem of piercing the earth's atmosphere. This envelope of air, which protects and sustains life at sea level, rapidly loses pressure and density until, at an altitude of about six miles, there is not enough pressure to support respiration. The effect of the atmosphere on a rocket destined for interplanetary space, however, can be largely neglected, since the resulting drag from the air can be generally considered as producing a velocity loss of less than two per cent of the rocket's terminal speed. (High-altitude sounding rockets and guided missiles, depending on configuration, give a somewhat higher figure.) This is not to say that air drag is unimportant, but only that, compared with the even more fundamental problems of gravity, it assumes a minor role. However, since the atmosphere reduces the operating efficiency of a rocket (described in the preceding chapters) and, in addition, creates aerodynamic drag and friction heating at high speed, it is advisable that we consider its constituent parts. We will have to come back down through it sooner or later.

Structure of the Atmosphere

This medium is composed of a number of gases: nitrogen (78 per cent), oxygen (21 per cent), and argon (1 per cent), mixed with minute quantities of carbon dioxide and traces of neon,

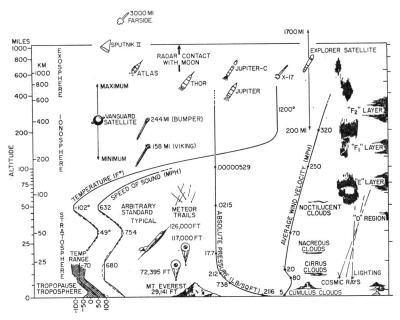

FIG. 7-1. Characteristics of the earth's atmosphere, and altitude attainments of various satellites, research rockets, and aircraft. (*Adapted from Douglas Chart.*)

helium, methane, and other gases. The composition remains more or less constant over its complete range. In a standard day atmosphere, the water-vapor content may range from 0.12 to 1.3 per cent by volume.

For convenience, atmosphere physicists divide the atmosphere into a number of layers. The first, the *troposphere,* is from 6 to 10 miles thick, and since 75 per cent of the atmosphere's weight is concentrated here, it is obviously the region most troublesome for the rocket. The troposphere is characterized by a rapid falling off of temperature with altitude and by the fact that all the earth's land mass is found within it (Mount Everest is about five and one-half miles high). The troposphere ends at what may be termed the *tropopause,* where an abrupt change in temperature gradient occurs. It is here that the *stratosphere* begins. The lower stratosphere displays an isothermal structure where, from six or seven to perhaps eighteen miles, the temperature is about constant. Above this is the upper stratosphere, or *mesosphere,* extending to about 45 miles, where the temperature first increases (to about 35 miles) and then falls off. Above some 45 miles, the temperature drops rapidly until open-space conditions are met; to describe this region the term *thermosphere* has been suggested. Within the stratosphere are the zones of maximum ozone concentration, and the word *ozonosphere* has been suggested for the region of 12 to 22 miles.

Man is only beginning to understand the thermal properties of the region above 40 to 50 miles, but it is known that large electron densities exist there. The general term *ionosphere* is employed for the region extending from about 45 to nearly 200 miles. Layers of maximum ionization are known to exist at about 45, 62 (electron density 2×10^5), 125 (electron density 4×10^5), and 185 miles (electron density 10^6). The ionosphere is a very important region, and at the present time is undergoing an enormous amount of exploration by sounding rockets.

Much of the significant research conducted in this region, so far, has been accomplished by the Aerobee-Hi and Viking series, which have probed up to 190 miles into this mysterious region. Research in the ionosphere by instrumented rocket has brought back a wealth of valuable information on its composition and its effect on radio waves and, consequently, on broadcasting.

During the current International Geophysical Year our atmosphere is coming under intensive study by rocket, four principal types of which will be used. For highest altitudes the type used is the Aerobee-Hi, some of which have already been launched from Ft. Churchill. Smaller rockets include Nike-Cajun, Rockoon, and Nike-Deacon. Launching sites are Ft. Churchill (where 34 Aerobees and 42 Nike-Cajuns are scheduled for launch) White Sands,

Point Magu, and Holloman Air Force Base. Some rockets will be launched from Guam, in the Pacific, and others from ships and from polar points. The United States will fire some 200 rockets in all, with experiments to be conducted in meteorology (meaning atmospheric structure: pressures, temperatures and densities, composition, and ionospherics) as well as such other phenomena as solar activity, air glow, aurora, cosmic rays, and geomagnetism. Atmospheric-structure experiments will be conducted with 60 rockets, wind studies with 18. Other atmospheric-exploration techniques will be carried out using balloon, anomalous propagation, searchlight probing, meteor observations, etc.

The atmosphere-structure programs will make use of a number of pressure-sensing devices, rocket-grenade techniques to determine wind and temperature, falling-sphere techniques to determine density, and aerodynamic techniques to derive pressures, densities, and temperatures.

The outer region of the atmosphere is sometimes referred to as the *exosphere*. Here, at the space frontier, the air particles bounce off their scarce neighbors, following elliptical paths as they fall back under the influence of gravitational attraction. The mean free path (the distance between air molecules) is one-millionth of an inch at sea level, 51 in. at 70 miles, over half a mile at 140 miles, and 43 miles at 250 miles.

The Problems of the Atmosphere

Aerodynamic drag is caused by the impinging of molecules of air on the surface area of a body traversing the atmosphere and is proportional to the density of the air, the velocity of the vehicle, and the configuration. In general form, it is customary to state that

$$D = C_d \tfrac{1}{2} \rho V^2 A \qquad (7\text{-}1)$$

where D = drag or air resistance to body

V^2 = velocity

C_d = drag coefficient

A = frontal area of body

ρ = air density

Equation (7-1) is not true for all conditions of flight, but it is sufficient for our purposes.

*Opening of Raketenflug-
platz Berlin, the experi-
mental station of the VfR
(September, 1930). In the
foreground is Wernher von
Braun wearing a trench
coat. (Courtesy Wernher
von Braun.)*

*Test stand No. 7 at Peene-
münde, Germany, after an
air raid. (Courtesy Wern-
her von Braun.)*

*A V-2 power plant on a static
test stand at Peenemünde, Germany, 1942. (Courtesy Wernher
von Braun.)*

*The He-112 with a rocket
engine built by Wernher
von Braun's team, Ger-
many, 1937. (Courtesy
Wernher von Braun.)*

The A-5, forerunner of the A-4 (V-2). About twenty-five were fired from 1937 to 1939. The A-5 had a complete gyroscopic guidance system, jet vane controls, radio guide beam, etc. (Courtesy Wernher von Braun.)

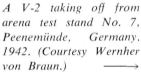

A V-2 taking off from arena test stand No. 7, Peenemünde, Germany, 1942. (Courtesy Wernher von Braun.) ——→

A typical A-4 firing under operational conditions in 1944. Note the camouflage by the forest and the paint pattern. (Courtesy Wernher von Braun.)

Carbon jet vanes in the A-5, 1937. (Courtesy Wernher von Braun.)

Test stand No. 1 in the closed position, Peenemünde, Germany. Built in 1936, this is probably the world's first really large liquid-rocket test stand. It could take 100 metric tons thrust and had removable side walls. The upper part of the floor could travel to the end of the rail for the test. (Courtesy Wernher von Braun.)

Wasserfall, a German antiair-craft guided missile, was developed at Peenemünde, 1943 to 1945. Note the radar (foreground) for target acquisition. (Courtesy Wernher von Braun.)

General Dornberger (left) and Dr. Wernher von Braun, 1944. (Courtesy Wernher von Braun.)

Rocket-engine assembly in V-2 pilot production at Peenemünde, Germany, 1943. (Courtesy Wernher von Braun.)

A motorized V-2 battery with three launchers set up experimentally at Peenemünde, Germany, in the spring of 1944. Actual firing operations were carried out under camouflage in forests. (Courtesy Wernher von Braun.)

An artist's conception of a method to recover cameras and instruments from extreme altitudes. This particular system was used with a converted German V-2 rocket at White Sands Proving Grounds, in New Mexico. (U.S. Air Force.)

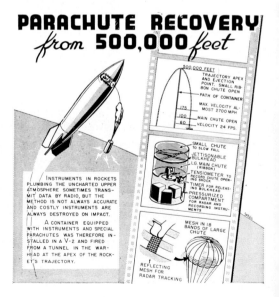

PARACHUTE RECOVERY
from **500,000** *feet*

500,000 FEET
TRAJECTORY APEX AND EJECTION POINT, SMALL RIBBON CHUTE OPEN
PATH OF CONTAINER

175 — MAX. VELOCITY ALMOST 2700 MPH
100 — MAIN CHUTE OPEN
60 — VELOCITY 24 FPS.

SMALL CHUTE TO SLOW FALL

JETTISONABLE BULKHEAD
LG. MAIN CHUTE (RIBBON)
TENSIOMETER TO RECORD CHUTE OPENING SHOCK
TIMER FOR RELEASING BULKHEAD
PRESSURIZED COMPARTMENT FOR RADAR AND RECORDING INSTRUMENTS

MESH IN 18 BANDS OF LARGE CHUTE

REFLECTING MESH FOR RADAR TRACKING

INSTRUMENTS IN ROCKETS PLUMBING THE UNCHARTED UPPER ATMOSPHERE SOMETIMES TRANSMIT DATA BY RADIO, BUT THE METHOD IS NOT ALWAYS ACCURATE AND COSTLY INSTRUMENTS ARE ALWAYS DESTROYED ON IMPACT.

A CONTAINER EQUIPPED WITH INSTRUMENTS AND SPECIAL PARACHUTES WAS THEREFORE INSTALLED IN A V-2 AND FIRED FROM A TUNNEL IN THE WARHEAD AT THE APEX OF THE ROCKET'S TRAJECTORY.

A photograph of the famous Bumper missile, composed of a German V-2 and a small American-made WAC-Corporal. For a long time Bumper held the world's altitude record of 244 miles. (U.S. Army.)

One of the first experimental V-2s, 1942. (Courtesy Wernher von Braun.)

Facing page, upper left: *An Air Force Boeing IM-99 Bomarc interceptor missile in firing position at the Air Force Missile Test Center in Florida. (U.S. Air Force.)* Facing page, upper right: *The Army-Firestone surface-to-surface Corporal 75-mile-range tactical missile being erected into launching position at the Redstone Arsenal.* Facing page, bottom: *A missile loader designed to transfer quickly three Army Hawk missiles at a time from storage area to launcher. This loader and other integrated units give the Hawk system high speed and mobility of operation. (U.S. Army.)*

The Talos Defense Unit, a land-based version of the Navy's shipboard missile system, has been turned over to the Army for evaluation. Equipped with a mechanical "brain" known as the Steering Intelligence System, it can carry a nuclear warhead. (U.S. Navy.)

Left: *Army Nike-Hercules surface-to-air guided missile on its launcher at White Sands Proving Ground. (U.S. Army.)* Above: *America's largest air-to-surface guided missile, the Air Force–Bell Rascal, with a range of about 100 miles, is shown being carried to a B-47 aircraft. (Bell Aircraft Corporation.)*

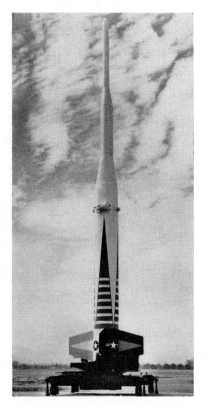

Above: *Army's huge Redstone missile being serviced prior to flight firing at Patrick Missile Testing Center in Florida. (U.S. Army.)* Below: *This Air Force X-17 test rocket weighs more than 6 tons and incorporates three stages. It is a Lockheed development utilizing the Army solid-propellant components. (U.S. Air Force.)*

A Cook Research parachute test sled being decelerated on the experimental high-speed track at the Air Force Flight Test Center, Edwards, Calif. These sleds are used for acceleration and deceleration tests and reach speeds well over 1,000 mph. (U.S. Air Force.)

Rocket power developed by a large missile engine is being measured on a static test stand at the Aerophysics Field Laboratory, North American Aviation. (North American Aviation, Inc.)

Above: *A missile flight performance is recorded by electronic equipment at the Lockheed Missile Systems Division in Van Nuys, Calif. At the upper left, tape recording goes on. The line of equipment in the rear transforms information from a taped record to decks of punched cards. In the foreground is shown a plotter which produces graphs from the information on the cards. (Lockheed Missiles.)* Below left: *Prior to testing the Vanguard, a modified Viking was used to check out a variety of components. This particular rocket reached an altitude of 125 miles and a range of 180 miles. It is shown here being serviced before launching. (U.S. Navy.)* Below right: *An artist's conception of the Vanguard rocket being serviced in its gantry. (Stanilla-Martin.)*

A telescopic photographic recorder (TPR) is capable of tracking and photographing an object the size of a Coca-Cola bottle 4 miles away. It was designed and built by the Air Research and Development Command and is under contract to Perkin-Elmer Corporation. It is a completely mobile unit. (U.S. Air Force.)

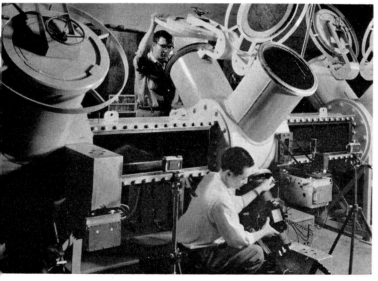

This pressurized test tank is used in high-speed experiments with the Ames light-gas gun, capable of propelling a model at 10,000 mph under laboratory conditions. The Y-shaped sections are shadowgraph stations, where pictures of the model are made in 1 ten-millionth of a second. Cameras in front of the rectangular windows record the streak of light created by high temperatures to which the model is subjected. Data derived are useful in intercontinental ballistic missile development. (National Advisory Committee for Aeronautics.)

Above: *An artist's conception of the separation of the second and third stages of the Vanguard rocket. (Stanilla-Martin.)* Below left: *The USAF–Bell X-2 rocket research airplane has reached 25 miles into the space frontier. It is the closest thing yet devised to a manned spaceship. (Bell Aircraft Corporation.)* Below right: *An artist's conception of a troop-carrying missile based on suggestions of Maj. Gen. John B. Medaris, Commanding General of the Army Ballistic Missile Agency. It is obvious that such a concept would be applicable to possible passenger transport. (U.S. Army.)*

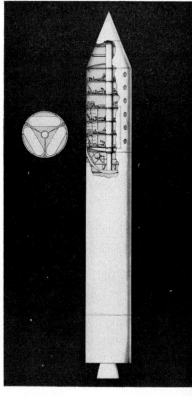

Von Braun has suggested a freight-carrying missile that would be launched from a supporting base on earth, rise into the satellite orbit, and then be controlled by a satellite-station crew. Here a missile is being launched rearward from the freight-carrying transporter. (U.S. Army.)

Three space pioneers: (Left to right) *Dr. Heinz Haber, Dr. Wernher von Braun, and Willy Ley. (Courtesy Walt Disney.)*

An artist's concept of tomorrow's interplanetary rocket. Notice the use of multiple engines. (North American Aviation, Inc.)

Left: *An artist's impression of the establishment of a power transformer on the moon. It is pointed out that lunar conditions will simplify the design engineer's problem. The lack of atmosphere will allow him to eliminate heavy insulation; and since there are no oxidizing effects, transformers should last indefinitely. (Camilli–General Electric Company.)* Lower right: *A Thor above its firing pad at the Air Force Missile Test Center, Cape Canaveral, Fla. An intermediate range ballistic missile developed for the Air Force by Douglas Aircraft Company, Inc., it is being manufactured with production tooling on the assembly line at the company's plant at Santa Monica, Calif. (U.S. Air Force.)* Upper right: *A Jupiter in vertical flight shortly after taking off. This is the Army's intermediate range ballistic missile. (U.S. Army.)*

Interstellar and internebular travel are already being studied in theory. Here we see nebulosity in Monoceros, in the south outer region of NGC 2264. (Photographed in red light, 200-in. photograph, Mount Wilson and Palomar Observatories.)

←———

A possible lunar objective, Ptolemy and Eratosthenes in the central region of the moon. (Mount Wilson and Palomar Observatories.

←———

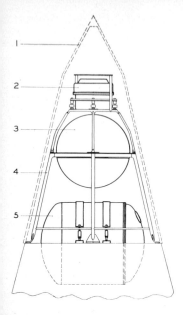

Arrangement of equipment in Sputnik II: (1) protective cone, (2) solar-radiation device, (3) capsule containing other instrumentation and the radio transmitters, (4) instrumentation-package frame, (5) animal chamber.

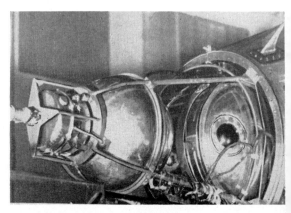

Installation of capsules with scientific instrumentation on Sputnik II.

The instrumentation by which Sputnik II traces not only the changes in intensity but also the composition of cosmic radiation.

Sputnik II instrumentation for the study of solar radiation. (Courtesy Soviet Embassy.)

Since the densest part of the earth's atmosphere is within 10 miles of the earth's surface, the drag upon a vehicle is most critical in this region. Fortunately for the outward trip, however, it is the nature of a large rocket to accelerate slowly from the earth's surface and not attain high velocity until it has passed through the denser regions of the atmosphere. The rapid falling off of density with altitude compensates for the increasing velocity. Velocity loss V_d can be expressed as

$$V_d = \int_0^T \frac{D}{m}\, dt \qquad (7\text{-}2)$$

where m is the rocket mass at time t and T is the upper limit of integration given as the time required to pierce the denser air layer.

Several solutions for offsetting this detrimental effect upon the rocket's performance have been advanced from time to time. One is to launch at a high altitude, say from any of several locations in South America, with suitable platforms ranging from 14,000 to 15,000 ft above sea level. A number of sites in Bolivia would be particularly attractive in that there are railroad communications to some of the remote areas. Mount Kilimanjaro, in Kenya, Africa, with its tablelike abutments, can also be considered for launching, although access to this region would be somewhat difficult.[1]

Another solution that has been advanced for a satellite-launching rocket is the use of balloons. A satellite rocket could be carried aloft by this method, using a helium balloon, thereby partially avoiding the loss of velocity and extra expenditure of propellant to overcome drag.

Balloon-launching of small rockets has been tried extensively in the Rockoon program, wherein Deacons have been able to explore the region from 50 to 75 miles up. Kurt Stehling, of the Naval Research Laboratory, has been an active proponent of balloon-launching an earth satellite rocket. His concept involves a three-stage rocket, with a 20-ton gross weight, launched from a 3-million-cu-ft plastic balloon at 75,000 ft. The payload would be 30 lb, which would be placed in orbit. Now his scheme seems to have borne fruit.

[1] G. Partel, Some Problems on Rocket Development, a paper presented at the Sixth Congress of the International Astronautical Federation, 1956.

Four preliminary attempts at firing a balloon-launched four-stage Air Force–Ford Aeronutronic rocket from a balloon 100,000 ft above the Pacific failed before the first successful shot. The 30-ft-long rocket is to take a small payload up to about 4,000 miles above the earth's surface. Data are to be telemetered back to the surface on University of Maryland designed equipment. Four Recruit rockets are to make up the first stage, a single one the second, four Asp-type motors the third, and one Arrow II motor the final, or fourth, stage. These solid rockets are to take the last stage to a burnout velocity of 17,000 mph. Called Project Farside, the program is expected to yield valuable information on cosmic rays, ionospherics, meteorites, and geomagnetism. Six rounds are to be fired. The vehicle's weight is 1,900 lb, and its payload only 3½ lb.

Still another solution is to launch the satellite rocket at high altitude from a fast-climbing airplane. The limiting factor here would be the maximum payload of the aircraft (consistent with speed and altitude objectives), together with the engineering problems involved in separation of the aircraft-rocket combination and the control of the angle of launch.

The Problems of Gravity

The second fundamental problem of escape is that of overcoming the force of gravity. Newton's inverse-square law states that every particle of matter in the universe attracts every other particle with a force which is directly proportional to the product of the masses of the particles, and inversely proportional to the square of the distance between them. This can be written

$$F = G\,\frac{m_1 m_2}{r^2} \qquad (7\text{-}3)$$

where G = gravitational constant
F = attracting force
r = distance between centers of the masses
Considering a two-body system and eliminating the mass terms, we may rewrite Eq. (7-3) as

$$g_r = g \left(\frac{R}{r}\right)^2 \qquad (7\text{-}4)$$

where g_r is the force of gravity at a distance r from the center of the earth and R is the earth's radius.

To escape the earth's surface it is necessary to create a force equal in magnitude and opposite in direction to the gravitational pull exerted by our planet. By considering the energy E required to move unit mass from R to infinity, it may be seen that

$$E = \int_R^\infty g \frac{R^2}{r^2} dr = gR \tag{7-5}$$

Hence, from Eq. (7-5), a body of unit mass projected to infinity would require an instantaneous velocity of

$$V_e = \sqrt{2\,gr} \tag{7-6}$$

Considering the earth's mean radius as 3,960 miles and g equivalent to 32.2ft/sec², the velocity required becomes 7 miles/sec, or 25,000 mph.

It is most likely that the first interplanetary voyage will not depart directly from the earth to its destination, since a prohibitive amount of energy would be wasted in traversing the first few miles of the gravitational field and the effects of drag, although small by comparison, should be avoided. Hence, the obvious solution is to launch our interplanetary vehicle from an earth-circling satellite. The energy required to move unit mass at a distance r from the earth's surface, or the point in space where the earth's attractive energy will just equal the energy required by a rocket to escape, is given by

$$E_r = \int_r^\infty g \left(\frac{R}{r}\right)^2 dr = g \frac{R^2}{r} \tag{7-7}$$

Hence, escape velocity becomes

$$V_r = \sqrt{\frac{2gR^2}{r}} \tag{7-8}$$

Considering the case of a satellite orbiting at 1,075 miles with a circular velocity of 4.39 miles/sec, it may be seen that the additional velocity required for escaping from both orbit and earth is only 1.76 miles/sec.

With these facts in mind, it immediately becomes apparent that the satellite vehicle will play an important part in the sequence of events leading to interplanetary voyages. Rocket designers must of necessity, for the time being at least, include in their calculations an already-existing satellite circling somewhere between 200 to 1,000 miles.

Based on known engineering techniques, any single-staged vehicle launched directly from the earth's surface and designed to land on, or circumnavigate, the moon without recourse to orbital refueling or construction would indeed be enormous (Chaps. 10 and 11). Regardless of all the technological advances in propellant chemistry and structural design, the size and weight problems associated with such an escape rocket may prove too severe a deterrent to any direct approach to space flight.

In previous chapters the relationship which determines the theoretical velocity of the rocket has been stated as

$$V = c \log_e \frac{m_o}{m_1} \qquad (7\text{-}9)$$

where $V =$ characteristic or final velocity of rocket

$\dfrac{m_o}{m_1} =$ mass ratio

$c =$ effective exhaust velocity

We now have to rewrite the equation to correct for air drag V_d and force of gravity g, which is assumed constant during powered flight for time t. Hence, the revised equation becomes

$$V = c \log_e \frac{m_o}{m_1} - gt - V_d \qquad (7\text{-}10)$$

If the speed attained is equal to, or greater than, the corrected escape velocity, the rocket will be projected to infinity. If the characteristic velocity is less than the escape velocity, the maximum altitude reached will depend directly upon the angle of launch and the rocket will theoretically return to the earth's surface at velocity V.

Escape velocity varies considerably throughout the solar system, and indeed throughout the universe. For example, the escape velocity at the moon's surface is 1.5 miles/sec, whereas at the surface of Jupiter it is 37.5 miles/sec (Table 7-1). From these two figures we can gain some idea of the range of escape velocities throughout our own solar system. Table 7-1 is a list of escape velocities for planets, satellites, and two selected asteroids.

TABLE 7-1   *Escape Velocities*

Planets

Body	Escape velocity, miles/sec	Gravity ratio
Earth	7.0	1.00
Moon	1.47	0.16
Mercury	2.2	0.27
Venus	6.3	0.85
Mars	3.1	0.38
Jupiter	37.0	2.64
Saturn	22.0	1.17
Uranus	13.0	0.92
Neptune	14.0	1.12

Satellites

Body	Primary	Escape velocity, miles/sec
Phobus	Mars	0.0009
Deimos	Mars	0.0003
Ganymede	Jupiter	1.74
Callisto	Jupiter	2.05
Titan	Saturn	1.78
Rhea	Saturn	0.76
Titania	Uranus	0.62
Oberon	Uranus	0.59
Triton	Neptune	1.05

Asteroids

Body	Diameter, miles	Escape velocity, miles/sec
Ceres	475.0	0.31
Eros	12.4	0.006

To delve a little further into the mechanics of rocketry, we shall now consider a variation of Eqs. (7-9) and (7-10). By inspection, it is noted that

$$\frac{m_o}{m_1} = e^{V/c} \qquad (7\text{-}11)$$

with gravitational and drag losses neglected. The equation in this form is most useful for performing graphical analysis. To illustrate a particular case consider the following example. Letting $V = 7$ miles/sec, $e = 2.718$, and c (the exhaust velocity) $= 3$ miles/sec, the mass ratio $\dfrac{m_o}{m_1}$ becomes a little better than 10.

Mass Ratios

It is immediately apparent that, with existing high-altitude rockets taken as a yardstick, where mass ratios in the case of V-2 and Viking missiles have ranged from 3.5 to 5, great improvements will have to be made if we are to escape. Our figure of 10 is derived with the assumption that exhaust velocities are available in order of 3 miles/sec, a very optimistic figure at this time, since no such exhaust velocity has been reached outside the laboratory. Furthermore, since gravitational losses are ignored in the calculations, accelerations would have to be assumed as infinite.

If and when exhaust velocities greater than, or equal to, 7 miles/ sec become available, escape by single-stage rocket will be theoretically possible. There are many associated problems, including propellant chemistry, acceleration characteristics, and structural-design limitations, which would make the vehicle fantastically large and unbelievably expensive. The answer to this dilemma—and the one to which, it seems, we must always return—is the earth-circling satellite. The first refueling satellites will probably be the final stages of multistaged rockets, adapted to this particular purpose by containing propellants as a payload. This convenient gas station will probably be the site for the construction of the first interplanetary vehicle.

The circular or orbital velocity of a satellite is a matter of celestial mechanics, since all planetary bodies obey the same laws. The gravitational attraction of the earth must equal the centrifugal force of a body rotating at a radius r about the earth. This can be expressed as

$$F_g = F_c \qquad (7\text{-}12)$$

Expanding these values we obtain, by substitution from previous equations,

$$g\left(\frac{R}{r}\right)^2 = \frac{V_r^2}{r} \qquad (7\text{-}13)$$

Therefore, circular velocity V_s becomes

$$V_s = \sqrt{\frac{gR^2}{r}} \qquad (7\text{-}14)$$

At this juncture it will be noted by inspection that, given a common gravitational level, escape velocity is $\sqrt{2}$ times greater than circular velocity.

By considering the period of time T required by a satellite to complete one revolution of the earth and by transposing the already determined circular velocity V_s, we obtain

$$T = \frac{2\pi r^{3/2}}{\sqrt{gR^2}} \qquad (7\text{-}15)$$

Equation (7-15) is simply the distance divided by the velocity and is well known as Kepler's third law of motion.

An equatorial orbit would be most favorable for departure, inasmuch a bonus of the earth's rotational speed would be added to the velocity of the rocket when launched eastward in the equatorial plane. Another advantage which can be gained by utilizing this natural asset is an increase in the amount of propellants and construction materials which can be carried into orbit by a given rocket over that by an identical rocket launched in an orbit having a polar plane.

Let us now consider the energy required to place a satellite into orbit at a distance r from the earth's center, against the gravitational attraction of the earth.

$$E = \tfrac{1}{2}V_s^2 + \int_R^r g\left(\frac{R}{r}\right)^2 dr \qquad (7\text{-}16)$$

From this expression we derive

$$E = Rg\left(1 - \frac{R}{2r}\right) \qquad (7\text{-}17)$$

Since the single-stage rocket, for the time being at least, appears incapable of meeting escape, or even circular, requirements, we must look for other means, namely the multistage or multistep rocket (Chap. 8). The advantage to be gained from a two-, three-, or four-stage rocket becomes immediately apparent when we consider the performance of the V-2–WAC-Corporal (Bumper) combination. The V-2 rockets fired in the United States typically reached altitudes of about 100 miles, while the WAC-Corporal might go as high as 40 miles, but the combination attained an altitude of 244 miles and a maximum velocity of 1.43 miles/sec. Jupiter three-stage test vehicles have flown thousands of miles by using staging techniques and have launched a satellite, and the Air Force Farside four-step rocket is designed to probe 4,000 miles into space.

The obvious advantage of the step over the single-stage rocket is that all stages subsequent to the first have the velocity of the prior stages imparted to them. If the mass ratios of all the stages are the same, as well as the performances of the rocket motors, the effective velocity of each stage can be added to the velocity of the next step. Hence, if at separation the first step is traveling at 2.5 miles/sec, the third step (by development) will have the final velocity of 7.5 miles/sec. This figure is calculated on the theoretical basis of ideal conditions, which, because of gravitational losses and drag in the lower atmosphere, we do not obtain.

The result, however, is indicative of the step-rocket's performance and points out the path that must be followed if we are to obtain the maximum possible results from our present-day knowledge of chemical fuels, materials, and launching techniques. When we reconsider our problem of escape in the light of orbital refueling and multistage rockets, we find that great energy losses and tremendous expenditures of fuel may be avoided.

Before continuing it should be pointed out that all staging is not of the tandem type. The British use wrap-around staging on many of their missiles today. The Martin Company has investigated lateral staging, wherein all stages would fire at the same time. High performance is the expected result. At all times propellant would be pumped from the outer to the inner stages; and when the outer ones emptied, they would drop off. Not only would higher thrust-to-weight ratios result, but all stages would be ignited before take-off. Professor Crocco of Italy presented a similar plan to the Fourth Congress of the International Astronautical Federation, in 1953 ("Le Ravitaillement dans l'espace et le problème des polistades"). There is one additional bonus to be obtained by entering circularity first, and this is angular launching. By rotating the rocket into an elliptical ascent curve after we have cleared the denser atmosphere, we reduce the gravitational losses by the very fact that an additional (centrifugal) force is now aiding our escape. Also, the rotational velocity of the earth will be taken into account when the velocity budget for any interplanetary voyage is fully contemplated.

The intriguing proposition of the escape of a rocket from the surface of this planet to a point outside the solar system has been theoretically investigated,[2] and it appears that, since the mass of all the planets combined is about a thousandth that of the sun, the influence of the planets can be neglected. This being the case, the authors find that the

energy per unit mass required to bring a vehicle from the surface of the earth to a position far outside the solar system is the sum of the increase in potential energy due to the earth's field plus the increase in potential energy due to the sun's field minus the kinetic energy corresponding to the orbital velocity of the earth.

Using the nomenclature found in "Physics of Rockets," it is shown that the energy required to take a unit mass outside the solar system can be expressed as

$$E = \frac{GM_e}{R} + \frac{GM_s}{S} - \frac{\frac{1}{2}GM_s}{S} = \frac{GM_e}{R}\left(1 + \frac{\frac{1}{2}M_sR}{M_eS}\right) \quad (7\text{-}18)$$

where G = gravitational constant
$\quad M_e$ = earth's mass
$\quad R$ = earth's radius
$\quad M_s$ = sun's mass
$\quad S$ = distance from earth to sun

From the fact that g equals GM_e/R^2 we arrive at

$$E = g_oR\left(1 + \frac{\frac{1}{2}M_sR}{M_eS}\right) \quad (7\text{-}19)$$

[2] Seifert, Mills, and Summerfield, Physics of Rockets, *Am. J. Phys.*, vol. 15, no. 3, pp. 261–262, May–June, 1947.

If M_s/M_e equals 3.32×10^5, R/S equals 4.26×10^{-5}, and $g_o R$ equals 6.79×10^8 ft-lb/slug, E equals 54.8×10^8 ft-lb/slug, about eight times the value required to leave the earth. This is a formidable proposition, requiring an immense power source.

An even greater problem of escape will eventually follow when scientists turn to the possibility of escape from our galaxy. The very thought of this stuns the mind, taxes even the most vivid of imaginations, but the past has proved that, in the remoteness of the future, all things are possible, and even probable.

BIBLIOGRAPHY

Kahn, F.: "Design of the Universe," Crown Publishers, Inc., New York, 1954.

Clarke, A. C.: "Interplanetary Flight," Harper & Brothers, New York, 1954.

Hoyle, F.: "The Nature of the Universe," Harper & Brothers, New York, 1950.

Seifert, H. S., M. M. Mills, and M. Summerfield, Physics of Rockets, *Am. J. Phys.,* vol. 15, nos.1–3, 1947.

Sutton, G. P.: "Rocket Propulsion Elements," 2d ed., John Wiley & Sons, Inc., New York, 1956.

Partel, G.: Some Problems on Rocket Development, paper presented at Sixth Congress of the International Astronautical Federation, Copenhagen, Denmark, 1955.

"Space Flight Problems," proceedings of the Fourth Congress of the International Astronautical Federation, Zurich, 1953.

Sears and Zemanski, "University Physics," Addison-Wesley Publishing Company, Reading, Mass. Formerly Addison-Wesley Press, 1954.

8

The Spaceship

Resources and Logistical Thinking

Spaceships present an entirely new concept of design and operation, one that is quite unlike that experienced in the common vehicles of today. The task of space flight is a tremendous one, undoubtedly demanding of the complete utilization of all of man's present resources. Present methods and techniques indicate that the ascent into space must be accomplished by brute force, by the consumption of vast quantities of propellants, and by voyages across space which will be divided into sections or phases.

A consideration of the force of the earth's gravity indicates that it is theoretically possible for a single, self-sufficient vehicle to be capable of making the shortest trip through space (i.e., to the moon). In fact, the ideal end product in the development of any vehicle is that it be self-sustaining. The spaceship of science fiction is such a vehicle: It is fueled, provisioned, staffed, and loaded on one planet (from which it takes off, sometimes from unprepared fields); makes a routine voyage across interplanetary space, lands, and perhaps refuels; and takes off for home or some other planet.

There is nothing wrong with this picture, except that it makes a questionable fundamental assumption: that the energy source on which such flights are based is both stupendous and abundant. Atomic energy is usually stated or implied. Since most interplanetary science fiction is a study of what happens as a *result* of

185

space flight, the problems of propulsion are not analyzed. Science fiction is primarily a study of people and how they react to situations of a scientific nature.

Propulsion is a problem for the engineers, and it is quite a problem. A broad statement of the general proposition relating this factor to others of the whole, follows.

It is desirable to gain access to other astronomical bodies because the natural resources of the Earth will eventually be used up, because other bodies may be colonized, and because the scientific knowledge gained in both the attempt at flight through space and the exploration made possible by it will repay the effort of undertaking the task. If this is true, the attempt should be made.

An inspection of the mechanics of the problem reveals that flight in space is theoretically very simple, once you are in space, but that the strong gravitational pull of planets requires large amounts of energy to be consumed in escaping from the planets. The presence of an atmosphere (air-friction heating) makes landing a hazardous operation; the absence of an atmosphere (no aerodynamic support) makes landing even more hazardous, and best dealt with by the consumption of more energy.

An inventory of energy sources reveals that a reaction device is the only one that will work both on the planet and in space and that the rocket engine is its practical expression. An inventory of available propellants for use in rocket engines reveals a number of possibilities: steam, modified explosives, liquid-chemical action, the controlled release of atomic energy, and the emission of light.[1]

The common feature of all these propellants is the fact that they are used by ejecting particles from the vehicle and moving by reaction to this ejection. Generally speaking, they are mentioned in the ascending order of energy content and in the descending order of size of particle ejected. Heat is involved in all cases, and the increase in energy consumption is accompanied by an increase in the amount of heat created.

All matter melts or evaporates if heated enough, so one limiting

---

[1] This also happens to be the chronological sequence in which they have appeared or will appear. The practicability of steam power for JATO should not yet be ruled out.

factor is the highest melting point attainable in the material of which the reaction engine and the vehicle are made. There is no such problem in the use of steam, but there is in the use of solid and liquid chemicals. Temperatures associated with atomic energy are so high that an atomic rocket in terms of present metallurgy is only just barely possible. The temperatures involved in the use of direct atomic energy, ions, or light are so great that the matter is now chiefly of academic interest.

A conventional steam rocket system cannot develop enough exhaust velocity to avoid a vehicle size so large that it would collapse under its own weight. A rocket using solid- or liquid-chemical energy for escape from earth could be built, and, although of tremendous size, is not beyond a supreme engineering effort. Atomic energy would produce a comparatively small rocket, but it has a serious radiation hazard for occupants and for observers in the vicinity of the take-off area. Steam is too weak, and atomic energy is too strong, so to speak. Everything beyond atomic energy is still "dreamwork." This leaves chemical energy. What can we do with chemical energy?

The above statement may seem rather long-winded, but it is the preliminary thinking that the scientist must do to get a desired result. Condensed, the procedure falls into the following steps:

1. Determination that there is a task which merits action
2. Determination of the nature of the task
3. A survey of alternative methods which may be utilized in solving the problem
4. Selection of the most feasible method
5. Determination of the equipment needed to follow the method
6. Designing, developing, and utilizing the equipment

A seventh step may be added later. Based on the experience gained in the utilization of the equipment, an effort should be made to improve the equipment and thereby secure more efficient performance.

Step 1 is somewhat subjective to man as a species, and motivation may range from greed to the ethos of adventure. Step 2 depends on the development of astronomical knowledge. Steps 3 and 4 have been underway since the turn of the century, and at the present time the following preliminary conclusions present themselves:

1. Chemical energy is the only energy source we can now manage.

2. Chemical energy is just barely equal to its task.

The idea of a single rocket of gigantic dimension (say, the size of the Empire State Building) was never seriously studied. The principle of the multistage or step rocket was well understood even by Ziolkowski, and the 1,000-ft rocket remained merely as a basis of comparison.

Some thought has also been devoted to step 5. Studies have been made to determine the structure of spaceships,[2] but it should be noticed that it was Oberth who first realized the true nature of the problem and made the first concrete suggestion that multistage rockets be used. Later, others inspected the situation and saw that Oberth had rightly assessed the mass-ratio problem and the way to overcome it. (Multistaging has been taken for granted ever since and was proven feasible experimentally by the two-stage Bumper.) Multistaging greatly reduced the size of the rocket system to be used, but even this was not enough. Oberth sensed this, and made the first concrete statement expressing the technical desirability of satellite vehicles, as an additional "permanent stage" in the system.

Here was a second degree of procedural breakdown, and when scientists studied the matter they found that not only was it necessary *to* space flight, but it was necessary *before* space flight. Multistaging brought the rocket into reasonable engineering size (but still large), and the space-station idea reduced the size a little further. The more the matter was studied the more it was realized that all aspects of space flight should eventually be divided into a large number of small, manageable packages. This applied even to construction, and this is where the novelty of the spaceship as a vehicle makes it appearance.

Nearly every purposive action is based on some sort of logistics.

[2] Even Ziolkowski had some sketchy ideas on the subject. See "L'Astronautique," *Science et vie,* hors de serie, pp. 18–27, Paris, 1952, for Ziolkowski's design and the designs of Von Hoefft, Hohmann, Valier, Oberth and others.

A need arises and means are surveyed, summoned, and used. If the need is simple, the logistics are simple; if the need is great, the logistics are also great. Making breakfast, for example, consists of the recognition of the need for nourishment and the survey of the means (almost instantaneous since the problem is repetitive and standardized): it is remembered that equipment for cooking is at hand, the food to be cooked is in the refrigerator, and the person to cook it, probably a wife, is at home. The summons is automatic, since she has accepted the role of family cook as part of the marriage bargain—and since she also is hungry. The means are all present, they are used, and the breakfast problem is solved.

A 1,000-mile motor trip is more consciously logistical but still not much of a problem, nor is the construction of a playhouse in the back yard for the children. A trip to the top of Mount Everest is highly logistical and takes a great deal of study, as does one to the bottom of the ocean. The logistical problems grow with the size of the project and the variations to be experienced in the environment. The size of the task confronting us in climbing into space against powerful gravitational forces into the most hostile environment conceivable is large indeed. In a certain sense, logistics is the science of supply, and in another sense it is the science of getting things and people from one place to another through the medium of transportation—which, in turn, implies the development of specialized vehicles designed to perform the task.

Because of the meager energy available in chemical propellants,[3] compensations for the mass ratio will have to be made until atomic energy can be made practical in rocket engines. The first step would be the use of atomic energy for heat and of water or hydrogen for reaction mass. This would make possible more performance for a given mass ratio or the same performance for a smaller mass ratio. Each improvement in propellant systems would make possible smaller and smaller mass ratios (or, to put it another way, the equivalent of larger conventional mass ratios) until finally the

[3] Anyone who has witnessed the impressive display of power in a rocket-engine static test or in the launching of a large rocket missile finds it emotionally hard to accept chemical energy as very "meager." Yet this very fact only points up the enormous power of the earth's gravity, and the tremendous energy required to overcome it.

"full" mass and "empty" mass of a spaceship approach some yet undefined limit.

Meanwhile, as noted in Chap. 4, propellants will have to be stock-piled in a circumterrestrial orbit for use in attaining escape velocity, for deposit in circumlunar or circumplanetary destination orbits, and for retard expenditure on returning to the earth's surface.

Bearing in mind the work prerequisites for achieving space flight (the development of large chemical rockets of the Von Braun type for assembly of a space station in orbit), it is clear that a voyage across space, once the frontier is reached, recommends further preparation. Since the trip to the moon cannot be made more often than once every 2 weeks, the spaceship should be large enough to provision for a 2-week stay, and it must be constructed to land where there is no atmosphere. Wings are useless on the moon, and so, for that reason, are landing wheels. In landing, a lunar ship will have only the power of its rocket engines to reduce gradually the terrific speed of its tail-first plunge toward the moon. Landing will require propellants; more propellants will be needed for take-off.

It may seem that the lunar spaceship, for example, is already at hand in the third-stage rocket. But consider that the payload of a von Braunian stage three is roughly 37 tons. The whole three-stage vehicle consumes over 6,000 tons of propellants to attain a velocity of 4.4 miles/sec. This results in the accomplishment of the 1,075-mile orbit, but to escape from the earth requires another 2.5 miles/sec. Whether the third stage, replenished with only 91 tons of propellants, could escape from the earth, land on its jet, take off with its jet, and return to the earth space station seems dubious. Even if it were possible, the margin for error would be very slim.

Ferry rockets of the third-stage type, then, should bring up materials to construct a ship in space—if we are to avoid the expensive alternative of simply scaling up an already-huge rocket—so that a third stage replenished in a 1,075-mile orbit would have enough propellants to make the trip across space. Space flight is a big operation, and procedures of this magnitude, which would make it even bigger, would not be lightly indulged in.

Multistaging, Atomic Frustrations, and Vehicle Specialization

What type of ship should be constructed? The fundamental problem of space flight is still the achievement of desired velocities, so the idea of multistaging, which helped us get to a 1,075-mile orbit, again comes to mind. Here some caution is needed. Multistaging should be used, but not in the same way. When ascent is made from the surface of the earth, the first and second stages will expire, be dropped, and, because of a combination of gravity and air friction, reach a maximum altitude, curve back to earth, and be recovered by special teams out at sea, where they will fall as planned.

If the same kinds of stage were dropped in the same way out in space, they would fall not back *to* earth, but into eccentric orbits *around* the earth at average altitudes higher than the space station. It would be a rather inconvenient and expensive proposition to chase them in small spaceships. Each flight to the 1,075-mile orbit will use about 6,000 tons of propellants, and this, added to other costs—such as maintenance, supporting services, and personnel salary (with incentive pay)—might come to a million dollars a flight. And each recovery flight, since it supports the transspace flight, must be calculated into that total cost.

There is a further objection. Dropped stages might adopt orbits of such high eccentricity that they would cross the orbit of the space station. It would only be a matter of time before a collision occurred. Numerous flights would deposit swarms of these bullet-like menaces to navigation over a period of time. But there is a final objection: cost. Stages are too expensive to be expendable as conventional steps, and retrieving conventionally-dropped steps would be, perhaps, even more expensive. What is the solution?

One solution is to use them as steps or stages, but change the manner in which the steps are used. Smaller ships, which were used numerous times to build the space station, might be used to build a large spaceship, one so large that the "first stage" need not be "dropped" until the ship is near the moon. But arriving at the moon, it would not be dropped by the stage above. Rather, it is the stage above that would be dropped. The third stage would then become a small landing rocket or ferry to go down to the moon's surface

and come back up to the circumlunar orbit, perhaps using the sec-
ond-stage propellants for both maneuvers. Then, leaving the first
and second stages attached and in circumlunar orbit, it would come
back to the earth satellite vehicle on its own tanks.

The stages left in orbit around the moon might be left there permanently and gradually refilled as an emergency supply station by
siphoning off special surpluses from other ships which came by
later. These ships would deposit their own first and second stages,
which would also have to be filled, but over a period of time, procedures and performance would improve, so that the resupply of
these orbiting tanks would gradually catch up with the rate of stage
collection in orbit around the moon.

Before landings are made on the moon, however, a flight around
the moon is likely to be made. Carefully designed and launched, a
spaceship for such a trip could be a single-stage affair less than
85 ft long and consisting of little more than engines, tanks, connecting framework, and a crew compartment—not even as big an
engineering job as the third-stage rockets sent up with the materials
to build it.

Following the degree of development where orbital deposit (in
lieu of discard jettison) is used, the "first" stage will probably be
very large, whereas the "second" stage or stages will consist of
space launches which land and come back and are either taken
inside or attached to the hull; after which the main ship returns to
earth orbit. Here we have a new kind of vehicle, a spaceship that
is built in space and stays there forever, like an ocean liner built
at sea to sail forever back and forth but never be brought to shore.
The name that is beginning to be associated with such a proposed
vessel is that of "deep-space" ship, the equivalent of a "high-seas"
ship on the ocean.

Such a vessel may be necessary for a long time. It will be necessary at first because of the logistic limitations imposed by the low
energy content of chemical propellants. With the advent of the
atomic rocket, radioactive reaction mass may be ejected harmlessly
from the deep-space vessel, improving its mass ratio (and increasing storage capacity), while chemical rockets are still used for
landing and take-off. Landing on an atomic jet would probably
create a radiation hazard around the base of the ship which would

make it unapproachable, or, conceivably, give the members of the crew a fatal roentgen dosage before they could get away from the ship.

Direct use of atomic energy would make the deep-space ship even smaller and more efficient, but would make the landing hazard even greater. And there is a joker in the atomic deck. In order to get atomic energy at all, it may be necessary to release it at such a slow rate that the thrust would be extremely low. This low thrust would make the middle (deep-space) part of the voyage very slow and long in duration. Also, the thrust would be too low to be used in the effective gravitational field of a planet. To rely on it would be something like bailing out of an airplane with a 1-ft parachute.

Examination of the atomic-energy picture in this light may arouse some suspicion. Something is very wrong here, the reader may say. There is vast power in the atom, and when properly released, it can do anything. This is only partially correct. There *is* vast power in the atom, but successful utilization of the power requires the knowledge of how to make metals contain an energy which is by nature greater than their own cohesive strength. The explanation of attractiveness apparently lies in the fact that atomic energy, even at low thrust, is better on a thrust-hour-dollar basis than chemical propellants. Although more expensive to prepare initially, a low thrust for a long time is cheaper than a high thrust for a short time. The longer the voyage the greater this advantage becomes. The atomic economy thus adds to the length of the voyage. It also requires special design compensations in the deep-space vessel so that it may support a large "ecological structure."

One other philosophy of voyage phasing should be noted. This is the regrouping system, wherein ships are designed for reuse by dismantling and reassembly in other shapes and personnel, propellants, and supplies are transferred from ship to ship as the regrouping schedule requires. With this system a fleet of ships could be constructed. In the case of the moon project there may be three ships, two passenger and one freight craft, each weighing about 4,400 tons and standing about 160 ft high. The freight craft would be left on the moon, most of it taken apart and reassembled into pressurized underground Quonset huts and the like.

In von Braun's Mars Project, a fleet of ten ships is required.

Some are left in orbits around Mars; some, equipped with wings of very high aspect ratio [4] are used as landing craft. Three landing craft are erected (wings attached, etc.) in the circum-Martian orbit and glide down. Upon landing, each craft elevates to vertical position a "small" rocket it has carried on its back. After a year's waiting period, these rockets are used to return to the circum-Martian orbit, leaving the big gliders behind. Deep-space ships are regrouped and consolidated and the return trip is made.

As flights through space become longer and longer, the nature of compromise with the ideal (self-sustaining) ship will depend on what is attempted with how much. The more ambitious the trip the more compromise (in the way of discard, deposit, or regrouping) will have to be made.

Looking back over what we have just surveyed on the general nature of spaceships, a number of facts stand out.

1. The key factor in space travel is propulsive energy.

2. Shortcomings in propulsive energy will require compensation in voyage procedure.

3. Compensations in procedure will demand special designs and hence different types of ship for different purposes until the ideal (completely self-sustaining) ship is perfected.

A brief inspection of the different types of spaceship shows what the compensations are and what the nature of the propulsion system has done to both design and procedure.

1. *Primitive.* Any of the rocket-powered supersonic aircraft made by Douglas and Bell which have flown from 80,000 to 126,000 ft may be regarded as very primitive spaceships of small capability. They have traveled in an environment which, for all practical purposes, is space equivalent. They use the thin air for lift, it is true, but if they go much higher, they will encounter an atmosphere so rarefied that the speeds required for aerodynamic support would burn them up. Human protection provided for these highest flights would probably keep a man alive in deep space.

[4] Ratio of span to chord; strictly speaking, the ratio of the square of the span to the area of the wing. The object here is improved lift to capitalize on the thin Martian atmosphere, which is approximately the density of earth atmosphere at the top of Mount Everest. Gliding down in this is vastly cheaper than landing on jets.

Carried into deep space by other craft, the aircraft could probably perform there.

2. *Satelloid.* This is a slightly more advanced spaceship designed for orbiting at 80 miles or other low altitude, using small rocket engines to prolong orbital time against small amounts of air friction. A manned, supersonic glider in configuration, this concept of Krafft Ehricke is half satellite vehicle and half spaceship.

3. *Ferry rocket.* This is a minimum spaceship designed to deliver men and supplies to orbit for construction and resupply of satellite vehicles such as the Ross or Von Braun space stations. Functionally it is a true spaceship, being limited only by fuel capacity. Because it is designed to "shuttle" between ground and orbit, it is equipped with wings and can land at conventional airports.[5]

4. *Deep-space ships.* This ship is essentially a "long-shuttle" craft of large size designed to fly between circumplanetary orbits but not to land. It may be simply a skeleton-like vehicle in which cabins, tanks, holds, and engines are merely attached together by girders of aluminum or thin stainless steel. Landing craft may accompany, or be attached to, it. On a short trip (earth to moon), the deep-space ship may also be the landing ship. For a long trip it is simply a low-thrust carrier.[6]

5. *Landing craft.* These ships vary in appearance with the nature of the celestial body on which they are to land. Moon ships are largely skeletal in appearance and have long-footed metal legs to rest on. Martian ships have long wings. A landing craft to descend on a body with an atmosphere essentially like our own might superficially resemble an earth ferry rocket. There would be certain differences, however. A ferry rises vertically, loaded, as the top of a multistage system and then glides down essentially empty. A landing craft, on the other hand, is designed to glide down, loaded, and to rise again vertically, essentially empty. It is a matter

[5] For the Von Braun design see C. Ryan, ed., "Across the Space Frontier," inside front cover, The Viking Press, Inc., New York, 1952. For the R. A. Smith design see R. A. Smith and A. C. Clarke, "The Exploration of the Moon," p. 38, Harper & Brothers, New York, 1954.

[6] The simplest deep-space ship is probably that of Von Braun's circumlunar manned probe. See C. Ryan, *op. cit.,* p. 51. A very advanced ship of low thrust for interstellar travel is shown in K. W. Gatland and A. M. Kunesch, "Space Travel," pp. 176ff., Philosophical Library, Inc., New York, 1953.

of wing-loading on the way down and strength of the gravity field on the way up. An earth ferry rocket might be able to land on Titan for example, but not take off, and vice versa.[7]

6. *Auxiliaries.* These include taxis and propulsion "guns" for individual men in space suits, or reaction power packages attached like outboard motors to large objects. Purists will probably reject these, though it does seem, in the case of the taxis, that a small craft which enabled the operator to use it without wearing a space suit would technically qualify as a small spaceship.[8]

Effect of Human Parameters on Spaceship Design

Aside from the design function of a spaceship, which determines the presence or absence of wings, wheels, legs, and so on, the spaceship has a further parameter: the human beings who must travel in it. The physiological considerations of man in space are treated in Chap. 10. Once the matters of function and, hence, propulsion have determined the general architecture of the vessel, it is necessary to modify the architecture to the requirements of the people who will ride in the ship. The factors which must be considered, somewhat in the order of urgency, are as follows:

1. Pressure
2. Acceleration
3. Breathing
4. Temperature

[7] Lunar landing craft may be found in C. Ryan, ed., "Conquest of the Moon," inside front cover, The Viking Press, Inc., New York, 1953. This shows all the essential elements of this particular era of space flight: the ferry rockets, satellite vehicle, and the combination deep-space and landing craft being assembled in orbit. A British design is shown in Smith and Clarke, *op. cit.,* p. 55. On page 51 of that book is a novel combination of the lunar landing rocket and a lunar probe, a robot rocket, in the act of touchdown. An interesting spidery-looking version of the lunar landing rocket appears in J. Coggins and F. Pratt, "By Space Ship to the Moon," front cover and pp. 38, 39, Random House, Inc., New York, 1952. On page 45 is an astronomical observatory, complete with dome, landing in one unit.

[8] Several interesting versions of the "space taxi" are found in "Across the Space Frontier," *op. cit.,* p. 107, center and lower right, as well as three more inside the front cover. See also "Exploration of the Moon," *op. cit.,* p. 31, and "By Space Ship to the Moon," *op. cit.,* pp. 26, 29. For propulsion guns, see "Across the Space Frontier," p. 79, and "The Exploration of the Moon," p. 29. About the only known picture of the "outboard motor" attachment is a sketch on p. 6, upper right, in "By Space Ship to the Moon."

5. Gravity
6. Radiation
7. Food and elimination
8. Meteor puncture

The order of urgency may be subject to debate, depending on some special conditions or missions of the vessel, but will serve as a point of departure. A sudden loss of pressure in the spaceship (caused conceivably by a faulty window giving way under pressure) would cause the air to surge out into empty space in a white jet. The sudden pressure drop inside, if the occupants had not been cannonaded through the porthole, would cause death by explosive decompression in 15 sec, long before the lack of oxygen could take effect.

In view of the difficulty of obtaining a high vacuum in the laboratory, with massive chambers and elaborate pumps, it may seem that the spaceship would have to be a thick-walled affair. Actually not. Despite the fact that metallic compression strengths are greater than tensile strengths, it is easier to keep pressures in than to keep them out. Present-day engineering techniques used to seal cabins of high-altitude aircraft are capable of designing an airtight hull in the same order of weight and strength. There is nothing in this that would alter the visual aspect of the basic design requirements, except perhaps some local precautions at portholes and the presence of a double-doored air lock.

The economics of propellant supply require as high an acceleration as possible to get into orbit at the earliest possible time. The ship must be braced for such accelerations, as well as for stress caused by the requirement of turning through the curve of synergy. This means more than an excessively massive exterior. Instruments, for example, must be specially designed and mounted to compensate for this stress. Air and propellant systems are moving fluids which themselves have inertia and must not flow in too great or too small quantities. Radar antennas, solar-furnace reflectors, and miscellaneous masts and booms of a comparatively fragile nature must be fastened securely.

Finally, there is man, the occupant. He is subjected to somewhat the same type of stress as the ship. His heart is a pump moving blood, which has inertia, and an inadequate or excessive pressure or supply of blood may cause physiological malfunction. (Human coordinations are interfered with.) It has been determined that a prone position is most desirable, since man in that position is less subject to the effects of acceleration.

Even so, men will probably still be operating at a disadvantage because the accelerations of the ship will be of the order of 3 g for several minutes. This is severe, and it means that computers and automatic-control mechanisms must be added to the ship so that maneuvers can be programmed into them while the men are lying all but helpless on their contour chairs. And these equipments themselves must be "ruggedized" to withstand the very accelerations they are compensating for. If the vessel in question is a deep-space vessel, the initial accelerations may be much less, but the same considerations may still hold, in reduced degree. Perhaps not even in reduced degree, for if thrusts are low, there will be an attempt to make the ship lighter, in order to take advantage of what little thrust there is. If so, the original problem is simply restated in a more subtle fashion.

Man must breathe. Breathing means oxygen, which is expensive and heavy. It will be brought in liquid form under pressure, which requires heavy containers, but this is a lighter and a better procedure than attempting to bring along the same amount in gaseous form in larger tanks. The pressure in the cabin provides a pressure differential so the lungs may inhale the oxygen, but a forced-draft circulation system may be necessary to prevent suffocation if there is no gravity in the ship, since convection depends on gravity.

Also, since human beings cannot breathe pure oxygen for long without a feeling of uncontrolled exhilaration, the oxygen must be diluted. Nitrogen, the diluent in the earth's atmosphere has the unfortunate property of causing "bends" with sudden changes (reductions) in pressure. Thus helium will undoubtedly be substituted. Sudden pressure drops are not anticipated in regular procedures, but helium (replacing nitrogen and thereby preventing bends) may be the difference between life and death by a few seconds during an emergency in space.

So far, the spaceship seems somewhat like a submarine in respect to breathing. But a submarine may carry vast quantities of oxygen with no particular weight problem, since there the problem is merely that of flotation. A spaceship would suffer a fantastic weight penalty; for that matter, space stations would have to be prohibitively large if the oxygen were simply brought along in tanks, breathed, and ejected after exhalation.

Machinery which can extract oxygen from exhaled carbon dioxide has been devised, but it requires a lot of power, which means more weight. Leafy plants and *Chlorella algae,* similar to pond scum, have been found to produce a high amount of oxygen for their weight in the process of their photosynthesis. The size of the spaceship can take into account the size of the cycling gardens, for such they would be, and additional oxygen in tanks would simply allow for certain losses, such as through the air lock.[9]

There may be an argument of fragility concerning dependence on algae or leafy plants. If some toxic element damaged or killed the cycling garden, there remains a question of whether or not another one could be grown before emergency oxygen supplies ran out. It would also have to be established, for example, that the gardens could survive starting accelerations and certain cosmic radiations that might filter through the hull (even though such radiations might not harm human beings). Conceivably the radiations could modify the plant chemistry to such an extent that the plants would produce something other than oxygen after a given period of time.

On the other hand, the cycling gardens would probably be vastly efficient on a volume per unit weight basis, and might have the additional advantage of helping to regulate the humidity (water-vapor content) in the ship. There is another argument in favor of cycling gardens: They can also produce food, since vegetables may be eaten in many cases without destroying the plants that produce them. A pumpkin may be eaten and the vine continue to grow. Tubers, such as potatoes, and vegetables of the carrot type contain their nutritive value in their roots, so starch must be obtained from other sources. Rice is high in starch but requires prohibitive quan-

[9] This raises a point: Why let the air escape from the air lock? It might be possible to pump it back into the ship, and none would be lost. It would have to be determined by a study whether the weight penalty for installing such pumps offsets the additional weight in oxygen that would have to be carried if leakage through the air lock were allowed.

tities of water. Corn is perhaps better, although it requires considerable space for growth. Figs and dates are very high-energy foods but might be tricky to grow.

Practically any vegetative substance has food value. Grass can be eaten but is largely undigestible by the human system, and palatability is an important factor. The *Chlorella algae* have been proposed as food as well as an oxygen-producing agency. Recollection of green pond scum does not arouse the appetite, but the algae would naturally not be offered in this state for consumption. The form the stuff might take is hard to visualize, but it would tax the ingenuity of a Paris chef to devise an inviting way of serving it. Perhaps, when processed, it would be completely tasteless and could be added to other foods as a fortifier or camouflaged as a lime-flavored gelatin dessert. In any event, the capacities of the cycling and food garden will be figured in the layout and weight factors of the vessel design. If a mechanical cycling system is incorporated, it will change the modification of the basic design in a different way.

Temperature will have an effect on the performance of machines, instruments, and men (and on the cycling garden if one is used). Surprisingly, the main problem in the earlier days of space flight will be that of keeping cool rather than keeping warm. Most of the flying will be in the general vicinity of the sun, and objects, particularly dark ones, will heat quickly on being exposed to solar rays. The shadow sides will not heat directly, but some heat will be transmitted to them by conduction.

One side of the ship might be painted partially or wholly black, and the other side polished to a mirror finish, so that the ship could be turned to adjust temperature. This, however, might require too much energy (in the form of propellants for power-driven flywheels), and consequently a heat pump [10] might be more feasible. In a deep-space vessel, it is possible that, if one set of propellant tanks lay in the shadow of another set, the contents of the former might either freeze or be so modified that the combustion properties of the propellant combination would be impaired when

[10] A heat pump would be something like a refrigerating system: Fluids of high heat-carrying capacity would take the heat from the sun side and dissipate it on the shadow side.

mixed in the rocket engines. If the ship were driven by other methods of propulsion, the introduction of additional heat might somewhat upset the delicate energy balances peculiar to the system. If this were not the case, it might be desirable to spin the personnel cabins (probably spherical in shape) in order to distribute the exposure to heat.

This spinning of the personnel cabins would probably be cheaper than spinning the whole ship and does not introduce any new problems about the direction of thrust applied for maneuvers. It also has the advantage of giving the crew a feeling of normal or near-normal gravity. Gravity provides the basis for automatic convection of air and restores the balance and tension elements of human action. On the other hand, it introduces some awkward problems in the operation of the ship, as all control connections (probably electrical) would have to be made through slip rings which might be rather inaccessible should a repair become necessary. The stars would probably circle at a dizzying rate of speed, which might further complicate the problem of navigation. Could the fixes be taken from a stationary part of the ship and transmitted electrically to the cabin with enough accuracy to trust? This would be a serious matter. Ordinary navigation is hard enough; navigation in space is demanding indeed.

Radiation will attack anything it strikes. Metals themselves suffer from various radiation effects, depending on their composition. The matter of hull substance will be of prime consideration in the general design of the ship; perhaps a special alloy must be perfected, so that one component can complement the shortcomings of the others. The metal must not fatigue in space or the ship will crack open under stress. Windows must have filters, so that ultraviolet and other radiations will not give the crew fatal burns or eye injury. Ordinary glass itself suffers deterioration under the assault of the radiations in space. The glass, and the substance of the filter, must not succumb to the rays, and, in fact, the very brilliance of the sun will demand tinting. Cosmic rays penetrate metal hulls effortlessly. Some shielding material, possibly a paraffin or other hydrogenous material (even water), may be used. This may conceivably have to be coated over the entire ship to protect even the bare metal. Perhaps not; possibly only the personnel cabin need be protected with a layer of radiation shielding. One thing seems certain, lead is so heavy that it will not be used unless science is desperate.

Food is a bodily necessity and a definite morale factor as well. Long trips in space will require a study of what can be brought and what can be grown, the energy content, composition, and palatability of each type, and the whole matrix will have to be balanced into a good diet and then made appetizing (within reason) so that the crew will not find eating an ordeal.[11]

The matter of reducing weight by supercondensation of nutriment (the "meal in a pill") is a chimera. Even if possible, it would gradually recondition the human body so that, after a long voyage, the reconditioned body, suddenly beset by emergency, would be unable to live on bulky food when the supply of food pills ran out. The human body develops with the advance of science and medicine, but a question does arise sooner or later as to whether the advances are setting up dangerous dependencies upon artificial agencies, which, by their nature, are not everywhere. This is not reactionism, it is horse sense.

Elimination of body wastes is a very serious problem in a closed-circuit environment such as a space station or ship. Chief wastes are exhaled air, sweat, salt, urine, and feces. Exhaled air may be handled by the cycling garden or similar agency, and at least part of the water, transmitted to the cabin air as water vapor, may be handled in this way; some may have to be absorbed by special machinery. Urine contains water, which may be removed by distillation, but the crystalline by-product is not only useless, but toxic. The use of dehydrated feces for fertilizer in cycling gardens should be regarded with caution. In some cases it can create a hygienic problem more serious than the ecological problem it "solves."

Food (normal bulk food, it is hoped) may have to be specially processed and shipped in reusable containers. Normal supplies would create an unbelievable mass of fruit rinds, coffee grounds, cans, papers, cartons, husks, stems, seeds, and miscellaneous pulps, pastes, and crumbs. No problem in a terrestrial kitchen, such materials would accumulate at an alarming rate in space and would be

[11] A. Ananoff, "L'Astronautique," pp. 397–399, Librairie Arthème Fayard, Paris, 1950.

hard to get rid of. In a space station they could be frozen into a block, tied to a rocket, and sent off in a retrograde path which would eventually take them down to incineration as the rocket struck the atmosphere.[12] This would require that the rocket used for the purpose also be brought up. Perhaps it would be cheaper to let the waste matter accumulate and tow it for a short distance behind a descending ferry rocket if that could be done without danger.

It may be necessary to reduce food to its digestible essence, deep-freezing everything, after removal of bones, rinds, unchewable pulp, stems, seeds, and cores. The remaining minimum packaging could be brought back on the ferry rocket. In a spaceship, however, actual removal of waste might be extremely expensive, as it would be necessary to counteract somehow the speed of the vessel, which might well be considerable. In the distant future, perhaps, the surpluses could be a blessing, for they might be powdered or liquefied and added to the basic reaction mass and thus be an assistance in propulsion.

It appears, however, that the problem of providing food in space may have been solved by research recently completed by the National Research and Development Corporation. In anticipation of the advent of the necessity or desirability of extended periods of flight, as well as the immediate need for an improved emergency food ration, they have just completed two years of research in the development of an entirely new bulk-providing concentrated food called Multi-Meal Tube, or MMT.

The nature of MMT is such that it provides a concentrated complete nutrient containing the food elements essential for the maintenance of normal body functions combined with a bulk producing substance which will provide the roughage-residue requirement for normal gastrointestinal function. The product is a homogeneous

[12] W. Ley in "Across the Space Frontier," *op. cit.,* p. 104. Ley points out that 6.25 lb of human waste per man will be created per day, of which 4 lb will be sewage. The other 2.25 lb will consist of per capita share of containers, indigestible leftovers, and foreign matter filtered out of the air and water systems. Simple ejection of wastes would merely result in explosion into a cloud of micrometeors. This would ruin observation in a space station and would not leave the vicinity of a moving spaceship, since there would be no airstream to sweep it away.

combination of cellulose gum, as a bulk-providing base; carbo-hydrates, fats, proteins, minerals, and vitamins in sufficient quan-tity to meet basic daily requirements; preservative factors; and flavoring elements to make the product palatable, all combined in semisolid form in a tube container. The container is so designed that its plastic cap may be removed with one hand and its contents easily squeezed directly into the mouth, thereby facilitating ease of ingestion and leaving one hand free for performance of piloting procedures, etc.

The MMT will maintain a sufficient proportion of its volume upon ingestion, digestion, and elimination to allow normal gastro-intestinal function. This complete food product provides more calories per unit weight and per unit volume than any other such product presently available. It is also the most complete food con-centrate containing the residual bulk necessary for normal gastro-intestinal peristalsis. Most of the material of the presently available food concentrates is immediately absorbed in the upper gastrointes-tinal tract, leaving no residual mass to be eliminated by the lower tract and thereby impairing normal intestinal motility and function. By providing a volume of palatable, edible, concentrated, high-caloric matter, compressed in a container, MMT provides desirable bulk without undesirable weight or waste of space. Because its entire mass is not absorbed, it accomplishes appeasement of hunger for longer periods of time than do the presently rapidly absorbed food concentrates. Also, it provides the psychological advantage of a feeling of fullness long after ingestion. Each tube will contain one complete meal of approximately 720 calories, will weigh approxi-mately 5.3 ounces, and will be approximately 1¼ in. in diameter by 5 in. long.

It is generally conceded that 2 lb of food per day per man is the very minimum amount required for normal metabolism and activ-ity. The product of the National Research and Development Cor-poration will provide 52.80 grams of fat, 10.80 grams of protein, and 50.40 grams of carbohydrates, totaling over 720 calories and 150.36 grams of bulk. This will save more than 1 lb per day per man in food weight, which amounts to a 50 per cent reduction in total weight of food to be carried. The 5-ounce container will occupy only 7.5 cu in., but will provide an amount of bulk normally requiring 17.5 cu in. of storage space. This will save 57.1 per cent of the space that would otherwise have to be devoted to food storage.

This saving of 50 per cent in food weight and 57.1 per cent in food storage space will permit considerable additional allowances for fuel or crew.

Ecology: Vest-pocket Logistics

Breathing, food, and elimination, taken together, represent basic requirements of the human being which must somehow be supplied from his environment. Since this is very limited, he must get air and food from the environment and contribute to the environment as many things as it can use, which means that he must devise a special environment that *can* use them. This consideration is in the province of a science called ecology.

Consider a fish tank. The breathing air for fish is provided by surface aeration, but carbon dioxide from the fish supports the plants. But assuming the plants *did* provide all the oxygen for the fish, the ecological problem in the tank would be this: How many fish will this tank support? How many of what type of plant will provide enough oxygen? What can be put in for a self-replenishing food supply for the fish? How many snails are needed to scavenge the bottom of the tank? How much oxygen from the plants would the snails use which could otherwise be used by the fish? And so on.

In a spaceship the problem is partly turned around. Once the target of the voyage is established, it is possible to determine how much of a ship it will take to get there, how many men it will take to operate the ship, how many more will be needed if there will be a landing, and how many of these roles may be combined in given men to make the ship smaller. Then, given a certain number of men in a sealed environment for a certain length of time, it is possible to adjust the environment. Before this is done, the spaceship will have been partly redesigned.

This matter of ecology is a subtle thing. The synonym for it is "bionomics," and both words are combinations from the words "biology" and "economics." As the words imply, ecology is a study of the relation between organisms and their environment. In space, the environment is a capsule surrounded by nothing, so to speak, and the ecology becomes a matter of profound urgency. The hull of the spaceship, in so far as it maintains pressure, figures in the ecological picture, but not, for example, in so far as it provides a structural basis for the attachment of rocket engines.

A definite hazard of space travel is puncture by meteors, metallic or stony bodies that travel in orbits through space, like huge clouds of gravel, at tremendous speed. Small granules striking a spaceship would explode under the terrific impact or might penetrate and explode partly inside. Larger ones would pass through the ship as if it were made of cheese. The granules in these clouds of gravel may be separated by anywhere from 20 to 300 miles, but since there are billions of them in a swarm, there is no room for complacency. If a ship wandered into one of the unchartered meteor swarms, it would be punctured a good deal faster than the crew could mend the holes—*if* the crew could mend the holes.

Puncture by meteors, or even by one meteor, provides an exit for air which is under relatively high pressure. This means explosive decompression would occur, as would all the other hazards that would be associated with a structural failure. Aside from the damage done to the ship, engines, tankage, instruments, and controls, there is also the likelihood of human injury or even death by a bullet-like penetration of the body. Constant etching by micrometeors (about the size of dust) would destroy any high finish meant to cool the hull or any coat of paint intended to heat it.

One solution to this danger is the "meteor bumper," a sort of high-velocity collision mat, suggested by astronomer Dr. F. Whipple. Preliminary researches suggest that, as the size of a meteor increases, the fewer such there are and the less likely is the chance of collision. Since no ship could be built stoutly enough to resist all possible meteors (some of them may weigh 50,000 tons), the problem becomes one of devising protection against the meteors that are likely to be met.

As it turns out, these appear to be rather small. A meteor about the size of a grain of sand, or perhaps the size of birdshot, would be the most dangerous normal meteor. The penetrations into aluminum are rather serious, but the use of stainless steel, which sharply resists penetration and produces a local explosive scattering effect, can provide a sort of second, outer, hull which would absorb these impacts. A bumper 33 ft square and 3/64 in. thick would weigh about 2,100 lb.[13]

Assuming the data on the meteor population and frequency are correct and that a meteor bumper would actually stop the sizes mentioned, there still remains the problem of how much of the ship should be protected in this way. Every square foot of hull area protected adds 2 lb of weight. It is evident that adequate coverage could quickly run into tons—tons which have to be brought up to orbit and which have to be lifted away from the earth in the process of escape.

It appears to be a difficult decision. A good-sized meteor striking an engine could wreck it, or it could let precious propellants out of a tank, or it could shatter the radar mast, or a window, or the air lock—practically anything would be fatal or near fatal. In the early stages of space flight we will be in a situation similar to that faced by the Wright Brothers. Conceivably they could have made their airplane a good deal safer, but it would have been too heavy for the engine they had and would not have flown. Much the same sort of thing may be said about the spaceship.

Looking at the cruel facts about meteors it may be said that meteor bumpers should probably be supplied for the personnel cabin and the engine area. If the propellant tanks are under no pressure, fluid loss will be low; and masts can be fixed. The rule of thumb, then, is to protect things that cannot be repaired in space, such as the rocket engines, and protect the people who ride in the vessel, so that they can fix what cannot be protected.

Finally, there is the factor of human thinking and feeling, which here we could possibly term "space psychology." The successful performance of any mission depends not only on the training of the men but also on their morale. Morale is an index of willingness to work as a team, to put the training to work. Confinement of an appreciable number of people in small quarters has a depressing

[13] M. H. Langton, The Mechanical Penetration of Bumper Screens, *J. Brit. Interplanet. Soc.,* vol. 13, no. 5, pp. 284, 288, 1954. This is a useful article for anyone wishing to examine a good, brief mathematical treatment of the basic problem. Langton considers bumpers made of copper, aluminum, stainless steel, and chrome steel; the penetration of iron and stone meteors, and the question of mechanical vs. thermal penetration.

effect on morale. This has been noticed in long voyages in airplanes and submarines.

Also, there is the matter of disorientation, which besets human beings in the weightless conditions of space, whether inside a ship or in a space suit. It may be necessary to learn new types of co-ordination which habit has told the individual under normal conditions are wrong or even dangerous. At tremendous velocities, which may be reached in the distant future of space flight, it may not be possible for the human being to rationalize some of the extremely fundamental changes of space-time relationships. It may be necessary to build controlling computers into the ship that cannot, under certain conditions, be countermanded by human operators, because under those certain conditions, the human being would most assuredly be wrong and would wreck the ship.

More fundamentally, there is a matter of man's notion of his position in the universe. It may seem abstruse and philosophical to those who stay on earth, but mankind will be confronted with basic issues of this type with a range, subtlety, and impact for which his training has never prepared him. In the early days of space flight, the question of survival will be so urgent that a return to the harsh tyranny of the clipper ships may be necessary.

The value of each man will transcend any moral attitude or act of his own. Such a thought represents a reversal of our cherished ideals of democracy and decency. The bald facts of space flight are that a lost man cannot be replaced and that each man lost represents a reduction of the collective survival probability. In space, if one man should murder another, and thus reduce the chances of survival, it would not do to have a trial and execute the man, however much he might deserve execution, for to do so would be to further reduce the chance of *anyone's* coming through it alive. Punishment here is no protection; it is stupid revenge.

On tremendously long trips in the distant future, very large ships with populations may embark for the stars. If they do, the morals of that society will be based on one thing: transferring the population to the new planet. Everything else will be secondary. Here is an amplified and vastly ramified version of the problem on the early spaceships.

Reviewing, then, it may be said that the self-sufficient spaceship is possible, but far in the future, awaiting superior fuels and metals that can stand their action. Until then, multistaging of rockets and division of voyages into a number of sections will be required. A key "section" of any voyage is likely to be the space station. The undertaking of any project, particularly a voyage of an expeditionary nature, is a matter of logistics and will require the stock-piling of propellants and the building of structures, notably space stations, refueling dumps, and spaceships, in space itself.

Ships will have to be highly specialized at first and will probably cover only one phase of a trip. The greater the trip that is attempted the more of a compromise with the ideal, self-sufficient rocket will be required. Compromises and specialization, however, will have certain advantages, as there are weight-saving omissions that can be made in structure. Finally, although there may be quite a variety of space vehicles which are unmanned—automatic ferry rockets, unmanned satellites, probes, and transspatial sounding rockets—a true spaceship must be designed around the physical and psychological necessities of man. But most importantly, man must improve *himself*.

There are those who will take issue with Protagoras on general grounds, but in space flight there can be little doubt that "man is the measure of all things." Man has never yet been confronted with a challenge to his maturity and intellectual honesty that he could not somehow evade, if he so desired, and emerge with the illusion of triumph. But now, if he seriously expects to undertake flight in space, he is so confronted.

BIBLIOGRAPHY

Ryan, C., ed.: "Across the Space Frontier," The Viking Press, Inc., New York, 1952. The chapter entitled Prelude to Space Travel gives data on the famous multistage design for ferry rockets, and also on a moon-orbiting spaceship, by W. von Braun.
———: "Conquest of the Moon," with contributions by W. von Braun, F. L. Whipple, and W. Ley: The Viking Press, Inc., New York, 1953. See especially chap. 3, Building the Moonships; chap. 4, The Personnel Spheres; and Appendix, p. 122.
Clarke, A. C.: "Exploration of Space," chaps. 6 and 9, Temple Press, Ltd., London, 1951.

Clarke, A. C.: "Interplanetary Flight," chap. 8, pp. 93–104, Temple Press, Ltd., London, 1950.

"L'Astronautique," Science et vie; hors de serie, pp. 18–27, Paris, 1952.

Ananoff, A.: "L'Astronautique," chap. 8, Librairie Arthème Fayard, Paris, 1950.

Ducrocq, A.: "L'Humanité devant la navigation interplanétaire," chap. 3, Calmann-Levy Éditeurs, Paris, 1947.

Oberth, H.: "Menschen in Weltraum," chap. 7, Econ Verlag, Düsseldorf, 1954.

Ley, W.: "Rockets, Missiles and Space Travel," chap. 11, The Viking Press, Inc., New York, 1951.

Stemmer, J., ed.: "Space Flight Problems," proceedings of the Fourth Congress of the International Astronautical Federation, Schweizerische Astronautische Arbeitsgemeinschaft, Zurich, Switzerland, 1954. The following papers presented at that conference, are applicable:

　　Golay, M. J. E.: The Application of Radio Interferometry to the Guidance of Interplanetary Rockets, pp. 71–74.

　　Kooy, J. M. J.: On Plotting Small-thrust Space Ship Orbits, pp. 107–114.

　　Crocco, G. A.: Le Ravitaillement dans l'espace et le problem des polistades, pp. 152–160.

　　von Braun, W.: We Need a Co-ordinated Space Program, pp. 206–211.

　　Truax, R. C.: We Can Have Space Flight in Our Time, pp. 212–213.

Gatland, K. W., and A. M. Kunesch: "Space Travel," chap. 6, Philosophical Library, Inc., 1953.

Sternfeld, A.: "Le Vol dans l'espace cosmique," chap. 9, Les Editeurs Français Réunis, Paris, 1954.

ARTICLES IN THE *Journal of the British Interplanetary Society*

Nicoll, N. R.: Design of the Life Compartment Necessary for Space Travel, vol. 13, no. 5, p. 277, 1954.

Langton, N. H.: The Mechanical Penetration of Bumper Screens, vol. 13, no. 5, p. 283, 1954.

Bowman, N. J.: The Food and Atmosphere Control Problem on Space Vessels, Part I, vol. 12, no. 3, p. 118, 1953; Part II, vol. 12, no. 4, p. 159, 1953.

Shepherd, L. R.: The Possibility of Cosmic Ray Hazards in High-Altitude and Space Flight, vol. 12, no. 5, p. 197, 1953.

Neat, W. N.: Some Limiting Factors of Chemical Rocket Motors, vol. 12, no. 6, p. 249, 1953.

Vertregt, M.: Calculation of Step Rockets, vol. 14, no. 1, p. 20, 1955.

Haldane, J. B. S.: The Purification of Air During Space Travel, vol. 14, no. 2, p. 87, 1955.

Kaeppeler, H. J.: On the Problem of Cooling Nuclear Working-fluid Rockets Operating at Extreme Temperatures, vol. 14, no. 2, p. 89, 1955.

Vergregt, M.: Calculation of Step Rockets, Appendix, vol. 14, no. 3, p. 152, 1955.

Bradfield, W. S., and J. G. Ballinger: A Comparison of Heat-transfer characteristics of Three Aerodynamic Shapes for Re-entering Earth's Atmosphere at Mach 12, vol. 14, no. 4, p. 185, 1955.

Ovenden, M. W.: On the Nature and Distribution of Meteoric Matter, vol. 6, no. 6, p. 157, 1947.

Ross, H. E.: Air-conditioning Problems of Rocket Travel, vol. 1, no. 9, p. 49, 1942.

Ovenden, M. W.: Meteors and Space Travel, vol. 10, no. 4, p. 176, 1951.

Clarke, A. C.: Meteors as a Danger to Space Flight, vol. 8, no. 4, p. 157, 1949.

Kooy, J. M. J.: Space Travel and Future Research into the Structure of the Universe, vol. 15, no. 5, p. 248, 1956.

Cross, C. A.: The Use of Probe Rockets, vol. 16, no. 3, p. 148, 1957.

ARTICLES IN OTHER JOURNALS

Neat, W. N.: Flight Into Space, *Spaceflight,* vol. 1, no. 1, p. 4, 1956.

Lehman, M.: The Coming of the Space Ship, *Sat. Eve. Post,* July 21, 1956.

Blanco, V. M.: An Astronomer Looks at Space Travel, *Sky and Telescope,* vol. 16, no. 7, p. 312, 1957.

Program Aimed at Manned Space Flight Started by USAF Group, *Missile Eng.,* vol. 1, no. 2, p. 33, 1956.

Ehricke, K. A.: Satellites et cometes artificials porte-instruments, *Interavia,* p. 960, December, 1956.

Solliday, H. S.: Shortcut to the Moon?, *Missile Away!,* vol. 4, no. 4, p. 24, 1957.

Stehling, K. R., and R. Foster: We Can Build a Moon Rocket Now, *Missiles and Rockets,* p. 58, October, 1956.

Proell, W.: Solid Propellants in Spaceships, *J. Space Flight,* vol. 8, no. 7, 1956.

Castruccio, P. A.: Ships for Space, *Missiles and Rockets,* vol. 2, no. 6, p. 72, 1957.

Cox, D.: Space Power, *Missiles and Rockets,* vol. 2, no. 4, p. 65, 1957.

9

The Architecture of the Universe

Mechanisms and Orders of Magnitude

The province of the spaceship is nothing less than the entire cosmic creation. However, nothing can be seriously entertained but the establishment of satellite vehicles in the neighborhood of our own planet at the present time, flights to the moon and planets within the century, and a voyage to Alpha Centauri in the unforeseeably distant future. This is a mere nothing when compared with even the known universe.

The development of astronomy has gradually shown the universe to be of staggering dimension—so large that the greatest human intellect is bewildered by an attempt to visualize its true size. The attempt is also unnerving, in that man has been trained to believe that he and the earth are the keystone of the whole affair. Each new discovery of an increased dimension of the universe reduces man's own importance in the scheme of things, inflicting heavy blows to his ego but otherwise causing little injury.

Despite the apparent hopelessness of even visualizing the universe, and the more staggering implications of its conquest in a spaceship, some preliminary statements which will at least offer one a little insight into the situation may be made. With so little known about the immense realm of space, it is not surprising to find some disagreement about its nature.

Many scientists believe that the best explanation so far is that of Thomas Gold, of England's Royal Observatory. He espouses the idea of a universe which, in a manner of speaking, was not created at some moment in the past, but has always been in existence and

212

always in motion. It has a sort of horizon, but is of no definitive size. Basic hydrogen appears, gathers, compresses, evolves into stars and galaxies, and the universe expands outward from the pressure of an eternal and continuous creation—thus a universe with a balance but no beginning or end.

These notions of unlimited space and time wrench normal human perceptive powers. With the growth of the apparent size of the universe, man has become lonely in space. Somehow the proposition of being lonely in unlimited time is even more frightening. His own lifetime, compared with a finite time, even several billion years, has some cold comfort, but a life-span compared to a real eternity apparently brings with it a paralyzing fear. With both aspects of himself measured against infinitude (in space and time), his very existence seems under challenge.

Unfortunately, lack of certitude is the rule in the universe, and all human knowledge, attitudes, and actions must reckon with the implacable laws of mathematical probability. Challenging these laws brings an equal probability of disaster.

It had long been a convenience of academicians to divide the universe into three categories of phenomena: (1) those below the observer (man) in the order of magnitude, called the microcosm; (2) man's world; and (3) those above man, called the macrocosm. These categories were not very definite, but dealt with realms so small, on one hand, that the eye could not detect the "little worlds," and so large, on the other, that one did not know where to look to discern the nearest part of "the big worlds." The terms were an expression of man's feeling that there were things both infinitely small and infinitely large, as extensions of his own perceptive order of magnitude, which, once perceived, would indicate a continuum of size and system throughout nature. Man still looks for this. Einstein's theories of relativity were mighty steps in the direction of learning the nature of this continuum; just before his death, Einstein proposed a unified-field theory in which he hoped to glimpse the continuity. As there does not seem to be any important discrepancy between Gold and Einstein, the following does offer to the informed layman a reasonable picture of the structure and activity of the universe. Some astronomers are certain to differ on details, but the picture is reasonably reliable in the important essentials.

The universe may be regarded as a surpassingly large volume of space, almost completely empty, dark, and cold. The exceptions to emptiness, which are rare, may be anything from an atomic nucleus, a grain of dust, or meteor, to a planet, star, or galaxy, and each is usually accompanied by a similar exception to complete darkness and coldness because of radiation or absorption. Taking the universe as a whole, any attempt to express as a percentage or fraction the degree of exception to the universal rule of the empty, dark, and cold would result in ridiculous notation.[1]

The smallest (and incomparably the most numerous) particles in the universe are atomic particles, nuclei, whole atoms, molecules, and submicroscopic particles of dust, ice, and gas. Empty as the universe is, these constitute the most numerous bodies and the greatest total mass of any category of matter in creation.

The whole universe, expanding from the central pressure of continuous creation, appears to be expanding more rapidly the more distant the observed bodies are from the earth. Some speeds have been recorded up to 134 million mph and present to the astronomer's spectroscopes an effect known as the *red shift*. This is a lateral displacement toward the red (meaning recession) of characteristic lines in the spectrum which is due to a phenomenon similar to the Doppler effect.

Scientists are suspicious of the increase of speed of recession with distance because it means the bodies are gaining energy as they go along. There is something wrong with that, and they wonder if the light from these bodies (which are really receding) "ages" with long duration en route or is changed in character by having to pass through incalculable trillions of miles of the submicroscopic particles just mentioned.

None of these particles is wandering around with complete aimlessness. Some of the smaller ones may be ejections from the explosions of stars or from the action of regular stellar cycles of nuclear fission and fusion in the dazzling brilliance of their atmospheres. Some of these—countless quintillions of them, but still very

---

[1] Astronomy is full of superlative comparisons. A popular one is that the shell of the Empire State Building, if it contained only six motes of dust in the whole empty volume within, would be infinitely more crowded with dust than space is with stars.

few—strike the atmospheres of relatively cold bodies, such as the earth, at tremendous speeds and disintegrate the upper layers until they are so saturated with degenerated atoms (ions) that they act as a screen to nearly all further penetration.

Some are slowed down by collision with other particles in space to the point that they assume orbits around planetoids, planets, or stars, possibly in some galactic cluster of low density, pursuing fragile orbits around the galactic center. Variations in a dominant orbit may occur from time to time as a particle begins a wide orbit around some body, only to be captured by another, and zigzag with no apparent control throughout the galaxy. Spiral galaxies, such as our own Milky Way and that of Andromeda, are rather "smoky" affairs, filled with some irregular but rather dense concentrations located more or less in the spiral arms.

Next in the order of size is an assortment of heavenly bodies in a fairly continuous gradation of size from a grain of sand to the planet Jupiter, which is some 88,000 miles in diameter. This clearly takes in everything in the solar system except the sun itself.

The smallest of these particles are the meteors, which range from the size of dust to metallic or stony bodies up to perhaps several hundred feet in diameter; they are widely thought to be the remains of comets, frequently found in the same highly eccentric orbits. Both the meteors and comets seem to have a common origin, still further back, with the asteroids, located in a similar but larger and more circular orbital belt between Mars and Jupiter. They may all be fragments of a planet in that belt that came too close to Jupiter and was pulled apart in a tug-of-war between that planet and the sun. The influence of Jupiter on all these remaining small bodies— the meteors, comets, and asteroids—is still very strong, and consideration of the very powerful gravitational pull of that planet can explain a lot of apparently chaotic relationships in the solar system.

Meteors

Meteors are the most numerous of these small bodies. They travel in swarms in orbits of high eccentricity, some of which cross that of the earth. There must be many of these orbits. Billions of meteors strike the earth's atmosphere daily (totaling one ton in weight), and were long thought to be local phenomena like lightning flashes. Approximate orbits were first worked out by Brandes and Benzeberg, in 1798, but there was no systematic study of meteors until the great shower of 1833. A radiant point (apparent origin) in the constellation of Leo was noted, and subsequent studies have found other families and named them after their radiant points (Table 9-1). Meteors are small and largely unexpected,

TABLE 9-1   *Meteor Showers and Radiant Points*

Constellation	Shower	Date of maximum	Miles/sec
Bootes	Quadrantids	January 3	29
Lyra	Lyraids	April 21	32
Aquarius	Eta Aquarids	May 4	41
Aquarius	Delta Aquarids	July 28	31
Perseus	Perseids	August 12	38
Orion	Orionids	October 22	42
Leo	Leonids	November 16	45
Gemini	Geminids	December 12	22

except for proven showers. This makes them hard to observe accurately, a fact which retarded studies of them for centuries. Several thousand reasonably visible meteors of varying composition fall each day and ignite, because of air friction, at about 50 miles altitude. A few are brilliant enough to be seen in broad daylight, but the majority burn to dust between 12 and 25 miles from the ground.

Velocities are extremely hard to determine, for the problem is complicated by the earth's own orbital velocity of 18.5 miles/sec. Meteors overtaking us (seen at dusk) will naturally have lower velocities than those we meet head on (at dawn), and it should be remembered that, even if the meteor had no motion at all, the earth's gravitational attraction would make it strike the atmosphere at about 7 miles/sec, which, of course, is the same as the earth's escape velocity.

The density of meteor swarms may be gathered from the net average fall of one meteor per 100 observing hours. Meteors are decelerated by the upper atmosphere, but a bit less so than they are accelerated by the earth's gravity. Sporadic meteors have velocities well below parabolic and behave like close-approaching asteroids. There are, loosely, two groups: type Y are siliceous and stony, and their spectra exhibit calcium lines; type Z are metallic, and their spectra exhibit no calcium lines. Meteors appearing in showers, as well as half of all sporadics, are stony. The remaining half of the sporadics are metallic. All shower type and half the sporadic type show calcium lines; the rest do not.

Air friction causes compression, heating, and incandescence at 2000°C and hence sometimes also crumbling or explosion. Some meteors arrive spinning and show a pinwheel effect. The size of those meteorites not recovered is based on a speed-brightness theory. For a meteor the size of a pinhead, the following approximations hold true:

Perseids	38 miles/sec	2nd magnitude
Giacobinids	14.3 miles/sec	5th magnitude

This is quite a difference. Second magnitude is the same brilliance as the North Star; fifth magnitude is barely visible. Fast, hot meteors sometimes bore a hole 0.6 mile in diameter and produce a peal of thunder. Oddly, meteors ignite at 51 miles, which happens to be about the coldest ($-90°C$) part of the atmosphere and the bottom of the ionosphere, where all manner of interesting things happen. Some dusty trails left by the largest meteors have lasted an hour and a half, and all meteors have been observed to cause static in electrical communications equipment.

Jupiter, like comets, raises havoc with meteoric orbits and, together with Saturn, in 1866, so diverted the Leonids that, even though we always meet them head on, we may never see another intense shower from that swarm again. The chance that the two planets will change the Leonid orbit back again is extremely remote.

The Perseids are annual, having their intensity peak about August 12. They are very evenly distributed along their orbit because they intersect the earth's orbit at nearly 90° and so never go near big planets whose attraction would cause bunching.

Meteors tend to travel in orbits with certain comets. Some common meteor-comet associations are:

Halley's Comet	Eta Aquarids and Orionids
Encke's Comet	Taurids
1862–III Comet	Leonids
Biela's Comet	Andromedes

We meet the orbit of Halley's comet twice a year (though, unfortunately, not the comet) and meet two showers having radiants in Aquarius and Orion. Loosely speaking, they are part of the same general swarm. The swarm of Halley's orbit is very diffuse, apparently because of numerous planetary perturbations. We have more or less lost track of the Bielids, or Andromedes, and this type of loss presents a rather serious problem in space flight. It is something like starting across a battlefield after losing a map of the enemy land-mine distribution.

We should note that, although meteors are fragments of disintegrated comets, the presence of meteors in a cometary orbit does not indicate that the comet is about to break up. There is a long attrition before this happens. Not all streams have comets, and it is reasonable to conclude that the comet associated with a stream has already collapsed.

Parabolic comets have no associated streams. This may be due to the fact that they remain fairly distant from both the sun and the planets through all of their orbits and have had no tearing effect exerted on them. Weak showers are hard to locate among the records of brighter sporadics and are evidence of short-period showers which overtake the earth's orbit at low inclinations.

Physical separation in swarms varies a great deal:

Leonids	18 miles
Bielids (Andromedes)	25 miles
Perseids	125 miles
Sporadics	310 miles

Thin meteor falls observed from the dense Leonids are evidence that we have only hit the fringes of the swarm since the planetary brush of 1866. The clusters originate around a comet (possibly within it) and gradually spread over the entire orbit. The Taurids are an extreme example of this, which is not surprising in view of their small orbit. The Andromedes are still highly localized.

It is interesting to note that the largest meteors, especially those surviving to be picked up, do not come from showers. Only those of comparable size stay together. This is due in part to the Poynting-Robertson effect: solar heat reradiated in the direction of motion retards the particle by reactive laws. Smaller particles are naturally more subject to this effect than are larger ones, and the gradations of size produce gradations in orbit. It would seem that the retarding effect, exerted more noticeably on the smaller particles, should bring those particles into somewhat smaller orbits around the sun, since for a given velocity there is a characteristic average distance from the parent body.

Meteorites, the solid masses which sometimes remain to be picked up, are usually named after the locality in which they fall, though they may be given some colloquial name before being collected for museums. Most meteors are in orbits of low inclination and hence overtake the earth. Heat of ignition liquefies the meteoric surface and blows the droplets off as sparks. The fire stops after air friction, which produced the fire, slows the meteor down. Stony meteors form glassy crusts, and metallic ones oxidize. The fiery erosion may carve and form the bodies as they fall. Stony meteors are very apt to shatter under air-pressure impact and land as a shower of pellets, like a titanic charge of buckshot. "Irons" may plunge 20 to 50 ft underground. Freshly fallen irons are just too hot to handle, while "stones" are milk warm.[2] They are never very cold, even at 100 million miles from the sun, and they are never burning when they land.

A great fall in Siberia, in 1908, created 10 craters, ranging from 30 to 150 ft across, and felled trees radially for over 18 miles. Had it fallen 4 hr 47 min later it would have leveled Petrograd. Weighing several hundred tons (about the same as a locomotive), it created an impact air wave which arrived in London about five hours later and shook seismographs all over Europe. And this is one of the *smallest* of the big fireballs which have left definitely identifiable craters! There are many so-called fossil craters which attest an extremely ancient impact. Meteoric bombardment is a favorite theory advanced to explain the origin of lunar craters. The average age of the meteors is very hard to place, but studies based on the low

[2] F. G. Watson, "Between the Planets," p. 149, The Blakiston Division, McGraw-Hill Book Company, Inc., New York. Formerly P. Blakiston's Son & Company, Philadelphia; then The Blakiston Company, New York. The latter was a subsidiary of Doubleday & Company, Inc., 1941.

radioactivity remaining in the meteors suggest that they are nearly as old as the earth itself.

Permanent membership of meteors in the solar system has been long suspected, though it is not yet established, but the more or less regular transition—from metallic, through metallic-stony, to stony —suggests a common origin for all. Strangely, a theory of lunar volcanic origin has been advanced, but in view of the theory that the lunar craters are caused by the meteors, it may be wise to reject both. Recent thinking leads to the tentative conclusion that all meteors came from a parent planet with a mass equal to that of the earth. According to this view, the metallic meteors would have originated in the core, the stony-iron part way to the surface, and the stones at the surface. This is a fairly neat theory except for the incongruous fact that some stony meteorites contain chondrules (inclusions of pyroxene and olivine), but, since pyroxene is a phenomenon of the metasilicates, we may have the same paradox with us on earth. In any event, the physical state of the fragments suggests a cataclysm of astronomically recent time. Looking over the gradations of size, the large meteors and small asteroids seem indistinguishable.

The largest known fallen meteorite weighs 60 tons and still lies where it was found, in Grootfontein, South-West Africa. The largest American meteorite, fourth largest in the world, fell at Willamette, Oregon, and was half rusted away before it was found and sent to the American Museum of Natural History, New York. Very large meteors produce craters from 50 to 3,900 ft in diameter. Ten major falls are known, of which the largest crater, in Arizona, is perhaps 5,000 years old.

Comets

Another important class of bodies in the solar system is that of the non-self-luminous comets. These number several hundred thousand and were thought by Tycho Brahe to have circular orbits, by Kepler to travel in straight lines, and by Halley to travel in parabolic paths. Halley, however, made the daring and successful prediction that the comet now named after him (and observed since antiquity) would return in 1758. Many comets are still listed as "parabolic" (in orbit) because their origin is unknown and there is at least a reasonable chance that many do appear only once. Since comets change in appearance, behavior, and orbit, it is possible that many comets listed separately are those previously seen but now changed beyond recognition.

Encke's comet (17th magnitude) has a period of only 3.3 years, the shortest known, and has been thoroughly established as having an elliptical orbit. Many comets have periods of less than ten years. An enthusiastic fraternity of amateur and professional astronomers watches for new comets and engages in regulated and sportsman-like contests to compute cometary orbits. Harvard and Copenhagen observatories act as coordinating and clearing houses for this sort of thing.

Some orbits of extreme eccentricity suggest that the comets in question must come from interstellar space on hyperbolic paths. Actually, they probably do not, since such a situation would introduce the probability of a preferred direction of approach to the solar system, and also some head-on meetings at fantastic speeds. Neither has materialized; there is no real evidence of either interstellar origin or hyperbolic orbit of approach. Parabolic orbits may simply be approximations of small parts of the ends of huge ellipses, and hence are merely to be regarded as orbits not yet confirmed as elliptical. Half of the orbits are retrograde to the planets and most of them move in orbits inclined about 90° to the ecliptic. A few have huge orbits and never come very near the sun. Some may be as much as several light years away at aphelion. If true, there is a definite (though remote) possibility that they could be captured by Alpha Centauri. This would be hard to check, however, since such comets would have periods of about 100 million years!

Comets with periods of less than 100 years are called *periodic comets,* move in the same direction as the planets, and generally have orbits tilted less than 45°. Jupiter, because of its immense size, exerts a very strong influence on a comet's orbit. It has a "family" of comets (those which it controls or has definitely modified), but the members are not as well organized into groups as the asteroids. Comets are divided into groups according to their period and are associated for their nominal control with certain planets, as follows:

Period, years	Control planet
5–12	Jupiter
13–18	Saturn
28	Uranus
49–81	Neptune
81 and on	?

However, the real control is by Jupiter, which can seize retrograde comets on certain near approaches and hurl them from the solar system in hyperbolic orbits, or, catching others in the opposite direction, can bring them into tighter and tighter rein each time they come by. The planet may take a retrograde comet and merely lengthen its period, or, catching certain other comets, cause their orbits to exhibit a progressive change.

Comets apparently consist of large transparent swarms of particles surrounded by a luminescent gas that evolves from the particles by heating when the comets make their close approaches to the sun. The heads of comets average the size of Jupiter but can be as large as the sun. They have tails, consisting of fine matter propelled away from the head by pressure of sunlight, which measure about 200,000 miles in length at aphelion and may grow to ten times that as they approach the sun, brighten, and have more material blown back.

The tails always point away from the sun, because of its pressure, and are somewhat curved, because of the path the comets follow and the hyperbolic orbits of the particles blown back. The tails seldom appear until the comet is inside the orbit of Mars, because, although sunlight may be blowing some of the dust back, the distance to the sun is not short enough for sunlight intensity to cause the tail gases to luminesce. The rate and degree of brightness is very erratic. Close (short-period) comets waste away rapidly, since they are always in a region of high sunlight pressure.

The mass of even a great comet is about a billion tons, only one ten-thousandth the mass of the earth, and so exerts no detectable effect on the earth. Our planet has already passed through tenuous comet tails whose composition includes elemental hydrogen, carbon, nitrogen, oxygen, cyanogen (CN), methyne (CH), carbon monoxide, nitrogen hydride (NH), and hydroxyl (OH). Although some of these constituents are toxic, the mean free path of several miles prevents any inhalation danger during tail penetration. The size of the particles in the head is apparently not very large, and a direct collision with a comet (the great meteor shower of Leonids in 1833 may conceivably have been a collision with the disintegrated head of a very ancient defunct comet) would produce only a shower of meteors.[3]

Approaching Jupiter or the sun sometimes causes comets to split into two or three comets (the smaller of which are called satellitic); sometimes they will have their mass depleted by solar radiation beyond a certain critical value. They will then collapse into a swarm of meteors spreading out along the former cometary orbit.

The origin of comets is unknown. There are serious objections to all theories, but it is believed by many astronomers that comets are native to the solar system, and, because of their observed rates of disintegration, must be generated from somewhere at all times; otherwise, they would probably all have crumbled before the dawn of human history.

The greatest comet is Halley's; the most durable (considering its closeness to the sun) is Encke's; and the oddest, perhaps, is Schwassmann-Wachmann, which follows a rather circular orbit just beyond Jupiter and exhibits fantastic variations in brightness. Generally speaking, the wasting away of comets, as noted by Watson, is from the following sources:

1. Material blown back into the tail

2. Collision with fine matter abroad in space

3. Electrical repulsion in particles induced by solar photoelectric effect

4. Poynting-Robertson effect, which sorts out large and small particles into different orbits

5. Splits due to near approaches to Jupiter and the sun

6. Collapse after reaching critical attrition point; insufficient gravity in cometary system to hold it together

7. Head-on collision with planets

8. Total loss due to sudden shift into hyperbolic escape orbit

[3] F. G. Watson, *op. cit.,* p. 85.

Asteroids

The asteroids, for the most part, pursue orbits located in the general path of an orbit that would be occupied by a planet according to Bode's law.[4] They were detected very slowly at first, because of their small size, but they are now recorded at the rate of several hundred a year. The official register, "Kleine Planeten," now shows 1,500 of them. Typically they are situated in an orbit (or belt of orbits) between those of Mars and Jupiter, but some have high eccentricity. Hidalgo has the largest and most eccentric orbit yet discovered; it reaches almost to the orbit of Saturn and is almost unique in that most of the larger asteroid orbits are rather circular. Periods between 3 and 6 years are common. Some orbits are highly inclined to the planets' orbits but none move in a direction opposite. They are mainly confined to the zodiacal band.

The highly inclined orbits are largely of long periods (10 to 12 years) and depend on how close to Jupiter they may come. These approaches to Jupiter may or may not be in a rhythmic phase related to definite fractions of Jupiter's own orbital period. A gravitational contest with the sun produces gaps in the belt, analogous to the gaps in the rings of Saturn and for a similar reason.

Jupiter also exhibits Trojan planetoids, located in its orbit 60° ahead and 60° behind it, establishing two adjacent equilateral triangles with Jupiter and the sun. Combined pulls of Saturn, the sun, and some planets can and perhaps do dislodge the Trojans occasionally, but similar forces may also capture the planetoids. Thus membership in the group may be long but not permanent.

Asteroids may number 100,000, of which 5,000 may be Trojans. Whether other planets have sufficient mass to have Trojans and whether there may be another asteroid belt between Jupiter and Saturn are questions that have not yet been answered.

[4] This law is ascribed to J. E. Bode (1747–1826), who was chiefly known for his "Uranographia," a collection of maps including 17,240 stars and nebulae. It was thought out previously by J. D. Titius, but is known as Bode's law and is based on the numbers 0, 3, 6, 12, 24, . . . in the series $n + 4/10$, $2n + 4/10$, $4n + 4/10$, which results in the number of astronomical units of the planets from the sun. Although subject to some serious objections, it has successfully predicted the asteroid belt, an approximation of Neptune's orbit, and, if Pluto is relegated to the rank of errant satellite, may be regarded as a fairly reasonable expression of the main orbital structure in the solar system.

A Japanese astronomer, Hirayama, has plotted thousands of orbits and has discovered that the asteroids fall into five general families. Several have made rather close approaches to the earth. Hermes, in particular, came within 700,000 miles, which by astronomical standards is a hair-raising near-miss. Ceres, the largest asteroid, is about 480 miles in diameter. The total mass of all asteroids would make a sphere only 600 miles in diameter (about the size of Ariel, satellite of Uranus), and, hence, they are not of the same order of magnitude as the planets.

Spectrographic analyses suggest gray, brown, and sometimes blue surfaces. Vesta shows small but odd variations and seems to be coated with dust, perhaps from collisions with meteors. The jagged shapes of most asteroids further suggest the possibility of an old and tiny planet, pulled apart in a gravitational tug-of-war between Jupiter and the sun and exhibiting the same distribution and annular gaps as the rings of Saturn.[5]

Satellites and Planets—Real and Ideal

Next in the order of magnitude are the satellites and planets of the solar system. The orbital character of natural and artificial satellites is dealt with in Chap. 4. An examination of Table 9-2 shows the satellites of the solar system in the increasing order of size. The chart does not tell us much, but it does suggest some speculations.

The planets in the solar system that have no satellites are Mercury, Venus, and Pluto. Kuiper, noting the extreme eccentricity of Pluto's orbit and the heavy tilt of Neptune's axis, has presented a plausible hypothesis that Pluto is not a planet, but an errant former satellite of Neptune. This same notion may conceivably be applied to Mercury as an errant satellite of Venus. Like Pluto, it has an orbital eccentricity of the order of four or five times (at least) the eccentricities of the planets between Venus and Neptune. Kuiper is also studying Venus and apparently already suspects a heavy

[5] F. G. Watson, *op. cit.,* pp. 41–42. Watson also suggests that a collision between the parent body and a moon of Jupiter could have done this, or that Jupiter pulled the nearer side of the former planet away from the further side, then repeated the process until the planet had crumbled to small bodies of the present size, which generally got no smaller because their own internal cohesive forces finally overcame the disruptive power of Jupiter.

TABLE 9-2   *Satellites of the solar system in ascending order of size*

Diam, miles	Name	Parent planet	Remarks
5	Diemos	Mars	Both seem too small to be genu-
10	Phobos	Mars	ine moons, probably captured from asteroid belt
15?	X	Jupiter	All of outer moons seem too
15?	XI	Jupiter	small to be natural, perhaps
20	IX	Jupiter	captured from the asteroid
40	VII	Jupiter	belt; larger moons further in
40	VIII	Jupiter	
100	V	Jupiter	
100	VI	Jupiter	
150?	Miranda	Uranus	Assortment and arrangement of
200	Phoebe	Saturn	sizes by distance from planet
200	Nereid	Neptune	or distance from the sun form
300	Hyperion	Saturn	no regular pattern
370	Mimas	Saturn	
400	Umbriel	Uranus	
460	Enceladus	Saturn	
600	Ariel	Uranus	
750	Tethys	Saturn	
900	Dione	Saturn	
900	Oberon	Uranus	
1,000	Japetus	Saturn	
1,000	Titania	Uranus	
1,150	Rhea	Saturn	
2,000	II (Europa)	Jupiter	Largest moons are generally
2,160	Luna (Moon)	Earth	around the largest planets,
2,300	I (Io)	Jupiter	with the odd exception of the
3,000	Triton	Neptune	earth
3,200	III (Ganymede)	Jupiter	
3,200	IV (Callisto)	Jupiter	
3,550	Titan	Saturn	

tilt of 32° of that planet's axis to its orbit.[6] It may be reading too much significance into the similarity, but one is tempted to feel that we may eventually hear from Dr. Kuiper that both the innermost and outermost "planets" of the solar system are not planets at all, but delinquent satellites, and part of the disrepute of Bode's law will have been removed.

It is probably demanding too much of the powers of inference

[6] Astronomy, *J. Astronautics,* vol. 2, no. 2, p. 69, 1955.

to place such faith in the obvious implications of this proposition, but a reconstruction of the solar system into what might have been the former "ideal solar system" is hard to resist and might look something like Table 9-3.

TABLE 9-3   *An ideal solar system*

Order from sun	Parent planet	Satellite(s) belonging to the planet
1	Venus	Mercury
2	Earth	Moon (as at present)
3	Mars	Aster, parent of: Asteroids Planetoids Comets Meteors Diemos Phobos Moons V–IX of Jupiter
4	Jupiter	I (Io) II (Europa) III (Ganymede) IV (Callisto)
5	Saturn	Nine moons (as at present)
6	Uranus	Five moons (as at present)
7	Neptune	Triton Nereid Pluto

This cleans up the solar system and provides each planet with a satellite system of net mass in the same order of magnitude. But this is not to be taken literally. It is a reconstruction only for the sake of illustrating the present state of the solar system, and it should not be taken as a theory of planetary evolution in the system.

Concerning the individual planets, vital statistics will be found in Table 9-4. It will be noted from the table that the planets vary in density and in the gravitational pull one might expect for a given size. All of the planets in this system are believed to have a common origin, and hence could be expected to have a common composition. Broadly speaking, they probably do, but allowance must be made for the possibility that the distribution of constituents

TABLE 9-4 *Planet Descriptions and Motions*

PLANET DESCRIPTIONS

	Diameter, miles	Volume [a] (Earth = 1)	Density [b] (Earth = 1)	Mass [c] (Earth = 1)	Gravity [d] (Earth = 1)	Escape velocity, miles/sec	Albedo	Temp of surf., max °F
Mercury	3,100	0.060	0.76	0.056	0.38	2.6	0.06	750
Venus	7,700	0.910	0.88	0.817	0.86	6.4	0.76	210
Earth	7,927	1.000	1.00	1.000	1.00	6.9	0.39	140
Mars	4,215	0.151	0.71	0.108	0.39	3.1	0.15	85
Jupiter	88,640	1,312.000	0.24	318.350	2.64	37.0	0.51	−200
Saturn	75,100	763.000	0.13	95.280	1.17	22.0	0.50	−240
Uranus	31,000	59.000	0.23	14.580	1.05	13.0	0.66	−270
Neptune	32,000	72.000	0.29	17.360	1.23	14.0	0.62	−330
Pluto [e]	3,500	0.900	0.96	0.700	0.90	6.5	0.16	−370
Moon	2,160	0.020	0.60	0.012	0.16 [f]	1.5	0.07	−240

PLANET MOTIONS

	Length of day, hr	Length of year, sidereal days	Mean daily motion	Distance from sun miles × 10⁶	Orbital velocity, miles/sec	Eccentricity of orbit	INCLINATIONS Equator to orbit	Orbit to ecliptic
Mercury	2,105.85	87.96	4.092	35.9	29.7	0.2056	0°	7° 0' 13"
Venus	718.23	224.70	1.602	67.2	21.7	0.0068	32°	3° 23' 39"
Earth	23.94 [g]	365.25	0.986	92.9	18.5	0.0167	23° 27'	0° 0' 0"
Mars	24.61	686.98	0.524	141.5	15.0	0.0934	24° 10'	1° 51' 0"
Jupiter	9.38	4,332.60	0.083	483.3	8.1	0.0484	3° 7'	1° 18' 20"
Saturn	10.03	10,759.53	0.034	886.2	6.0	0.0558	26° 47'	2° 29' 25"
Uranus	10.75	30,686.48	0.012	1,782.8	4.2	0.0471	98°	0° 46' 23"
Neptune	15.80	60,188.82	0.006	2,793.5	3.4	0.0085	151°	1° 46' 28"
Pluto [e]	155.61	90,471.33	0.004	3,616.0	2.8	0.2486	...	17° 08' 34"
Moon	654.04	27.32 [h]	13.200	0.24 [i]	0.64	0.0549	6° 41'	5° 08' 43"

[a] Where Earth = 1.083×10^{27} cu cm. [b] Where Earth = $H_2O \times 5.52$. [c] Where Earth = 6.6×10^{21} tons. [d] Where earth = 1 g = 32 ft/sec². [e] All values for Pluto should be considered doubtful. [f] Estimates range from 0.16 to 0.20. [g] Based on Newcomb's sidereal day of 23 hours 56 min 4 sec. [h] The lunar "year" is the same as our month and the lunar day. [i] From Earth.
SOURCE: "Practical Work at the Threshold of Space," General Astronautics Corporation.

varies from planet to planet and that certain events and stages in the evolution of the solar system operated to modify what would eventually have been a close similarity among the planets. Typical among such events might have been a solar flare-up of titanic violence when all the planets were still fiery gas balls. This could have blasted away the upper gas layers from the protoplanets and perhaps from the protoearth's protomoon. Such a blast would possibly not have reached Jupiter, and all the planets and satellites from there out to Pluto might be expected to show a common set of certain basic differences from those on the other side of the asteroid belt. The belt, incidentally, was probably of much more recent origin.

The planets, generally speaking, have reasonably concentric orbits, which, with the exception of Mercury and Pluto, are close to the ecliptic. Axial tilts from the orbital plane are widely assorted and the fixity of axes in true space causes most planets to present a variety of visual aspects to earth-bound telescopic observation.

Planets close to the sun, of course, have higher orbital speeds than those farther out. Rotations vary between 9 and 24 hours for all bodies but Mercury and Pluto. The rotation of Venus is unknown; estimates range from 50 to 500 hr, which may be within the right range, but the variance from the others arouses suspicion.

Of particular interest to astronautics are the gravities, escape velocities, and orbital speeds of the bodies of the solar system. Consideration of these will determine the steps to be taken in the climb to interplanetary space and the course to be taken once in space. Flight to the moon, for example, has only the gravities of the earth and moon to reckon with. A flight to Mars is a transfer between circumsolar orbits which must also reckon with the pull of the sun. A similar problem occurs in escape from the galaxy, but this will not be a practical problem for many centuries.

Comparison of temperature (distance from the sun) and gravity (ability to retain an atmosphere against the kinetic energy of its particles, which tends to produce escape) indicates for a given planet the habitability by man or any other form of life. Extremes of temperature and gravity will affect the course of space travel, since they will make all but hopeless demands on technology.

The detailed composition of the planets can only be guessed at carefully, but an inkling of the history of the solar system and a knowledge of what gravity and temperature will do to distributions allow some reasonable estimates to be made by using the composition of the earth (also incompletely known) as a basis of inference.

The earth is roughly 8,000 miles in diameter. It has a surface area of approximately 200 million square miles, which, but for the vertical irregularity of contour, would be completely covered by a thin film of water. Tensions in the body have produced massive continental prominences which limit the film to 80 per cent of the surface. This film, known as the oceans, is extremely thin (between two and three miles deep on the average), was the origin of all life on the planet, and provides for an important amount of climatic stability for the planet as a whole.

The great mass of the globe is thought to be nickel and iron of density that increases with approach to the center. Geological opinion is divided on whether the core is intensely hot or whether volcanic phenomena are a result of radioactivity near the crust. By conventional measurement the earth may be said to "weigh" 66 sextillion (66×10^{21}) tons.

The atmosphere of the earth is found as far up as the ocean, on the average, goes down: the first three miles. The remainder of the atmosphere, which becomes incredibly rarefied, extends to many hundreds of miles, possibly 800. Researchers at Stanford University have strong evidence that ionized particles exist out to 6,000 miles, and possibly as far as 20,000 miles. Tests using radio signals were conducted under Office of Naval Research sponsorship. The globe of the earth has a complex assortment of mutations, wobbles, and tilts, but these are chiefly of interest to astronomers.

Knowing these elementary aspects of our home planet, we can consider what little is known of the other planets and draw our own conclusions. Looking at Mercury, we see a body very like our own moon. No one has seen it well enough to know whether it has craters, but it is practically airless, waterless, slow of rotation, utterly lifeless, subject to even greater extremes of temperature, and may conceivably prove to be a former moon of Venus—though one must not jump too readily to this conclusion. Venus, of about earth size, has an atmosphere that is like a pea-soup fog and consists largely of carbon dioxide, a good heat absorber. Depending on the presence of water (which cannot be established from the upper layers of the atmosphere), Venus could be either a constantly tornado-ridden sandy desert or a sweltering, steaming jungle like the interior of Brazil. It could conceivably be completely covered by ocean, but there is no evidence to prove this. There is no firm basis yet for assuming conditions conducive to the formation of life there. While most astronomers feel that Venus rotates on its axis in the same time it revolves once around the sun, radio astronomical observations suggest that the period may be 22 hours.

Mars apparently has a little water, stored chiefly in the polar ice caps. These appear to melt seasonally; and there are seasonal changes in the rest of the planet's coloration. There is a small amount of evidence to suggest that the "canals" may actually exist, but whether these are waterways, natural or otherwise, is fruitless speculation. The atmosphere is about as thin as that at the top of Mount Everest; it probably has traces of oxygen and may support life in the form of primitive mosses and lichens. A higher form of life, especially human life, either does not exist there or is some form of life which modern earth biology is not equipped to understand at the moment.

More than any other planet, Mars has been the object of recent intensive study. In September, 1956, it came to within a shade over 35 million miles from the earth, the closest in more than 30 years. Preliminary reports on observations made at that time were presented at an American Astronomical Society meeting in December, 1956; and in June, 1957, the International Mars Committee met in Arizona to offer further anxiously awaited information.

The International Mars Committee reports "very strong evidence" of some sort of life on the planet, and in support of this cited work done under an Air Force contract wherein tough soil bacteria were taken from desert regions and propagated in an artificial atmosphere approximating that of Mars. Spectrographic work also indicated the presence of carbon-hydrogen molecules, which are characteristic of vegetation.

Studies of the dark areas of Mars, whose color is apparently a neutral gray and brownish near the poles, suggest that they may be lava flows, with scattered vegetation on top. All astronomers agreed that, during the opposition, there was, in general, a marked lack of contrast. Dust storms were viewed, and the characteristic blue haze studied. The latter cleared occasionally, and it is felt to consist of frozen-water ice particles. As for water vapor, none was found, nor was molecular oxygen detected. The conclusion is that Mars can have no more water vapor than would make a film of 0.08 in. if it were condensed on the planet's surface. The value in reality is probably more like 0.002 mm! In addition, radio measurements at 3.15 cm wavelengths were made and thermal emission detected. Both moons were photographed and studied. Richardson reports distinctly seeing canals twice in the southern region, namely Simois and Thermadon, as "dark straggly streaks." Photographs did not pick them up.

Jupiter and Saturn, the titans of the solar system, are very much alike, except for the latter's rings. Both have an assortment of moons, strong gravity, and fast rotation, and both probably have comparatively small rocky cores, encased in gigantic layers of ice, perhaps 15,000 miles thick, followed by atmospheres of hydrogen from 10,000 to 15,000 miles high, on which have been observed clouds of ammonia and methane. These factors, and prevailing temperatures of at least $-200°F$, make them attractive neither as places to land nor as the abode of any life at all. Jupiter is known to give out strong radio signals. Signals taken at 18.3 megacycles give a fairly accurate point source on the planet, and are suggestive of large electrical storms.

Uranus and Neptune, because of their distance, are even less completely known. The concept for Uranus is based on the same plan as that for Saturn and Jupiter, and, like them, was developed by Wildt.[7] Here is a rocky core of 14,000 miles, followed by 6,000 miles of ice, 3,000 miles of "gas" (probably hydrogen) and, again, the clouds of ammonia and methane. Its high escape velocity of 13 miles/sec would seem odd in the presence of a gravity less than Earth's, but is explainable by the planet's lower density. As noted in Chap. 4, Uranus proceeds pole first along its axis (at two points

[7] P. Moore, "Guide to the Planets," p. 158, Eyre and Spottiswoode, London, 1955.

of its orbit, at least), and it may be in rather violent activity in the atmosphere, or even at the surface. The absoluteness of axial orientation leads to days and nights of about 20 years in the polar areas, and comparatively normal days and nights for 50 years in between.

Neptune has an inclination much like the earth's and hence its days, nights, and climate are patterned, basically, as are the earth's. The period of Neptune is about 165 years, and the fact that the planet was discovered in the last century was due partly to the happy coincidence that it was on the same side of the solar system as Uranus when the science of astronomy was ready to deal with such matters as perturbations. Had it been on the opposite side, it might not have been seen until much later. According to Wildt, it has a rocky core 12,000 miles in diameter, an ice layer 6,000 miles thick, and an outer gas envelope 2,000 miles high. The prevailing temperature ($-360°F$) freezes all the ammonia out of the atmosphere, but hydrogen and helium have been observed. Its satellite, Triton, is of uncertain size, but may prove to be a rival of Titan and also have an atmosphere. Because of the low temperature, we may expect a rather quiet condition out there. Neptune also has a small satellite (Nereid), which has an almost cometary eccentricity of orbit.

Finally, there is Pluto. Everything about this planet is suspicious. Its odd orbital behavior has been mentioned. New measurements suggest an incredible density, ten times that of Earth, a very high escape velocity, and a temperature of $-400°F$ in which the entire atmosphere, except for hydrogen, helium, and neon, lies frozen solid on the surface. Perhaps there are oceans: methane. The whole planet must be abysmally dark, cold, dead, motionless, and lonely.

But even this may not be the outermost. Pickering has been observing perturbations of Neptune and Pluto which indicate the possibility of a planet about seven billion miles from the sun.[8] If Pluto is uninviting, the dark coldness of this "Planet P" defies conception. It has never been directly observed, and may not even exist, so slender is the information on it.

[8] *Ibid.,* p. 178.

The Universe at Large

Beyond the solar system comes a new order of emptiness and magnitude. The reference shifts from small and cold planets to the fiery stars which range in size from that of Jupiter to 390 times the size of the sun. Our own sun is a very average, perhaps even mediocre, star in size, temperature, and all other respects. Density varies inversely with size. White dwarfs, such as the companion to Sirius, are so dense that a volume the size of an ice cube would weigh well over half a ton on earth, a red giant, such as Antares, is only one two-thousandth of the density of our atmosphere at sea level. Stars range in temperature between 5000 and perhaps 5,000,000°F.

In brilliance, the stars vary from one-millionth of the sun to about 600,000 times and are measured in magnitudes (which in the star atlas are "apparent magnitudes"). There are many ways of considering "magnitude," but the easiest to visualize is the apparent, which ignores intrinsic brightness, distance, emissions at various wavelengths, and a number of other items. Some apparently faint stars are actually brighter than others, but appear dim because they are farther away. About 2,000 stars are visible at one time, but telescopes reveal that the number in our galaxy may run into the billions.

The sun is 93 million miles away and the nearest star something like 24 million million miles, or 4.4 light years. The center of our galaxy is something like 30,000 light years away, and the total dimensions may reach 100,000 light years in diameter by 10,000 light years thick at the hub.

The light emitted from stars is caused by continual nuclear fission and fusion, much like exploding hydrogen bombs. Looking at the night sky, we have become accustomed to lay out the celestial hemisphere into constellations, in order to help remember where the individual stars are. This practice, although it provides a convenient method of approximate location, may also confuse the novice, since stars in a constellation vary tremendously in distance —something not evident from the flatness of star maps—and key stars in one constellation are very likely to be related to key and secondary stars in several others.

The sun is moving toward the constellation Hercules at about 12 miles/sec. Other stars travel at speeds up to 84 miles/sec but not all are going particularly in the same direction. Hercules is not a place but a direction from Earth. Generally speaking, all stars are moving in vast orbits around the center of the galaxy, according to the basic rule of high speed nearer the center and slower speeds farther out. Depending on what is taken as a reference, some stars may appear to be moving retrograde to the general movement of the spiral arms.

Stars may be single, double, or multiple. Double stars move about each other and may eclipse each other if their orbits are edge on to the solar system. Others are gathered in globular clusters, or in loose thin clusters, like the Pleiades, which may be involved in large gas clouds which they illuminate. Vast clouds of dust, gas, and ice particles, particularly in the spiral arms of the disk of the galaxy, make up the preponderance of matter in the galaxy, and where there are no nearby stars to create nebulosity, there will often be dark clouds, such as the famous "horsehead" nebula in the direction of Orion. Looking at the Milky Way, we see through the plane of the disk, but elsewhere we are more or less looking "up" or "down" out of the disk.

Our galaxy is one of about a dozen in a "local group" shaped like a lemon and measuring about a million light years through the long axis, which is aimed at Messier 31 (the great spiral of Andromeda) on the other end. Beyond these, in all directions, within a radius of 10 million light years, are about 1,025 galaxies of assorted types, known as elliptical, spiral, barred, and so on. Investigations have been made with the 100-in. telescope indicating about 100 million galaxies in a radius of 500 million light years, with an approximately uniform distribution of about 2 million light years between individual galaxies. There is some reason to suspect that the dust, gas, and ice particles are associated with the galactic systems and that only between the great galaxies is really pure, total, clean emptiness.

The distances of intergalactic space are incomprehensible. The 200-in. telescope seems to have pushed the frontier of the universe back to about two billion light years, with no certainty that this is the limit. Telescopes today receive light from these remote galaxies which started from them before dinosaurs roamed the Earth (in some cases even before there was any life on this planet) and has been traveling at 186,000 miles a second ever since. This is quite a distance.

The student of space flight ponders this and notes that man has not yet reached the planets in a small system engulfed in the vastness on one of these millions of galaxies. He has not landed on the moon of his own planet. He has only just established unmanned satellites around his earth. As a matter of fact, man himself has only achieved about 20 miles of altitude. Why, then, all the fuss about space flight? Isn't it a bit silly?

Actually not. The basic ingredients of space flight are at hand: rocket power, automatic control, and the disciplines of space medicine. These need sifting and development. There is nothing in the main problem that millions of man hours and billions of dollars will not ultimately solve. Getting into an orbit around the earth, as Von Pirquet pointed out, is the hardest part by far. Once that has been done, flight to the moon and planets is simplified by a whole order of magnitude.

The perfection of the techniques of space flight which will permit systematic reliable transportation, on a more or less scheduled basis, among the 40-odd planets and satellites, will keep man busy for centuries. When atomic energy, ionic drive, and light beams have been harnessed for propulsion, combined perhaps with anti-gravity, flight to the stars may be possible, but then only the nearest ones, unless some way has been found to get around the serious limitations imposed by what now seems to be the absolute speed of light itself. If there is any such way, the best minds of the world cannot now visualize what it would be.

The suggestion that spaceships may eventually travel faster than light will cause most astronomers to throw up their hands in horror, and for excellent mathematical and physical reasons outlined in Einstein's theory of relativity. But science is still in its extreme infancy. It is a bit fatuous to think we have approached any ultimate realities, or are very likely to until science is several thousand years older than it is now.

Even if man could do these things, he is not equipped to solve the technical and social problems he would probably encounter.

He cannot manage to get along in the womb-like utopia of a lush planet. He cannot adequately feed, shelter, clothe, or educate himself, or prevent vast bigotry, crime, and war—even when all the cards are stacked in his favor. What would such a clown do if at large in the galaxy?

BIBLIOGRAPHY

Kahn, F.: "The Design of the Universe," Crown Publishers, Inc., New York, 1954.

Rudaux, L.: "Sur les autres mondes," Librairie Larousse, Paris, 1937.

Rudaux and de Vaucouleurs, "Astronomie: Les Astres de l'univers," Librairie Larousse, Paris, 1948.

Zim and Baker, "Stars," (a Golden Nature Guide), Simon and Schuster, Inc., New York, 1951.

Baker, R. H.: "Astronomy," 4th ed., D. Van Nostrand Company, Inc., Princeton, N.J., 1946. Chapters 1 and 2 are useful for orienting the novice to the unfamiliar outlook of three-dimensional cosmic space as seen from the earth. Chapter 5 deals with the moon; chap. 10, with the sun; chap. 14, with stellar atmospheres and interiors; chap. 15, with interstellar matter; chaps. 16–18, with clusters, galaxies, and the cosmos.

Gallant and Hess, "Exploring the Moon," Garden City Books, New York. Formerly Garden City Publishing Company, Inc. Division of Doubleday, 1955.

Antoniadi, E. M.: "La Planète Mercure," Gauthier-Villars, Paris, 1934.

de Vaucouleurs, G.: "The Planet Mars," Faber and Faber, Ltd., London, 1955. (Distributed in America by The Macmillan Company.)

Antoniadi, E. M.: "La Planète Mars," Librairie Scientifique Hermann et Cie, Paris, 1930.

Flammarion, C.: "La Planète Mars," 2 vols., Gauthier-Villars, Paris, 1909.

Moore, P.: "Guide to Mars," Frederick Muller, London, 1956.

———: "The Planet Venus," Faber and Faber, Ltd., London, 1956.

Strughold, H.: "The Red and Green Planet," University of New Mexico Press, Albuquerque, N.M., 1953.

Peek, B. M.: "The Planet Jupiter," Faber and Faber, Ltd., London, 1958.

Watson, F.: "Between the Planets," The Blakiston Division, McGraw-Hill Book Company, Inc., New York. Formerly P. Blakiston's Son & Company, Philadelphia; then The Blakiston Company, New York. The latter was a subsidiary of Doubleday & Company, Inc., 1941. (See for discussion of asteroids, meteors, comets, etc.)

Ley, W., and C. Bonestell: "Conquest of Space," The Viking Press, Inc., New York, 1949. Contains many paintings of landscapes on other planets, based on solid scientific knowledge and legitimate inference.

Jones, H. S.: "Life on Other Worlds," Mentor Books, New York, 1949. (Author is the former Astronomer Royal of England.)

Kuiper, G.: "The Earth as a Planet," University of Chicago Press, Chicago, 1954.

————: "Atmospheres of the Earth and Planets," University of Chicago Press, Chicago, 1952.

White and Benson, eds.: "Physics and Medicine of the Upper Atmosphere," University of New Mexico Press, Albuquerque, N.M., 1952.

Hoyle, F.: "Frontiers of Astronomy," William Heinemann, Ltd., London, 1955.

Abetti, G.: "The Sun," The Macmillan Company, New York, 1957.

Sidgwick, J. B.: "Amateur Astronomer's Handbook," Faber and Faber, Ltd., London, 1955.

————: "Observational Astronomy for Amateurs," Faber and Faber, Ltd., London, 1955.

————: "Introducing Astronomy," The Macmillan Company, New York, 1957.

Born, M.: "The Restless Universe," Dover Publications, New York, 1951

10

Human Factors in Space Flying

The Big Picture

It is a sign of the times that handbooks on human engineering and texts on aviation and space medicine are finding a place on the aeronautical engineer's desk or drawing board. As science explores the speed ranges from the lower Mach numbers, man himself has become such a limiting factor that no engineer can now afford to develop a high-speed aircraft design without first seeking counsel from the medical doctor.

The same may be said about altitude. The planes of today are pressing higher and higher toward the extreme limits of the mechanically and physiologically effective atmosphere. Flights to the borders of space have already been made in such rocket-powered research aircraft as the Air Force Bell X-1A and X-2 and the Navy Douglas D-558-2. At the 15- to 25-mile heights reached by these planes, pilots have had to be protected from what have come to be known as "space equivalent" conditions, conditions that, in so far as the human being is concerned, are the same as those found in space itself.

Balloon flights have also been important in allowing *sustained* observations of human performance and reactions at high altitude. Captain Kittinger, USAF, reached 18 miles in June, 1957, remaining aloft for somewhat over two hours. This broke the 14-mile Navy Strato-Lab record of November, 1956, and the previous National Geographic Society–Army Air Corps record set in 1935 (a little more than 13 miles). More recently, Major David G. Simons spent 32 hr aloft, part of the time at the 19-mile level.

Present developments in the aeronautical sciences demand the acknowledgment that we have already arrived at the space frontier, a fact resulting in the establishment of a Department of Space Medicine under the Air University's School of Aviation Medicine. Not too many years ago it was announced that one-seventh of Air Force funds available for aviation medicine were allocated to space medical research, and this percentage has undoubtedly been increased to keep pace with, or precede, progress in aircraft and missile design. The Navy is equally interested in space-medical research, and much important work is being done within their aviation medical structure. In 1948, the armed services collaborated with various agencies and firms in the first aeromedical symposium, which since has been followed by others, including a meeting held from June 17 to 19, 1957, on problems common to the fields of astronomy and biology. This was sponsored by the International Mars Committee and the Astronomical Society of the Pacific, and it surveyed astrobiology, spectroscopic evidence of vegetation on Mars, the behavior of microorganisms under Mars-simulated environmental conditions, and other topics. A month earlier the Aero Medical Association's space-medical branch held a symposium on weightless conditions, space-cabin simulators, sealed-cabin atmospheres, and medical aspects of extreme-altitude balloon tests. One of the basic books in the field of physics and medicine of the upper atmosphere is a compilation of the papers presented at the 1951 symposium, held in San Antonio, Texas. A number of other books (see bibliography) dealing with space medicine in the United States have been published, and a wide variety of articles on the subject has appeared in *The Journal of Aviation Medicine* and other periodicals.

The Russians also have been very busy and animals as large as dogs have been sent up in rockets and recovered. These dogs wore special "space suits" and from birth had been trained for the rocket tests. So far they have been recovered from close to 70-mile altitudes by parachute. They reached a falling speed of 2,000 mph prior to parachute opening. It is rumored that the Lesgaft Natural Science Institute may be reorganized into an Institute of Cosmo-

Biology to study life possibility on other worlds and aspects of sustaining human life in spaceships. A new book, entitled "Medical Problems of Interplanetary Travel" has been published; it contains much non-Russian work, with analysis and commentary by Soviet medical scientists.

We owe much of the early progress in space medicine to the German workers, who, during World War II, developed the fundamentals from which most subsequent investigations have progressed. Many of the key German aero- and space-medical scientists are now in this country, and they represent a curious blending of the engineer, astronomer, and physician. The physical and medical studies of high-altitude and space flight have progressed so rapidly that we now have (to name only a few organizations) the Space Medical Association, the Civil Aviation Medical Association, Air Force Space Biology Laboratory, the Air Force Atmosphere Physics Laboratory, and the Lovelace Foundation for Medical Education and Research, which is closely connected with space-medical progress. A Human Factors Society has been even more recently established.

One of the more important concepts that have evolved from work carried on during the years since World War II involves the *aeropause*. This is a transition term as applied to the human being and the vehicle in which he rides and indicates the general region where the atmosphere ends and space begins. There is, of course, no exact point where we can assert this. The aeropause is indefinite, in that it relates man and vehicle to a variety of atmospheric and space conditions, all of which have a particular effect on bodily or vehicular functions.

The space-medical scientists prefer to think of the atmosphere as being divided into several functions, that is, the function of providing man with the air he must breathe and the climate within which he lives, the function of filtering out a variety of matter and radiation of cosmic origin, and the function of supplying mechanical support to aircraft. It is useful to recall these functions when discussing the interrelationship of the cosmos, the atmosphere, and man and vehicle.

As a general rule, it is felt that space-medical scientists should maintain a status at least 15 years ahead of the vehicle designers.

They have demonstrated conclusively that they must be consulted before any advanced piloted-vehicle design can be considered feasible and that the problems which must be solved to permit manned flight at the borders of space are either the same as, or are directly applicable to, those that must be solved for direct space flight.

The physical conditions which man must survive in flight above 10 miles are essentially the same as those he would have to endure at 100, 1,000, or 10,000 miles into space. From the medical point of view, man has already flown in space, and the work being accomplished *today* by aeronautical and rocket engineers, astronomers, and medical scientists is helping to open the doors to one of humanity's oldest dreams: exploration of the earth's upper atmosphere and the eventual conquest of planetary space. The road to space may be far shorter than we have suspected, for man may *have* to travel into space if he wants much greater speeds than he has attained today.

Until quite recently the airborne-vehicle designer was at best only moderately concerned with the eventual occupants of the craft on his drawing board. It was undoubtedly his desire that the seats be comfortable, that instruments be placed in convenient locations, and that certain safety devices be furnished, but there the engineer's interest in the passenger usually ceased. Speed, acceleration, deceleration, areas of operation, ambient conditions, and a host of other factors were considered largely in terms which ignored man, the rider.

That was yesterday. Today, engineers are acutely aware of factors once neglected or ignored. While science races ahead, man is still man, a rather frail creature when pitted against the performance of modern jet and rocket planes. Modern man has a life span longer than that of his grandfather, because of rapid advance in the field of medicine; nevertheless, his physical body performs under the same limitations that the bodies of his forefathers did. He cannot survive under water for more than a few minutes, for example, unless he brings with him an approximation of his normal living conditions. He cannot survive long under very high or very low pressures, nor can he endure exaggerated temperature extremes. The human organism objects to extreme acceleration and deceleration, and may object to prolonged states of weightlessness. Yet today, as the conquest of the upper atmosphere and space frontier approaches, man must, of necessity, subject himself to extreme conditions that would delight a connoisseur of Gothic tales. Faces contorted by high accelerations, bodies bloated by sudden drops in pressure, cell damage produced by severe radiation, and nausea resulting from extended periods of reduced or zero weight may soon be not uncommon. It will be the tremendous task of the aviation and space physician to see that the hazards of high-speed, high-altitude, and space flight are reduced to limits compatible with human endurance.

It is perhaps unnecessary to point out that these hazards will always be present and may well become more severe as higher altitudes are sought. It is interesting to note that we are now beginning to hear the unusual term "distance from earth" in connection with upper-atmospheric missiles and space vehicles.

We have progressed considerably since Samuel Johnson wrote, "We now know a method of mounting into the air [balloons], and, I think, are not likely to know more. The vehicles . . . can gratify no curiosity till we mount with them to greater heights that we can reach without . . ." These "greater heights" are indeed creating many problems today, but as long as the element of curiosity remains in his mind, man will bear anything to gratify it. Balloons have exceeded Johnson's small expectations for them and do offer a convenient method of reaching great heights, but, as we have seen, the rocket is the only means presently capable of carrying men and materials beyond the atmosphere.

We should note that the atmosphere ends at a variety of altitudes, none exactly placed, depending on what bodily or vehicular function we are concerned with. To the astronomer it may end hundreds or thousands of miles up, while to a pilot it may terminate where oxygen and pressure conditions no longer support life. This is the *hypoxic zone,* less than three miles up, where the decreased oxygen pressure brings human psychological and physiological discomfort. In the *anoxic zone,* about ten miles up, explosive decomposition becomes a serious problem. Here *man can consider himself in space,* just as if he were in a spaceship or on the surface of the moon. The D-558-2, the X-1A, and the X-2 airplanes have already flown in regions where 97 to 99 per cent of the atmospheric mass was below them and to 3 to 1 per cent was above. And the X-15 will probably take man out to 100 or more miles. What preparation has man made for this? What are his limitations?

We human beings can suffer arctic cold, Amazon heat, desert dryness, and pummeling rains of India. The temperature span may seem wide to us, but when viewed against values found throughout the universe, it is extremely narrow. Man is conditioned to certain atmospheric pressure, serious deviations from which will cause discomfort or death; he must have water at fairly regular intervals, and in sufficient amounts; without food he will surely expire within a few weeks; several days of sleeplessness leave him exhausted; his ability to withstand radiation is limited. A creature of the planet Earth, man has adapted himself to that planet, and will perish elsewhere unless he is able to take with him a close approximation of home conditions.

Present information indicates that man has not exceeded a speed of 2,500 mph, nor has he yet reached altitudes of even 30 miles. He has experienced zero gravity for a period of perhaps 40 to 60 sec and has undergone only moderately high accelerations for any important length of time. He has survived temperature changes from far below zero to the upper hundreds of degrees centigrade in a matter of seconds, and has endured abrupt variations in pressure under controlled experiments. These are notable achievements, but much more must be known before the human being can safely and repeatedly fly at the outskirts of the atmosphere and into space.

Man, of course, is quite accustomed to the convenient conditions found at the bottom of the atmosphere. "Normal" gravity of one unit is not only pleasant to him, but acts to keep his atmosphere attached to his planet, and produces "normal" sea-level pressure of nearly 15 lb/sq in. This atmosphere transmits a "normal" amount of light and heat from the sun, keeps out dangerous primary and much secondary cosmic radiation, controls the amount of ultraviolet light that reaches the surface, and effectively pulverizes all but the most stubborn meteorites.

The atmosphere's ability to stabilize temperature is too well known to enlarge upon, but above 10, 15, and 20 miles, radical changes occur. Meteoric intensity rises, and even though relatively unimportant until altitudes of 70 to 90 miles are reached, it is nevertheless a factor to be considered. Pressures drop severely, air thins dangerously, and radiation intensity rises sharply. The puncturing of a pressurized cabin wall enclosing a high-flying pilot would be fatal. Let us consider, then, what all these changes will mean to man and what he proposes to do to provide protection for himself. A mixture of physical, biological and psychological questions becomes interlaced in a discussion of this kind.

Radiation

Since radiation represents one of the most difficult problems that man will have to solve in terms of continuous exposure at high altitudes, it may well be considered first. Radiation comes from the cosmos in general and from the sun (visible heat, ultraviolet, radio, and X rays) in particular. It is known that, above approximately 20 miles, continuous exposure to primary cosmic particles will produce considerable cell damage. Primary cosmic radiation includes protons, alpha particles, and a good variety of heavy atomic nuclei, quite capable of killing human cells. At the same time it is known that the human body would not feel them; it would have no sense of being "hit," so to speak. Space physicians and the upper-atmosphere physicists must tell the vehicle engineer more about these particles, how much actual damage they may be expected to inflict upon cells. It is known that they are chiefly naked nuclei, and thus in the main positively charged. They are ionizers, and when they collide with particles of our atmosphere, they dislodge electrons, leaving positive atoms, or ion pairs. These ion pairs may be dangerous, and it is through the process of ionization that cell damage may arise. Artificial-satellite-borne instrumentation, such as on Sputniks and Explorers, helps gather vitally important cosmic-ray information prior to manned ventures for extended periods in space.

Secondary cosmic radiation forms another, though lesser, problem, one affecting man before he reaches the borders of space. Such radiation includes neutrons, electrons, gamma rays, neutrinos, X rays, slow protons, heavy recoil nuclei, and mesons, together with surviving elements of primary radiation. This is apparently quite a barrage, but it does not represent an impossible condition.

Soft X rays are not considered dangerous. Hard ones, formed occasionally from activity in the sun's corona, can do damage, but little information on them is available.

Ultraviolet light presents another danger. On the earth's surface it is practically nonexistent, having been filtered out by the ozone layer. Above that layer it would be deadly, but not necessarily fatal, since metals and special windows can stop the radiation. Perhaps the major problem posed by the ultraviolet is that it will, in time, do damage to coating materials of a spaceship's hull. Unfortunately, when exposed to the full intensity of the sun's very short-wave electromagnetic radiation, the chemical structure of most, if not all, suitable coating materials is decomposed. This is a side problem of radiation that will be brought up again later.

As for the genetic effects of radiation, Nobel prize-winning Dr. H. J. Muller believes that there is "every reason to anticipate that we can be successful in extending our conquest of the third dimension without genetic or other radiation damage to humanity that will correspond at all with the benefit to be derived . . ."[1] Many problems must be solved, but most medical experts feel that we can protect ourselves from radiation, though probably for not more than relatively short periods. It is hoped that some form of protective chemical, which may be administered internally, will be developed to counteract these effects.

Vision

The so-called *functional border* of space, in so far as vision is concerned, may reach right down to earth on a clear desert night. Optical conditions would then be space equivalent. On this fairly definite threshold of sensation, the eye would always see jet blackness in shadows. In space, since there are no air molecules to diffuse light, the sun is a blinding, brilliant orb, and any object lying in the shadow cast by another will be totally invisible. The sharp contrasts of the desert night are not precisely space equivalent, but are a close approximation. This matter is partly a matter of local

[1] H. J. Muller, Genetic Effects of Cosmic Radiation, in "Physics and Medicine of the Upper Atmosphere," University of New Mexico Press, Albuquerque, N.M., 1952.

brightness and depends upon the zenith distance of the sun, the difference in azimuth between the sun and the point of observation, and, of course, altitude. In addition, two less obvious factors enter the picture: the average reflectivity of the earth and the absorption of atmospheric ozone. All these factors become more pronounced with increasing altitudes and involve inconvenience, sensory fatigue, and bodily danger.

Respiration

At some altitude between 50 and 70 miles, diatomic oxygen ceases to exist, being replaced by the monatomic variety that is produced by hard-hitting ultraviolet radiation, which splits the oxygen molecule into two atoms. This oxygen is unfit for human respiration. Actually, the real limit to metabolic use of atmospheric oxygen is quite a bit lower than 50 miles. Red cells store inhaled oxygen, taking it from the lungs to the tissue. The higher we climb, the more red cells are required for this exchange. However, a limit to this compensatory mechanism is reached at about nine miles; beyond this, no matter how hard a pump might work to compress outside air, there would still be an inadequate oxygen supply— even with a maximum possible number of red blood cells.

In the old days a pilot, when he reached 15,000 ft, would put on his oxygen mask and feel perfectly all right. But when better air-planes carried him above some 40,000 ft, the mask failed, because oxygen pressure inside the mask was too much higher than ambient atmospheric pressure. Pressurized cabins have superficially solved the problem but may be dangerous at extreme altitudes: should they rupture, explosive decomposition would take place, killing the occupants within seconds. Gases would explode in the thorax and gastrointestinal tract, and unconsciousness and death would follow. It would be as if a deep-sea diver, accustomed to extreme pressures on the ocean floor, were suddenly to expose himself to normal sea-level pressure. Up to about 15 miles, air from the atmosphere could theoretically be used, but above this altitude the density would be so low that it would be unfeasible to employ the huge compression pumps (and radiators to dissipate heat of compression) which would be necessary. From about 12 to 15 miles the concentration of ozone is such as to make the atmosphere unfit for human use. Goody [2] reports the mean daytime height of the ozone layer was, during a month of tests, 22.7 km (14.1 miles), with maximum variation from 20.4 to 24.7 km (12.7 to 15.3 miles).

A common phrase used by the space physician is *time of useful consciousness,* or *time reserve,* which refers to the time that a man, traveling in a pressurized cabin, will have to save himself after he realizes that his cabin has ruptured and that his life-giving air and pressure are disappearing rapidly. This time interval decreases with altitude, from about 80 sec at 5 miles, until it reaches a minimum of about 15 sec at less than 9 miles. From this point upward, it stays the same, for at this distance from the earth's surface man reaches the functional border of space in terms of respiration. He is in space equivalent.

Let us follow this respiration question a little further. The lack of oxygen is not the only specter facing the space crew. It is well known that carbon dioxide and water vapor form in the lungs. These accumulate on the lung tissue's surface as they are deposited by the blood. Now, as the altitude increases, the lung pressure decreases, *but* the combined pressures of carbon dioxide and water vapor do *not* decrease, since they are being continually furnished by the blood. When the atmospheric pressure drops to somewhat over 10 per cent of the sea-level value (at 9½ miles), the entire volume of the lungs is taken up by the waste gases. From then on, inhaling and exhaling mean nothing—the ambient air would not even *enter* the lungs! Even a healthy air environment would be useless. Man would again be in space equivalent, because the oxygen would no longer have enough pressure to force its way into the lungs against carbon dioxide and water-vapor pressures.[3]

[2] R. M. Goody, "The Physics of the Stratosphere," Cambridge University Press, London, 1954. *Note:* Regener, in a chapter, Atmospheric Ozone, *op. cit.,* reports the ozone peak (maximum ozone density) average altitude to be 19.8 km (12.3 miles) varying from a low of 15.2 km (9.45 miles) to a high of 22.9 km (14.2 miles). However, when the ratio of the number of ozone molecules to the number of air molecules is determined, the peak lies about 24.4 km (15.4 miles). The value of this ratio is stated to be about 5×10^{-6}, vs. a surface average of 2×10^{-8}.

[3] The danger of nitrogen bubbles forming in the blood is also acute, so acute that it has been suggested that a 60 per cent helium–40 per cent oxygen atmosphere be carried into space.

Table 10-1 shows the amount of air, of which about 21 per cent

TABLE 10-1 *Air requirements of man*

Work level	Air breathed, liters/min	Oxygen consumed, liters/min
Resting	6–15	0.2–0.4
Light work	20–25	0.6–1.0
Moderate work	30–40	1.2–1.6
Hard work	40–60	1.8–2.4
Severe work	40–60	2.5–3.0

is oxygen, a man will inhale under various working conditions. In a closed environment, adequate flows of oxygen will be needed at all times. It is pointed out that a peak flow rate of 90 to 120 liters/ min may be required, since peak requirements can be three to four times the regular flow rate.

The Blood Boils

At above 12 miles the atmospheric pressure drops so much that the blood actually boils from the body's own heat. As ambient pressures lower, so do boiling points, so that, when pressures drop to below 6 per cent of sea-level values, a new functional border of space is reached. According to H. Haber, "The boiling point of body fluid is reached at an altitude where the barometric pressure becomes equal to the vapor pressure at body temperature" (that is, 47 mm Hg at 37°C).

Animals are commonly placed in chambers where the barometric pressure is 30 mm Hg (more than space equivalent). For test purposes, it is pointless to subject them to more. At 30 mm Hg pressure, respiration becomes deep and rapid, the abdomen distends with gas expansion in the intestine, and collapse occurs within 8 sec.[4] Exposures of more than 2 min are normally fatal.

Acceleration, Extreme Weight, Weightlessness

The factor of weight is demanding close attention. When we step on a scale, we read a measurement of the downward force

[4] F. A. Hitchcock and J. Kemph, Boiling of Body Liquids at High Altitudes, *J. Aviation Med.,* vol. 26, no. 4, p. 290, 1955; J. E. Ward, The True Nature of the Boiling of Body Fluids in Space, *J. Aviation Med.,* vol. 27, no. 5, p. 429, 1956.

exerted on the platform. Weight increases as the downward force increases, and is due to the gravitational attraction of the earth. Gravitational forces act in directions of lines joining the centers of bodies acting upon each other. This is a universal phenomenon; all bodies act on each other.

Space medicine, however, prefers to think of weight of a body a little differently. Haber defined it as equal to the force of its *support,* and independent of the force of gravity.[5] It would be the force of inertia which, if added to the normal weight, would give a

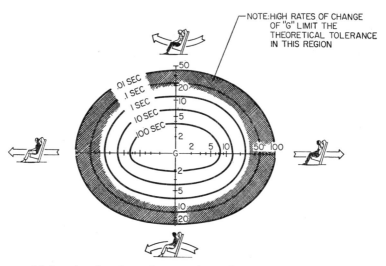

FIG. 10-1.   Acceleration tolerance. (*Douglas Aircraft Company, Inc.*)

plus value, or if subtracted, would give a minus, or perhaps even zero, value.

Now, why has this apparent difference in defining weight arisen between space doctors and the classical physicists? The reason is that weight, as Newton defines it, is too closely associated with the force of terrestrial gravity. Yet, within the earth's gravitational field, variations in weight can take place. A man can weigh ten times normal, or can weigh nothing, and still be close to the surface of our planet or even below it. Haber has worked it out as follows:

[5] H. Haber, "Physical Environment of the Flyer," USAF University, 1954.

"We shall define weight from the standpoint of man's experiencing it with his own body." [6] When he sits on a chair, gravity attracts him, but the downward force is balanced by the elastic forces of the chair which push upward. The downward force and the upward force being equal, the man moves in neither direction. But whereas Newton talked about weight as being due to the "pulling-down" force of gravity, we shall speak of it as "an elastic force brought to bear upon an individual by an external material agent physically in contact with him, such as a chair." [7] Directions have been reversed: that is all.

Where does this get us? Consider increased weight. If we ascend in an elevator, we feel pressed toward the floor. This is the same feeling one gets in pulling out of a dive in an airplane. The pilot of a rapidly accelerating rocket airplane feels much the same, except that the force is also directed toward the rear.

Now this increased weight is inconvenient to man. For one thing, the blood becomes rather heavy. At 7 g it is about like liquid iron. The soft veins yield under this unusual weight and pools of blood accumulate in the stomach and legs. The head (assuming that the direction of acceleration is from head to feet) receives none. Colonel Stapp, an Air Force space-medical doctor, showed that 45-g acceleration can be sustained if the load is distributed over 218 sq in. of the surface of the body.

Experiments with animals have resulted in a considerable increase in knowledge concerning this aspect of space medicine, and centrifuge tests with human occupants have supported the new knowledge with empirical data. Centrifuges have been used to simulate the experience a crew would undergo in a large three-stage rocket missile. One series of three tests was reported recently [8] wherein test subjects were first warmed up by 1-, 4-, 6-g runs, following which the desired tests under 8 g were made, spread out over a 6-min interval. The results of these tests demonstrated that experience is an important factor in terms of conditioning man to

[6] H. Haber, "Man in Space," Sidgwick & Jackson, Ltd., London, 1953.

[7] H. Haber, *ibid.*

[8] H. Preston-Thomas et al., Human Tolerance to Multistage Rocket Acceleration Curves, *J. Aviation Med.,* vol. 26, no. 5, 1955. See also R. R. Hessberg, Accelerating Forces Associated with Leaving and Re-entering the Earth's Gravitational Field, *J. Astronautics,* Spring, 1957.

high-*g* acceleration: "Inexperienced subjects showed a greater tendency toward deterioration under *g* than did those accustomed to the centrifuge." Following an analysis of the test data, it was concluded that it is likely that "manual control can be depended on during three-stage accelerations of the type studied."

There are also large, high-velocity sleds that accelerate human occupants to incredible values of *g*. One of these is Cook Electric's rocket sled, powered by a North American Aviation single-chamber rocket motor developing 50,000 lb of thrust. Others are Northrop Aviation's rocket-sled track, upon which twelve 2,000-lb-thrust engines develop high accelerations and speeds, and the Hunter-Bristol-McDonnell sled which has 14 solid rockets developing 11,000 lb of thrust each. Reaction Motors is developing engines for even more powerful models. An Army sled built by Aircraft Armaments, Inc. can reach 1,300 mph in just 2½ sec. The longest track is Snort, at the Naval Ordnance Test Station, California, where test speeds of nearly 2,400 mph can be achieved. At Muroc Dry Lake, 35 gravity-deceleration tests were carried out under conditions where a slowdown from 150 to 75 mph can be made in ⅕ sec. A Radioplane, Inc. sled has reached 1,100 mph, while a man, Col. J. P. Stapp, has traveled 632 mph on a sled operated by Cook Electric Corporation. It is expected that man will soon ride to 800 mph, which is equivalent to 1,800 mph at 40,000 ft.

Results have shown that, while man in no way enjoys undergoing abnormal accelerations, he is by no means conquered by them. If the *g* forces work across his chest—i.e., if he remains in a prone or supine position—he can withstand quite a bit. Under 10 *g,* man can still move a leg and an arm, but for periods extending into minutes, no more than 4 *g* are tolerable.

Now we shall go to the opposite extreme, man and weightlessness. Suppose a man were to have his chair pulled out from under him? During his period of fall, gravity would pull with one-unit acceleration. Inertia's upward-pulling force works in the opposite direction. Now the two forces acting on one body are equal, and since they work in opposite directions, we must subtract one from the other. Result: the man's weight during free fall is zero—during his drop to the floor he was, in effect, weightless. Near-zero weight is experienced by the diver, the jumper, and the parachutist, though all actually weigh a few pounds because of aerodynamic drag.

A curious interplay of physical forces, under certain conditions, will leave a missile, or airplane and occupants, without weight. In the rocket world, this happens when motors stop functioning and the craft begins to coast. It can happen to a satellite vehicle revolving around a primary body such as the earth. In all cases, the gravity of the earth is effectively "canceled." The orbit may be circular or elliptical or, for that matter, any celestial trajectory formed from a geometric cone (hyperbola, parabola, ellipse, circle, or line) followed by a nonaccelerating missile will result in zero gravity. Disregarding random atmospheric effects, rocket missiles —like planets, meteorites, satellites, and planetoids—follow Keplerian orbits. They rank as celestial bodies and obey the laws of celestial mechanics.

We have seen that an external force must bear on a body for the sensation of weight to be present. In space there is none, and therefore no weight, unless the rocket engines are firing. If this be the case, "up-pushing" reaction force (produced by the actual mass of the thrust-exerting discharge gases) must then be taken into account, and weight will increase as the acceleration or force acting on the rocket increases. When the motors stop, weight disappears, and bodies undergo continued "fall." The need for a new concept of weight in this light becomes clear.

Experimental work is being done with animals to check our theories on the new kind of "weight." Rats, guinea pigs, and monkeys have been shot up in missiles and have undergone free fall (zero weight) for many minutes. At Holloman Air Force Base, rockets have subjected animals to 15 g for 1 sec and 4 or 5 g for 45 sec. Cameras have recorded their reactions, and many technical devices have transmitted key data to space physicians back on the ground.

Can we arrange flight conditions today so that a pilot can observe himself under weightless conditions, and so that the medical scientist may determine his reaction? Yes, but for only very short periods. Here we must call on the rocket specialist and aeronautical engineers who create rocket-powered high-altitude research airplanes. While in flight through the atmosphere, two forces act:

the propelling force of the motor or motors and the aerodynamic force of lift and drag. If *one* could be canceled, the plane would be freed from all effective external forces, would travel (even inside the earth's atmosphere) in a ballistic trajectory (Keplerian orbit), and weightless conditions would result.

Experts of the American Space Medical Association have shown that zero gravity *can* exist in today's research rocket planes for more than 60 sec. There are various pilot reports of zero-gravity sensations being encountered for as long as 30 to 40 sec in Douglas and Bell rocket airplanes undergoing special zero-gravity flight.

Gerathewohl and other Air Force investigators have used both T-33A and F-94C airplanes to obtain gravity-free conditions for up to 45 sec. Some results were presented at the 1956 International Astronautical Federation Congress, in Rome, when it was revealed that 8 out of 16 subjects enjoyed the zero-gravity situation. By 1958 one pilot had over 30 hr of accumulated zero-gravity flight time logged, and he has stated the experience had been pleasant. With century series planes the Air Force expects to obtain about 80 sec weightlessness per trajectory. This period will extend to minutes when manned ballistic rocket flights are made, and to hours with satellites.

Major Charles E. Yeager, USAF research test pilot, experienced zero gravity for 25 to 30 sec. In his words: [9]

When getting to a point of pulling zero gravity, it feels as though the blood pressure is increasing. You get a swelling of the head. . . . But after two or three experiences of about 25–30 seconds of zero gravity, I don't see any reason why a man cannot change his habits so that he counteracts and compensates. But so far as physical effects of extended periods of time of weightlessness are concerned, I don't know, and I don't think anyone does, because there have been no experiences and there won't be any experience along that line until we have zero gravity that will extend into possibly hours or days.

It is exceedingly difficult to come to grips with something that cannot be studied for even a full minute.

In the June, 1957, issue of *The Journal of Aviation Medicine,*

[9] "Frontiers of Man-controlled Flight," proceedings of a symposium, Institute of Transportation and Traffic Engineering, University of California Press, Berkeley, 1953.

Walton describes a device to artificially produce alternating gravitational forces, "including intermittent gravity-free state." The device, called the *graviton,* can work over long periods of time. Free fall occurs in a vertical tube.

Orientation and Control in Space

This brings us logically to the problem of human orientation and control in space. Without weight, vision may be utilized to form a base upon which man may orient himself. But can man orient himself by vision alone? The answer is perhaps, but only with practice. This is somewhat alarming, since human survival, hinged to only one sense, is precarious indeed. Dr. Hubertus Strughold, a pioneer in the field, stressed the point. He said:

The conquest of the outskirts of the atmosphere, and eventually space, is a revolutionary event, comparable only to the transition of the aquatic animals to the land in geologic times.[10]

It is important to know the reason for disorientation in free falls. In the body there are microscopically small receptor organs apparently able to detect changes of mechanical stress or tension existing in the tissue. As the value of gravity reduces to zero, the stress on the tissue reduces to zero. When this happens, a "hollow" feeling in the stomach is likely to occur, and the receptors no longer provide any useful orientation capability. But it is under these very conditions that man may have to operate machines, work controls, feed himself, and generally perform routine observational and navigational tasks of a space voyage.

What control has he then over voluntary actions? It seems that the control of voluntary movements is performed in three ways: (1) through touch receptors of microscopic size, (2) through muscle spindles which are mechanoreceptors that lie in the tissue (the excitation of which is related to muscle tension), and (3) through microscopic corpuscles which rest in man's connective tissue, especially near the muscles, and which are excited by tension. The characteristics of the stress on these latter sense receptors allow for modifications of limb posture, apparently independently

[10] H. Strughold, *op. cit.,* Basic Environmental Problems Relating Man and the Highest Regions of the Atmosphere as Seen by the Biologist.

of the sensory receptors in the muscles, and of touch. Touch may provide some sort of base for orientation. Zero-gravity experiments with animals, using bars and meshed screens, have suggested an encouraging avenue of research.

Detailed investigation has also been conducted with the labyrinthine organs. One type supposedly responds to angular motion; another, the otolith organ, to linear motion. Both have considerable control over man's normal balance and orientation but may be completely useless under zero-gravity conditions, as was the case of the mechanoreceptors.

In the final analysis, zero-gravity orientation may be possible, with practice, for some individuals but not for others. Some people may never adapt. Furthermore, with no rapport between sensation on the one hand and perception on the other, there is some danger of psychological difficulties. Though a man may not be consciously afraid of a situation, reference habits ingrained in him since time immemorial may be too subtle to fight adequately.

Artificial Cabin Environment

On earth, even without artificial ventilation, a natural circulation results from the differing densities and weights of warm and cold air. One seldom stops to think that gravity indirectly causes this natural ventilation, even in closed rooms. Since there will be no weight in freely coasting space rockets, and hence no possibility of natural air circulation inside the crew chambers, it is obvious that a very effective ventilation system must be provided.

But before we can ventilate a cabin, oxygen has to be supplied. The human organism consumes about an ounce of oxygen per hour, under normal conditions. This, of course, increases when heavy work is performed, and creates an important weight factor, especially when long trips and a large crew are considered. Steel bottles, containing 20 lb of liquid oxygen (liquid oxygen is 800 times more compact than gaseous oxygen and boils at $-184°C$), weigh about 150 lb each and present a serious payload problem. Space travel could be prohibitive on this basis alone. But this is not all. Carbon dioxide and water-vapor problems will be present in rockets and satellite vehicles. Since the human animal inhales oxygen and exhales unwanted carbon dioxide, however, it would appear expedient to extract the oxygen from carbon dioxide for future reuse.

Before we attempt to see if this can be done, we must realize that, in a closed cabin, carbon dioxide cannot be allowed to accumulate; in fact, a concentration of more than one-half per cent CO_2 is toxic to the human. Carbon dioxide is so stable that its dissociation $(2CO + O_2 \rightleftharpoons 2CO_2)$ is only 1.8 per cent at 1100°C. It is easy to visualize the magnitude of the problem that would be posed aboard a satellite vehicle or space rocket where there was not enough power available to extract oxygen directly from CO_2. There could not be enough, and the equipment required would be entirely too heavy. Instead, we must turn to nature for a solution. In the well-known carbon cycle, the processes of combustion, decay, fermentation, and animal and human respiration result in heavy CO_2 production, which is indispensable to green-plant life. In sunlight, chlorophyll is formed and catalyzes the endothermic reaction $6CO_2 + 5H_2O \rightarrow C_6H_{10}O_5 + 6O_2$, which is sustained by external heat from the sun.

The $C_6H_{10}O_5$ is starch, or cellulose. Through this reaction plants purify the air, returning oxygen to the atmosphere. Here, then, may be a way to solve the oxygen problem in space. It is not difficult to see why the space-travel planners are consulting the biologist in seeking a solution to the vital oxygen problem. Experiments have shown that 290 sq ft of green leaves can give enough oxygen to replace that used by one man. German plant botanists found that even 11 sq ft of pumpkin-leaf surface would furnish enough for a man at rest. Water plants such as the *Chlorella algae* are known to be excellent oxygen suppliers. Alga offers the further advantage of being highly nutritive, and in one form or another it may be expected to be consumed as food, possibly being itself fed by human waste products. The aesthetic aspect of the cycle is less than ideal, but largely because it is a direct and immediate simplification of what goes on in a more subtle way in nature. The importance of algae is that they spell the difference between life and death to men in space. The reality is a stern one; even here on earth it has been estimated that, should plant life cease, animal life and oxidation processes would use up all oxygen in the atmosphere within a few thousand years.

As prestated in Chap. 8, however, a possible solution to the food problem in space has been found by the National Research and Development Corporation in their development of MMT, a highly concentrated food tube. By providing a volume of edible, palatable, concentrated, high-caloric matter, compressed in a container, MMT provides desirable bulk without the undesirable weight or waste of space. It affords a saving of 50 per cent in food weight and 57.1 per cent in food storage space, which will permit considerable additional allowances for fuel or crew.

Turning again to water vapor, it should be noted that perspiration and diffusion are the main sources. Experimentation with flying personnel shows that one-half a gallon, conservatively, is lost by the human body per day by diffusion, under normal conditions. Much more can be lost from the body in a day under dry desert conditions, perhaps up to four or five gallons.

It is evident that, under closed-cabin conditions, the water-vapor accumulation would rapidly become serious unless something were done to handle it. Somehow the water will have to be extracted from the air and reused for drinking, which is also necessary from the point of view of weight conservation. Specially designed air purifiers must accomplish this, taking out of the cabin atmosphere not only the vapor but other undesirable elements, such as carbon monoxide, ammonia, and chlorine. We are presently conducting experiments with closed-cabin environments, simulating as far as possible space conditions (or at least extreme-high-altitude conditions). Typical chambers are Convair test environmental chamber, simulating altitude conditions to 20 miles and temperature from -100 to $500°F$, and the Wright Air Development Center chamber, where a scientist successfully simulated an altitude of practically 40 miles. Litton has a chamber in which a subject has undergone simulated 95-mile-altitude conditions. Some experts now feel that, by taking full advantage of acclimatization and a little pure oxygen, a specially trained crew could operate in a cabin under a pressure of only 2 lb/sq in., which approximates conditions met at about eight and one-half miles. The week-long February 1958 endurance test of an airman in the small space-flight simulation chamber at Randolph Air Force Base proved that man could operate for extended periods in a completely closed environment.

At a symposium held in Great Britain in July, 1957, space-flight experts heard space-medical experts talk of *sensory deprivation,* which is the psychological effect of being outside the normal world of sensation. Man will suffer hallucinations if he is kept seated in a dark, silent room; if he wears frosted glasses in an illuminated room where normal sounds are obliterated or obscured by a steady hum; if he is placed at the bottom of a water trough with diving-type equipment for extended periods; or if he is put to bed and cut off from touch sensations by gloves. Colonel J. P. Henry felt that a space flier might suffer a mental breakdown in a matter of a few hours unless proper stimuli were provided. This condition is much like the *break-off phenomenon* reported in the April, 1957, issue of *The Journal of Aviation Medicine.* The report dealt with the feeling of separation pilots experience when in high-altitude aircraft; presumably the phenomenon would be more pronounced in space. The effect was described as "a condition of spatial orientation in which the pilot conceives himself to be isolated, detached, and physically separated from the earth so that he is no longer in contact with it."

Heat Problems

Many early space-flight enthusiasts thought that keeping warm would be man's most urgent problem. Today we wonder how we shall keep cool. For one thing, the absolute-zero "coldness of space" is a myth: space, being a vacuum, can have no temperature; the absolute-zero figure of $-273\,°C$ merely refers to the absence of molecular or atomic motion.

In the upper atmosphere, aerodynamic heating encountered by rapidly flying vehicles will prove troublesome, though it seems that heat-barrier material problems are gradually coming under control by the use of magnesium-thorium and other alloys. The magnesium offers great weight savings, giving excellent strength-to-weight ratios. The addition of the thorium provides great strength and should solve manned-flight problems in the speed regime below 2,200 mph, where temperatures of some $750\,°F$ will be generated. In space, the naked sun will have no ocean of air abating its fury. Paints or ceramic coverings with high reflecting values will be required, although how long they will stand up under ultraviolet and micrometeoric battering is still questionable.

Another item, *earthshine,* will be felt. The intensity of earthshine will depend on (1) cloud coverage, (2) the portion of the earth facing the vehicle, (3) the season, and (4) the earth's albedo (that portion of the sunlight that is reflected by a body into space). This albedo will strongly influence flight at extreme altitudes and in space, since about 35 per cent of solar radiation is reflected out.

We may here remind ourselves of the difference between temperature and heat: The former is a measure of the mean kinetic energy of molecules and atoms (hence the term "absolute zero" in referring to space), while the latter is a measure of the total heat energy a body contains. Knowing this, we realize that what we shall be measuring in space will be the skin temperature of a body, such as a rocket vehicle. The heat energy from the sun and earth, transmitted by electromagnetic radiation, will act to warm the rocket. Painting the body black will cause more absorption of the sun's radiations, and hence the temperature will go up; by painting it white or silver, it will reflect a high percentage of the radiation and tend to maintain a lower temperature.

The temperature of a spaceship may be expected to be influenced by the radiative exchange between it and (1) the sun, (2) the cosmos, and (3) the nearest planet, if applicable. Konrad Buettner [11] has given examples of a sphere, a plate facing the sun, and a plate facing away from the sun, which he used to work out temperatures on an object in space. He assumes that they are in orbit around the earth at 120 miles, are black-, white-, or nickel-surfaced, and are at equilibrium temperature. A black sphere would reach 63°C; a black plate facing the sun, 122°C; and a black plate facing away from the sun, 68°C. White objects would reach −42°C (sphere), −51°C (plate facing sun), and −13°C (plate facing away from sun), while nickel objects would get very hot (239, 347, and 231°C). At night they would all drop in temperature to −68, −29, and −270°C.

In order to keep a man and vehicle cool in space, it will be necessary to determine the radiative properties of many metals. We know that 98 per cent of the solar radiation can be reflected by certain polished surfaces, but what about infrared? Aluminum, a

[11] Biochemistry of Manned Rocket Flight, in J. P. Marbarger, ed., "Space Medicine," University of Illinois Press, Urbana, Ill., 1951.

good solar radiator, is a very poor infrared radiator. Buettner calculated that a spaceship with a polished aluminum hull would rise to 425°C in open, direct sunshine, because of infrared absorption. Metals appear not to be good shielding materials.

Nonmetallic materials may possibly be better infrared reflectors. White magnesium oxide appears promising, and calculations indicate that a spaceship covered with this substance would maintain −18°C temperatures. With men and machines giving off heat, plus the use of a simple heating system (possibly a solar mirror), a comfortable temperature should result. Someone has even suggested using a sort of venetian blind to regulate temperatures: one side would be black to absorb heat; the other side, highly reflective to allow for near-total reflection. As the temperature went up or down beyond comfortable margins, the blinds would be adjusted to preserve livable conditions within the craft.

Returning to man, the occupant, medical science would like to know exactly what he can endure. Recent experiments show that he can withstand temperatures of around 150°C for 10 to 12 min following artificially induced *environment-cooling breakdowns*. This is not much time, but it is something. Studies utilizing modern environmental cabins such as government-operated 20-man, 4-man, and 1-man chambers continue. The Martin Company has designed one that can change temperatures from −74 to +77°C almost instantly, as well as test toxic conditions, temperature extremes, and so on. The Litton Industry Company has a 30-ft-long, 15-ft-diameter space laboratory which will allow humans to carry out functions required during space travel. In August, 1957, man simulated an altitude of 90 miles in this chamber, and by fall the record had gone up to 95 miles. The goal is 160 miles. At −40°C, for example, man cannot live long without the protection of special suits, several of which we shall discuss shortly. But before we do, we should first consider what may prove to be the most serious of all heat problems, the so-called thermal barrier.

Thermal Barrier

Part of the air through which an airplane or missile travels is brought to a dead stop. Onrushing air has considerable kinetic energy, so that, when it is abruptly halted, it is "stopped hot."

Kinetic energy is converted into heat energy at the point of stagnation (stagnation temperature refers to the temperature of air coming to a complete rest along the craft's surface) and is transferred through the boundary layer to the skin of the vehicle. Moreover, the entire "side" surfaces of the airplane or missile—surfaces not receiving the direct force of air—are also heated, in this case by so-called friction heat, or heat from air "slipping" by the air frame.

Any vehicle carries a very thin "sheet" of air, called the *boundary layer,* that adheres to its surface and does not move at all. As the distance from the skin increases, the air moves faster, since the absolute friction is less. Onrushing air is forced through this transition, or boundary, layer and in so doing loses a part of its kinetic energy.

Here, also, some parts of the air may not only lose speed, but stop completely. Loss of kinetic energy is accompanied by an increase of heat, which envelops the vehicle. At all costs we must keep the temperature of the high-altitude airplane (and arriving or departing space vehicle) from reaching critical values. The air frame can absorb a certain amount of heat during a flight of very short duration, but after a certain time damage to craft and injury to the pilot will result. The heat must somehow be dissipated if the vehicle cannot absorb it. This means refrigeration systems, which unfortunately mean weight penalties.

Not only is it necessary for us to control the heat problem adequately, we must know how long a man can survive at various temperatures. We must know, again, the time reserve. According to Buettner,[12] it drops to about ten minutes at 150°C temperatures (light clothing assumed; the heavier the clothes, strangely, the

[12] K. Buettner, Effects of Extreme Heat on Man, *J. Am. Med. Assoc.,* vol. 144, no. 732, 1950. The author discusses the important problem of determining how heat is transferred to the human being. He says, "Principally, the flow of heat toward man is caused by the following factors: (*a*) conduction and convection of hot air, (*b*) contact with hot objects, (*c*) radiation from hot areas and gases, and (*d*) inhalation of hot air." In discussing the four cases, Buettner notes three ways of protecting man by coverings: i.e., by using dry clothes and coverings, wet clothes and coverings, and metal-coated clothing. "The protection against heat that clothing can provide to man depends on its heat conductivity, density and specific heat," and the extent to which heat will penetrate clothing depends principally on the cloth's specific heat and heat conductivity. Aluminum-coated clothing is shown to be especially useful as protection against radiation.

greater the heat resistance of the subject). The only solution, it seems, is to fly in space when possible and minimize the time spent in transatmospheric flight. At Mach 4, for example, 820°C may be expected; at Mach 6, over 1650°C. At Mach 8, we might expect more than 3000°C temperatures, yet they might not go nearly this high, because of the so-called *relieving effect*. When air hits the missile's skin at these speeds, it will dissociate into atomic nitrogen and oxygen and then into free radicals. The energy so used will reduce the temperature caused by the passage of the missile.

Emerson once remarked, "In skating over thin ice our safety is our speed." In traveling through the thin upper air, speed is necessary, but speed alone will not ensure our safety. Should the cooling system break down, the man-made rocket vehicle might become a fiery meteor.

Speaking of thin ice and thin air, the predicaments of the skater and the high-speed pilot do seem similar. A man can go skating over ice which is too thin to support him if he be standing still; a rocket plane can fly at Mach 5 speeds through the thin upper atmosphere, which at slower velocities could not supply the aerodynamic lift to support it. This aerodynamic force of lift naturally falls off in proportion to air density, but it increases in proportion to the square of vehicle speed.

It would seem, offhand, that the faster we go through the thin upper air the greater the possibility that the craft would be held up by the atmosphere. It would, but the speeds necessary in such thin air would be high enough to create dangerous heat from air friction. This is an ironic situation for the airplane. If it did not go fast enough to burn up, it would fall! We shall simply *have* to fly in space if we want to increase speeds.

During the reentry phase of space flight, much greater problems face the engineer. This is because heat transfer increases with speed and density, the latter causing more difficulties to high-speed returning vehicles than to slowly accelerating rockets pushing upward against gravity from the launching pad. Heating rates are expected to be very high, and for this reason much nose-cone research is being performed today. For example, the Giannini Research Laboratories have developed plasma jets with 20,000°F temperatures, while General Electric and the University of Chicago have produced a water-stabilized arc plasma flow at more than 25,000°F.

If a winged reentry vehicle entered, it would operate under a small flight-path angle to the point where temperatures became nearly intolerable, at which time it would move outward, cool, and reenter. Materials and vehicle heat capacity would determine exact timing of this maneuver. It is obvious that such a vehicle might have to circle the earth many times before it could stay in the atmosphere and land. Ballistic missiles descend at steep flight-path angles, and must be fitted with special, blunt nose cones.

Escape Capsules and Space Suits

At intermediate speeds, temperatures that might be endured by the vehicle would kill a pilot not furnished with some protection in the form of a special suit. Furthermore, pilot and crew might have to escape from a fast-moving craft. They would need special protection from cold, low pressures, radiation, and lack of oxygen until they were in an environment where they could survive without it.

The ejection or escape capsule must be as foolproof as the cabin of the vehicle from which it is discharged. So must the space suit be. According to H. Haber,[13] a pilot exposed to a 310-mph air stream would have an aerodynamic load of nearly 800 lb on his face. At higher speeds, his mouth would probably be forced open and his tissue would begin to tear.

While, at speeds above 300 mph, escape capsules are desirable to ensure pilot safety, at least one man has survived a supersonic (777 mph) bail-out, unprotected.[14] Test pilot G. F. Smith, bailing out of an F-100 airplane, was subjected to 40-g decelerative force, giving him a weight of 8,000 lb. This is assuredly one of the most amazing escapes in aviation history.

Both escape capsules and space suits are being developed today. The Navy and Air Force provide capsules for pilots of high-flying, superspeed aircraft, fitted to permit controlled descent to the ground. Protective suits are also worn by today's aviators. The Air Force Aeromedical Laboratory at Wright Air Development Center

[13] H. Haber, "Physical Environment of the Flyer," *op. cit.*
[14] Force of Ten Hurricanes Buffets Ejected Pilot, *Aviation Week,* Nov. 14, 1955.

has produced a model T-1 partial-pressure suit, good for use where extreme temperatures, pressures, and oxygen deficiencies are involved. An S-2 model and a V-3 exposure suit have been proven capable of protection at temperatures from −60 to 70°C.

New partial-pressure emergency suits include the MC-3 and the MC-4, which has a built-in antigravity feature for high accelerations. The world's simulated altitude record of 38 miles was made with the MC-4, which was also used in X-2 rocket-airplane flights and in the Navy strato-lab balloon flight. This suit eliminates reverse breathing and can be put on more easily than the T-1. The MA-2 is a special suit that is ventilated for travel through the thermal barrier, and the MA-1 is a new ARDC helmet.

At the Navy Aeromedical Laboratory, in Philadelphia, similar suits have been found promising. In fact, one of the suits could be used today in planetary space, since it carries its own oxygen, pressurizing, and air-conditioning systems. Reports are that it has already been tested at over 60,000 ft altitudes. A so-called antigravity suit has proven feasible. With it, pilots can tolerate accelerations of 3 g above normal endurance. During high acceleration, the heart "output pressure" must increase, so the suit assists the body in keeping the brain adequately supplied with blood. By compressing the legs and lower torso, the body is encouraged to develop higher pressures in the upper blood system, which feeds the brain. These protective suits show one trend of thinking and indicate that actual progress is being made toward space flight.

Biological Test Arrangements

The United States and Russia have both undertaken biological testing at high altitudes. The earliest American rocket experiments took place with V-2s under the Blossom Project, conducted by the Air Force Cambridge Research Center. Monkeys and mice were carried up to gain data on pulse rate, heartbeat, and respiration of mammals undergoing moderate and high acceleration, and zero- or subgravity states. Also, cameras were used to record sensations, particularly in the absence of gravity. Aerobee rockets were later used, and specimens were recovered alive. Results showed that such normal functions as respiration, heartbeat, and arterial and venous pressures were not disturbed by subgravity states.

A wide series of high-altitude balloon flights have been made, carrying to altitude animals, flies, seeds, etc. Balloons have gone up to 140,000 ft, but most flights range from 90,000 to 120,000 ft, with flight times lasting more than a day. Holloman and Wright Air Development Center workers are making plans to send up an animal-carrying satellite, sometime after the close of the Vanguard program. The advent of Sputnik II with its Laika dog payload marks an important step into this field of biological experimentation.

Meteors

Above some 70 to 90 miles the ability of the atmosphere to afford protection from meteors has largely disappeared and any object above this approximate altitude would be exposed essentially to space conditions. The probability that space vehicles will be damaged or destroyed by meteoric matter is not great but is important enough to cause concern, especially when an extended flight is being considered. Experts know that space-rocket hulls can never be made to stop all meteors. The weight of armor involved would be outrageous. A rather small, average-speed meteor of, say, 6 mm diameter, can penetrate a sheet of aluminum 2.5 cm thick. It has been determined that thin hulls will be the rule, so that under no circumstance would an explosion take place because of meteor impact. Rather, the larger celestial projectiles would "whistle clean through."

To provide some protection, however, meteor "bumpers," which would consist of thin shields placed a short distance away from the hull, have been suggested. They would serve to break the impact of oncoming meteoric particles. When hits were registered, the meteor would, in most cases, break up, and the smaller particles would do no damage to the hull proper. Of course, larger ones would get through, but astronomers believe that large meteors are rather rare and that the chances of hits are low. Any hole made in the hull would cause air to escape and pressure to drop. This pressure problem is probably the chief nightmare of space flight. Sensitive pressure instruments would have to be provided to detect slight pressure drops and give the crew adequate warning.

Micrometeors, dust, and granular particles might be expected to do an indirect damage in that they would pit and gouge the surface of the space vehicle, thereby reducing its reflectivity. Heating due to sun and earth would then soon make the ship unbearably hot. In space, it seems that no sooner do we apparently solve one problem than another appears to leave us more perplexed than before.

Satellite Vehicles

"The ship, a fragment detached from the earth, went on lonely and swift like a small planet." Thus speaks Conrad. Such is, in reality, the artificial, man-made satellite which began, in October, 1957, to accompany our planet in its celestial movements. It balanced the force of gravity with the centrifugal force imparted to it, and moved in a curved, closed orbit exactly as theory predicted. In Chap. 4 a full discussion of satellites is given; here we mention satellites in so far as they relate to the functional borders of the atmosphere.

In the earth satellite we come to another of the borders of space, this time the mechanical border. Beyond a point between 150 and 200 miles from the earth's surface, drag due to collision with air molecules will cease. As far as the mechanical effects of the atmosphere upon rockets and satellite vehicles are concerned, the atmosphere can be considered nonexistent. This is not a precise frontier; a safety factor of up to 250 or more additional miles may well be provided. We shall probably see permanent satellites placed in orbits outward from 300 miles, but lesser orbits are employed where permanence is not mandatory. Explorer I, with a perigee of 220 miles, may last 5 years or more.

The Ultimate Development of Space Medicine

Space begins at less than 10 miles up for man, the animal. To an extent, conditions become more serious as the distance from the earth increases, but the human being will require about the same order of protection for sustained flight at 10 miles as he would for flight at 10,000. We have seen that the key to the whole science of space medicine is the artificial environment, made possible largely by specially designed cabins.

The environment must be preserved at all costs; should it be punctured by a meteor, or should some breakdown occur in the interior, it would have to be amenable to immediate repair. If we can once develop and perfect an artificial environment capable of permitting a trip to the moon, it would also be physiologically possible, in theory, to make a voyage to Mars, Pluto, or a planet revolving around a distant star.

From a space-medical point of view, an interstellar voyage would not necessarily be more of a problem than a "simple" trip to the moon. We would be faced with the problem of carrying more of everything, of course, but physiological considerations should be much the same. A trip to Mars along the most economical route would last perhaps 250 days; to Jupiter, about 1,000 days; to Saturn, 5½ years; and to Pluto, the outpost of the solar system, a rather forbidding 30 years.

We may, in the future, be able to develop propulsion systems capable of driving a spaceship along hyperbolic routes (Chap. 13), so reducing travel time considerably. Even so, elapsed times to the outer planets will probably be measured in months or years, unless science can somehow develop a spaceship able to attain important fractions of the speed of light. If that ever happens, even a trip to Pluto would present no serious difficulty. By that time, however, man will have trained his sights on the stars, and voyages measured in years will come back into the picture. Even so, a ship traveling *at the speed of light* would require more than four years to reach the nearest star.

Now, any trip in a closed environment and restricted quarters lasting months or years will subject man to terrific psychological strains, and we shall probably someday see a companion science to space medicine: space psychology. Being alone at the South Pole would seem like a picnic when compared to an interstellar voyage lasting 25 years.

The relation of medicine and psychology to extremely long voyages is hazy and has not been subjected to any rigorous theoretical examination, but the subject is more than academic. Within the next 3 to 5 years we *may* have manned earth satellites orbiting above us, and because of the tremendous expenses involved in moving men and supplies from the surface into orbit, the changing of crews may be made only after tours of duty of several months duration. Approximately the same problems will face a crew spending a month or two in orbit as would face a crew undertaking a trip of similar duration in space, except possibly in the latter case the sense of loneliness would be more aggravated. New problems of medicine which take on the aspect of public health enter on extremely long flights. So far, things of this sort have been treated only in science fiction. In that literature, interstellar travel has long been taken for granted. The more audacious writers speed up their spaceships to light velocity or more, while the less adventurous carefully work out a system of "generation travel." They are undismayed by a trip lasting hundreds or thousands of years, an intriguing possibility that allows them to analyze a myriad of sociological, religious, technological, and philosophical-psychological questions.

The magnitude of the interstellar concept is huge; the generation-travel concept is almost incredible. One story based on it was written by two French authors, Groc and Zorn.[15] They assumed a trip to a distant star in the spaceship *Cosmos,* a vehicle capable of attaining 1,800 miles/sec. The distance of the destination star was such that the voyage was to last 430 years, a period which would permit only the descendants of the pioneers to enjoy the reward of reaching the target stellar system.

The idea of generation travel is so immense in its philosophical scope as to befuddle the twentieth-century imagination: the dedication to a purpose that neither the parents nor their children or grandchildren could ever hope to realize directly would be amazingly difficult to instill. To live for one's children seems natural; to live only that one's remote descendants can land and live on an alien planet is at best difficult to imagine. After several generations had been born, had matured, and had expired, the relationship of the spaceship and its occupants to the home planet would become quite vague.

Alone in the cosmos, these people could know of the earth of their grandparents only through books and by word of mouth. Elaborate sociological systems would have to be worked out, together with an extremely refined version of space psychology and perhaps even a specialized religion. We can be sure that some psychological props would be necessary. The predicament of those space travelers would be a vastly intensified version of life on earth.

[15] L. Groc and J. Zorn, "L'Univers vagabond," Le Sillage, Paris, 1950.

Nothing would be essentially different; life would simply be a little more realistic. It would have to be: the alternative would be sudden death.

As space medicine evolves from a primary concern with travel in the aeropause to the advanced and complex physio-psychological discipline of space, it will lift man from an essentially two-dimensional to a three-dimensional existence. And in so far as he becomes increasingly conscious of time in its ultimate sense (as he projects himself across almost inconceivable distances), it may become appropriate to think of him as living in four dimensions.

There seems every reason to believe that medical scientists, working closely with the engineers, will somehow develop methods of keeping man alive, and perhaps even happy, in his ventures across space. Physically the human body is a weak step in the staircase to the stars, but if the brain it supports can seriously entertain interstellar travel, it should be able to devise ways to endure what it conceives.

BIBLIOGRAPHY

Lundgren, W. R.: "Across The High Frontier," William Morrow & Company, Inc., New York, 1955.

Ananoff, A.: "L'Astronautique," Arthème Fayard, Paris, 1950.

Kuiper, G., ed.: "The Atmospheres of the Earth and Planets," University of Chicago Press, Chicago, 1952.

————: "The Earth as a Planet," University of Chicago Press, Chicago, 1954.

Burgess, E.: "Frontier To Space," chap. 4, Chapman & Hall, Ltd., London, 1955.

Newell, H. E., Jr.: "High Altitude Rocket Research," Academic Press, Inc., New York, 1953.

Haber, H.: "Man in Space," Sidgwick & Jackson, Ltd., London, 1953.

Leyson, B. W.: "Man, Rockets and Space," E. P. Dutton & Co., Inc., New York, 1954.

Mallan, L.: "Men, Rockets and Space Rats," Julian Messner, Inc., Publishers, New York, 1955.

Haber, H.: The Physical Environment of the Flyer, *USAF School of Aviation Medicine Report,* 1954.

White, C. S., and O. O. Benson, eds.: "Physics and Medicine of the Upper Atmosphere," University of New Mexico Press, Albuquerque, N.M., 1952.

Goody, R. M.: "The Physics of the Stratosphere," Cambridge University Press, Cambridge, 1954.

Boyd, R. L. F., and M. J. Seaton, eds.: "Rocket Exploration of the Upper Atmosphere," Interscience Publishers, Inc., New York (Pergamon Press, Ltd., London), 1954.

Ley, W.: "Rockets, Missiles and Space Travel," The Viking Press, Inc., New York, 1957.

Marbarger, J. P., ed.: "Space Medicine," University of Illinois Press, Urbana, Ill., 1951.

Haber, H., ed.: "Symposium on Frontiers of Man-controlled Flight," Institute of Transportation and Traffic Engineering, University of California Press, Berkeley, Calif., 1953.

ARTICLES IN JOURNALS

Space medical and upper-atmosphere physics articles appear in a wide variety of publications, including the *Journal of Aviation Medicine, Journal of the American Medical Association, Journal of Astronautics, Journal of the British Interplanetary Society, Astronautica Acta, American Journal of Roentgenology and Radio Therapy, Proceedings of the National Academy of Science,* USN and USAF Schools of Aviation Medicine reports, *Geochimica* and *Cosmochimica Acta,* and publications of the *American Meteorological Society* (meteor studies appear in most astronomical publications, as well as in geophysical and physical journals). Articles below are generally organized by subject.

Beyer, D. H., and S. B. Sells: Selection and Training of Personnel for Space Flight, *J. Aviation Med.,* vol. 28, no. 11, 1957.

Marbarger, J. P., et al.: The Occurrence of Depression Sickness Following Denitrogenization at Ground Level and Altitude, *J. Aviation Med.,* vol. 28, no. 2, p. 127, 1957.

Rocket Flights of Mammals to 200,000 Feet, *J. Brit. Interplanet. Soc.,* vol. 12, no. 1, p. 7, 1953.

Sleds Speed Answers to Supersonic Unknowns, *Jet Propulsion,* vol. 27, no. 4, p. 422, 1957.

Mayo, A. M.: La Locomotion spatiale: Considerations techniques fondées sur l'adaptation au milieu, *Interavia,* p. 435, June, 1956.

Wakeford, R. C.: High Altitude Biological Laboratories, General Astronautics Corporation Technical Report, No. 8, Feb. 1, 1957.

Segal, H.: Space Medicine, *J. South African Interplanet. Soc.,* vol. 2, no. 3, p. 24, 1954.

Haldane, J. B. S.: Space Physiology, *J. South African Interplanet. Soc.,* vol. 2, no. 3, p. 67, 1955.

Haber, H.: Manned Flight at the Borders of Space, *J. Am. Rocket Soc.,* vol. 22, no. 5, p. 269, 1952.

Haber, H.: Human Flights at the Limits of the Atmosphere, Second Symposium on Space Travel, New York, October, 1952.

————: Human Flight at the Limits of the Atmosphere, *J. Brit. Interplanet. Soc.,* vol. 12, no. 1, p. 32, 1953.

Armstrong, C. R.: Space Physiology, *J. Brit. Interplanet. Soc.,* vol. 12, no. 4, p. 172, 1953.

Henry, J. P.: Physiological Laboratories in Rockets, *J. Astronautics,* vol. 2, no. 1, 1955.

————: Flight above 50,000 Feet: A Problem in Control of the Environment, *J. Astronautics,* vol. 1, no. 1, 1954.

Ordway, F. I., and H. E. Canney: The Respectability of Astronautics as Reflected by Recent Developments in the United States; Section IV: Physical and Medical Research of the Upper Atmosphere and Approaches to Space, contribution to "Bericht uber den V. Int. Astronautischen Kongress," Springer-Verlag, Berlin, Vienna, 1954.

Strughold, H.: Space Equivalent Conditions within the Earth's Atmosphere, *Astronaut. Acta,* vol. 1, no. 1, p. 32, 1955.

————: Comparative Ecological Study of the Chemistry of the Planetary Atmospheres, *USAF School of Aviation Medicine Report,* December, 1953.

————: Life on Mars in View of Physiological Principles, *USAF School of Aviation Medicine Report,* March, 1951.

————, and S. J. Gerathewohl: La Medicine des vitesse supersoniques, *Interavia,* p. 61, January, 1957.

Hitchcock, F. A.: Present Status of Space Medicine, *J. Astronautics,* vol. 3, no. 2, p. 41, 1956.

————: Some Considerations in Regard to the Physiology of Space Flight, *Astronaut. Acta,* vol. 2, no. 1, p. 20, 1956.

Marlos, L. R.: Problemas medicos Astronauticos, *Astronautica,* vol. 9, no. 12, p. 102, 1956.

Greider, H. R., et al.: Subjective Thermal Comfort Zones of Ventilated Full Pressure Suit at Altitude, *J. Aviation Med.,* vol. 28, no. 3, p. 272, 1957.

Simons, D. G.: Improved Techniques for Exposing Animals to Primary Cosmic Ray Particles, *J. Aviation Med.,* vol. 27, no. 4, p. 317, 1956.

Konecci, E. B., and M. B. Danford: Biological and Medical Aspects of Ionizing Radiation, *USAF School of Aviation Medicine Report,* September, 1956.

Swann, W. F. G.: Story of Cosmic Rays, Parts I–VI, *Sky and Telescope,* 1954, and reprinted as a booklet, Sky Publishing Corporation, Cambridge, 1955.

Yagoda, H.: Frequency of Thindown Hits by Heavy Primary Nuclei in

Emulsion and Tissue, *J. Aviation Med.*, vol. 27, no. 6, p. 522, 1956.

Shepherd, L. R.: Possible Cosmic Ray Hazards in Space Flight, *Bull. Phila. Astronaut. Soc.*, vol. 2, no. 6, p. 115, 1954.

————: The Possibility of Cosmic Ray Hazards in High Altitude and Space Flight, *J. Brit. Interplanet. Soc.*, vol. 12, no. 5, p. 197, 1953.

Schaefer, H. J.: Cosmic Radiation, *Bull. Pacific Rocket Soc.*, vol. 6, no. 1, p. 1, 1953.

————: Biological Significance of the Natural Background of Ionizing Radiation Observations at Sea Level and at Extreme Altitude, *J. Aviation Med.*, vol. 26, no. 6, p. 453, 1955.

————: Optimum Altitudes for Biological Experimentations with the Primary Cosmic Radiation, *J. Aviation Med.*, vol. 27, no. 6, p. 512, 1956.

————: Protection of Humans from Heavy Nuclei of Cosmic Radiation in Regions Outside the Atmosphere, *Astronaut. Acta*, vol. 1, no. 2, p. 100, 1955.

————: Exposure Hazard from Cosmic Radiation at Extreme Altitude and in Free Space, *J. Am. Rocket Soc.*, vol. 22, no. 5, p. 277, 1952.

Chase, H. B., and J. S. Post: Damage and Repair in Mammalian Tissues Exposed to Cosmic Ray Heavy Nuclei, *J. Aviation Med.*, vol. 27, no. 6, p. 533, 1956.

Singer, S. F.: Cosmic Ray Effects on Matter at High Altitudes, *J. Aviation Med.*, vol. 27, no. 2, p. 111, 1956.

Simons, D. G.: Biological Effects of Primary Cosmic Radiation, paper presented at the Seventh Congress of the International Astronautical Federation, Rome, 1956.

Bergeret, P.: Biological Problems of the Earth Satellite Vehicle, *J. Brit. Interplanet. Soc.*, vol. 10, no. 6, p. 301, 1951.

Beischer, D. E., and S. Born: The "Boiling" Phenomenon of Living Tissue at Low Atmospheric Pressure, *J. Aviation Med.*, vol. 28, no. 2, p. 154, 1957.

Grant, L.: The Atmosphere of a Spaceship, *J. Space Flight*, vol. 8, no. 4, 1956.

Campbell, P. A.: Aeromedical and Biological Considerations of Flight above the Atmosphere, *J. Brit. Interplanet. Soc.*, vol. 14, no. 1, p. 1, 1955.

Nicoll, N. R.: Design of the Life Compartment Necessary for Space Travel, *J. Brit. Interplanet. Soc.*, vol. 13, no. 5, p. 277, 1954.

Bowman, N. J.: Nutritional and Other Physiological Aspects of Extended Space Flights, *Chicago Rocket Society Collected Tech. Repts.*, vol. 2, no. 41, 1951.

————: The Food and Atmosphere Control Problem on Space Vessels, *J. Brit. Interplanet. Soc.*, Part I, vol. 12, no. 3, p. 118; Part II, vol. 12, no. 4, p. 159, 1953.

Story, V.: Biological Aspects of a Space Journey, *Chicago Rocket Society Collected Tech. Repts.*, vol. 1, no. 48, 1949.

Haldane, J. B. S.: The Purification of Air during Space Travel, *J. Brit. Interplanet. Soc.*, vol. 14, no. 2, p. 87, 1955.

Strughold, H.: Medical Problems Involved in Orbital Space Flight, *Jet Propulsion,* vol. 26, no. 9, p. 745, 1956.

Haber, H.: "Physics and Engineering of Rapid Decompression," *USAF School of Aviation Medicine Report* 21–1201–0008, No. 3, August, 1953.

Randel, H. W., et al.: Further Studies of Medical Aspects of Partial Pressure Suit Indoctrination, *J. Aviation Med.,* vol. 28, no. 2, p. 134, 1957.

"Oxygen Poisoning," *USAF School of Aviation Medicine Report* 56–40–56, No. 44, June, 1956.

Gilbert, A.: L'Utilization des plantes pour la régénération de l'oxygène à patir du gaz carbonique, *Fusées et recherche aeronaut.,* vol. 2, no. 1, p. 65, 1957.

Haviland, R. P.: Air for a Spaceship, *J. Astronautics,* vol. 3, no. 2, p. 31, 1956.

Ward, J. E.: The True Nature of the Boiling of Body Fluid in Space, *J. Aviation Med.,* vol. 27, no. 5, p. 429, 1956.

Hitchcock, F. A., and J. Kemph: The Boiling of Body Liquids at Extremely High Altitudes, *J. Aviation Med.,* vol. 26, no. 4, p. 289, 1955.

Ross, H. E.: Air Conditioning Problems of Rocket Travel, *Bull. Brit. Interplanet. Soc.,* vol. 1, no. 9, p. 49, 1946.

————: Green Plants as Atmosphere Regenerators, *Bull. Brit. Interplanet. Soc.,* vol. 2, no. 1, p. 7, 1947.

Demetriades, On Decompression of a Punctured Cabin, *Jet Propulsion,* vol. 24, no. 1, 1954.

Strughold, H.: The U.S. Air Force Experimental Sealed Cabin, *J. Aviation Med.,* vol. 27, no. 1, 1956.

Luft, U. C., and W. K. Noell: The Manifestations of Sudden Brief Anoxia in Man, *USAF School of Aviation Medicine Report* 55–86, January, 1956.

Burkhardt, W. L., et al.: Explosive Decompression, *USAF School of Aviation Medicine Report* 21–23–005, No. 2.

The Invisible Force, *Gen. Elec. Rev.,* May, 1955.

Henry, J.: Acceleration as a Limit in Rocket Flight, *Chicago Rocket Society* Collected Tech. Repts., vol. 1, p. 45, 1949.

Haber, H.: G Forces and Weight in Space Travel, *Sky Tales,* vol. 10, no. 97, 1950.

Crosbie, R. J.: Directional Control of Accelerative Forces in Centrifuge by System of Gimbals, *J. Aviation Med.,* vol. 27, no. 6, p. 505, 1956.

Gell, C. F., and D. Cranmore: Dislocation of Organs and Tissues of Rats Exposed to Acceleration Stress, *J. Aviation Med.,* vol. 27, no. 6, p. 497, 1956.

Zuidema, G. D., et al.: Human Tolerance to Prolonged Acceleration, *J. Aviation Med.,* vol. 27, no. 6, p. 469, 1956.

Dorman, P. J.: Effect on G Tolerance of Partial Supination Combined with the Anti-G Suit, *J. Aviation Med.,* vol. 27, no. 6, p. 490, 1956.

Edelberg, R.: Comparison of Human Tolerance to Accelerations of Slow and Rapid Onset, *J. Aviation Med.,* vol. 27, no. 6, p. 482, 1956.

Brown, J. L., and M. Lechner: Acceleration and Human Performance, *J. Aviation Med.,* vol. 27, no. 1, p. 32, 1956.

Lewis, D. H.: An Analysis of Some Current Methods of G-Protection, *J. Aviation Med.,* vol. 26, no. 6, p. 479, 1955.

Preston-Thomas, H.: Human Tolerance to Multistage Rocket Acceleration Curves, *J. Aviation Med.,* vol. 26, no. 5, p. 390, 1955.

Stapp, J. P.: Measurement for Survival, Ordnance, vol. 40, no. 216, p. 975, 1956.

———: Effects of Mechanical Force on Living Tissues: Abrupt Deceleration and Windblast, *J. Aviation Med.,* vol. 26, no. 4, p. 268, 1955.

———: Crash Survival, *Missile Away!,* vol. 2, no. 2, p. 23, 1954.

——— and W. C. Blount: Effects of Mechanical Force on Living Tissues: A Compressed Air Catapult for High Impact Forces, *J. Aviation Med.,* vol. 28, no. 3, p. 281, 1957.

Raffone, J. J.: Acceleration Force and the Space Pilot, *J. Astronautics,* vol. 2, no. 3, p. 100, 1955.

Hessberg, R. R.: Accelerative Forces Associated with Leaving and Re-entering the Earth's Gravitational Field, *J. Astronautics,* vol. 4, no. 1, p. 6, 1957.

Slater, A. E.: The Balancing Mechanism of the Inner Ear, *J. Brit. Interplanet. Soc.,* vol. 9, no. 1, p. 18, 1950.

Biget, P. L., and H. Boiteau: Quelques aspects physiologiques du vol "sans pesanteur," *Fusées et recherche aéronaut.,* vol. 2, no. 2, p. 161, 1957.

Gerathewohl, S. J., et al.: Sensomotor Performance during Weightlessness, *J. Aviation Med.,* vol. 28, no. 1, p. 7, 1957.

———: Personal Experiences during Short Periods of Weightlessness Reported by Sixteen Subjects, *Astronaut. Acta,* vol. 2, no. 4, p. 203, 1956.

Slater, A. E.: The Problem of Weightlessness, *Spaceflight,* vol. 1, no. 3, p. 109, April, 1957.

Grant, L.: Life under Low Gravity Conditions, *J. Space Flight,* vol. 8, no. 8, 1956.

276 HUMAN FACTORS IN SPACE FLYING

Simons, D. G.: Review of Biological Effects of Subgravity and Weightlessness, *J. Am. Rocket Soc.*, vol. 25, no. 5, p. 209, 1955.

Buettner, K.: Effects of Extreme Heat on Man, *USAF School of Aviation Medicine Report* 21–26–002, Nos. 1–3, 1951.

Problems of Escape from High Pressure Aircraft, symposium including eight contributions on escape, capsules, ejection, etc., *J. Aviation Med.*, vol. 28, no. 1, p. 57, 1957.

Haber, H.: Escape and Survival at High Altitude, *USAF School of Aviation Medicine Report,* September, 1953.

Wilcox, E. J., Psychological Consequences of Space Travel, *J. Brit. Interplanet. Soc.*, vol. 16, no. 1, p. 7, 1957.

Slater, E. T. O.: Psychological Problems of Space Flight, *J. Brit. Interplanet. Soc.*, vol. 9, no. 1, p. 14, 1950.

Ovendon, M. W.: Meteor Hazards to Space Stations, in "The Artificial Satellite," British Interplanetary Society, London, 1951.

Grimminger, G.: Probability that a Meteorite Will Hit or Penetrate a Body Situated in the Vicinity of the Earth, *J. Appl. Phys.*, vol. 19, no. 10, p. 947, 1948.

Whipple, F.: Meteoric Collision Factor in Spaceship Design, *Aviation Week,* vol. 16, no. 6, p. 25, 1951.

Ovendon, M. W.: Meteors and Space Travel, *J. Brit. Interplanet. Soc.,* vol. 10, no. 4, p. 176, 1951.

"Possible Hazards to a Satellite Vehicle from Meteorites," Project RAND, Santa Monica, 1946.

Rinehart, J. S.: Some Observations of High Speed Impact, *Popular Astronomy,* vol. 58, p. 468, 1950.

Langton, N. H.: Mechanical Penetration of Bumper Screens, *J. Brit. Interplanet. Soc.,* vol. 13, no. 5, p. 283, 1954.

Clarke, A. C.: Meteors as a Danger to Space Flight, *J. Brit. Interplanet. Soc.,* vol. 8, no. 4, p. 157, 1949.

Ovendon, M. W.: Nature and Distribution of Meteoric Matter, *J. Brit. Interplanet. Soc.,* vol. 6, no. 6, p. 157, 1957.

Whipple, F. L.: Meteors, *Astron. J.,* February, 1947.

——— and L. G. Jacchia, The Orbits of 308 Meteors Photographed with Super-Schmidt Cameras, *Astron. J.,* vol. 62, no. 1, p. 37, 1957.

Mysteries of Meteoric Dust Begin to Unfold, *Jet Propulsion,* vol. 27, no. 2, p. 207, 1957.

Singer, S. F.: The Origin of Meteorites, *Sci. American,* vol. 191, no. 5, 1954.

———: A Crucial Experiment Concerning the Origin of Meteorites, *University of Maryland Physics Dept., Tech. Rept.* 47, July, 1956.

Leonard, F. C.: The Classification of Meteorites, *Sky and Telescope,* vol. 16, no. 8, p. 370, 1957.

Ordway, F. I.: Instrumentation for High Altitude Research Vehicles, (Sections on ESVP, Vanguard meteor detection experiments), *General Astronautics Corporation Tech. Rept.* 23, June, 1957.

Porter, J. G.: The Discovery and Nomenclature of Meteor Streams, *J. Brit. Astron. Assoc.,* vol. 62, no. 3, p. 101, 1952.

Struve, O.: Meteorites and Their Effects, *Sky and Telescope,* vol. 15, no. 7, p. 292, 1956.

Opik, E.: Meteor Astronomy: A Critical Review, with Comments on Meteor Vehicles in Particular, *Irish Astron. J.,* vol. 3, no. 5, p. 144, 1955.

A number of papers presented to the Aero Medical Association, during 1956 and 1957, dealt with the over-all problems of food and atmospheric control as they pertain to high-altitude and space flight. Key papers include:

Finkelstein, B., et al.: Effects of Altitude and Oxygen upon Taste Sensitivity.

Moore, J. A.: Flight Safety through Proper Nutrition.

Simons, D. G., et al.: Selection of a Sealed Cabin Atmosphere.

Smiley, J. R.: The Relationship between Meal Times and Landing Accidents.

Taylor, A. A.: Preventive Aspects of Flight Feeding.

Buettner, K.: Temperature of a Space Satellite and Human Heat and Water Balance in It.

11

Communications in Space

Equipment and Sources of Interference

In looking back over the development of the notion of space flight, as we did in the first chapter, we came upon an intriguing facet of that idea: the desire to communicate with other planets. Men pondered the likelihood of inhabitants and how to exchange information with them. This was communication, but not in the sense that technologists usually understand the word. Professor Gauss and others who speculated carefully on Pythagorean triangles—what would constitute a recognizable message and what could be identified as the answer—had in common the reservation that none of them was sure there would actually be anyone at the other end.

Today we feel that there will be. Although our knowledge of the planets of the solar system and their habitability by life as we know it has given scientists a disappointingly negative answer, it now seems that there will be someone from *this* planet out there to get the message. In this light, the proposition is simplified by several orders of magnitude, for the people at the other end will be human beings like ourselves. This removes the thorny semantic problems and the need for huge enterprises of civil engineering such as colossal bonfires in the Sahara, triangles of wheat and forestation in Siberia, or huge solar mirrors to write fiery symbols on the sands of Mars.

Radio makes things much cheaper, by and large, than such large civil-engineering projects, but only in the local sense. The immediate cost of equipment will be vastly lower, but the cost of putting

278

the equipment where it will do some good may reinstate the higher costs of the Siberian and Sahara proposals.

Radio communication on earth has many problems, but it also has the advantage that the earth is fixed with regard to the communications system being used. That is to say, England is always so far away in the same direction, and the same amount of power with the same atmospheric conditions will always establish the same degree of contact. To accomplish global contact, radio waves of varying frequencies are made to bounce off the "ceiling" presented by the ionosphere and the "floor" presented by the earth's surface until they have lost so much strength that they cannot be detected any longer. Well within this range lies the location of the intended recipient.

Low frequencies are in the long-wave bands used by standard-broadcast, police, and certain marine networks. Where the short waves "begin" is a somewhat moot point, but it may be conveniently thought to start somewhere around 3,500 kilocycles (3.5 megacycles) and stretch to about 40,000 kilocycles (40 megacycles). Beyond these limits is a variety of very high frequencies extending up to any limit at which one can obtain stable oscillation. In the top regions, radio waves behave very much like light and are often beamed at the intended receivers with parabolic reflectors.

Long, short, and very short waves are used for different purposes because of their behavior. Long waves, generally speaking, require high power, but are thought to be more reliable over relatively short distances because they bounce back and forth a large number of times within their useful transmission-distance limits and thus "saturate" the area. This dense coverage is desired by a standard-broadcast station because its survival depends on advertising sponsors' money, which is based on the number of people the station can reach in any given area. Scheduling strategy tries to make programs so attractive that people will tune to the particular frequency.

Despite high power, the large number of bounces soon attenuates the signal from the transmitter. Sometimes, only 100 miles away, the station cannot be heard. At the same time, it can perhaps be heard 2,000 miles away. The interval between points of *hearability* is known as the *skip distance*. The proposition of skip distance can be very bewildering in detail, but for the purposes of this chapter it is enough to notice that, as the frequencies get higher (and the wavelengths shorter) the skip distance tends to increase, because higher and higher levels in the ionosphere are reached. By the time the frequency reaches 100,000 kilocycles, the first skip (depending on atmospheric conditions) may be so long that it misses the surface of the earth entirely. Beyond this point, higher and higher frequencies penetrate the atmosphere more and more thoroughly and behave more and more like beams of light. The highest frequency thus far obtained for practical communications is about 30,000 megacycles, which is of the order of wavelength of $\frac{1}{10}$ mm.

We note that, generally, higher frequencies obtain longer distances with a given amount of power. However, in the very high frequencies there are a number of difficulties not encountered in broadcasting or short-wave transmission. Very-high-frequency equipment must be built in special ways, because odd lengths of wire and structural elements in vacuum tubes are in the same order of length as the wavelength they handle, and so become absorbers and antennas where they are not desired. It is often necessary to conduct these frequencies in copper tubing of rectangular cross section (called waveguides) so there will be some power left to radiate by the time it gets to the antenna. Also, there is a certain amount of resonance to these waves in the human body: a therapeutic effect known as *diathermy,* which is a good thing when it is wanted. So we see that very short waves are desirable, but that there are problems in equipment.

Assuming suitable equipment can be developed, there is still the problem of propagation. In conventional radio this is a matter of antenna design (which can be maddeningly subtle and tricky) and choice of bands and operating periods to capitalize on known effects of the ionosphere and atmosphere. It adds up to an attempt to obtain the strongest and clearest signal with the least fade and interference noise (popularly called static). Space communication, in this respect, is a proposition of high penetration of the atmosphere of the earth, the transmission of the signal over staggering distances (by terrestrial standards), continuous contact between two bodies moving with respect to each other, and competition with radioactivity and other effects abroad in interplanetary space.

Penetration of the atmosphere, of course, requires high frequency, begins at about 40,000 kilocycles, and becomes more complete and thorough as frequency rises. Also, as the frequency rises, radio waves lend themselves to beaming—which is lucky, for beaming causes all (or nearly all) radiated energy to travel in the same direction. None is lost by going in directions where, we know in advance, there are no stations to receive it.

Spaceships and planets are small indeed, considering the wide sweep of the heavens, and the great distances will tax the radiating power of transmitters. Every bit of energy available will be needed. A typical radio broadcasting station has a power of 10,000 watts, but may run to 50,000 watts. The high cost of operating such transmitters is attested by the formidable prices industrial sponsors must pay for time. Special communications systems used in space will not run all the time, of course, and will not cost much in the sense of absolute time; but since a great deal of money must be spent in developing special equipment producing very high power at very high frequencies over very long distances, as compared to earth, they may cost just as much in the final analysis.

Von Braun has calculated [1] that 60,000 watts at 600,000 kilocycles would just reach the planet Pluto, with doubtful readability, using an antenna of 10^6 sq cm. Sixty kilowatts is quite a transmitter at six hundred megacycles, and a million square centimeters is quite an antenna, but both are technically possible. Reading Pluto is not necessary for the foreseeable future of space flight (and von Braun is aware of this), but it is a useful frame of reference to show the range of values we are working with. Since it is not necessary, for the time being, to travel to planets further away than Mars or Venus, we have a reserve of power that can be converted into other important aspects of signal quality.

There are three major cases of communication from the surface of the earth in the astronautical sense: to a satellite vehicle, to a moving spaceship, or to a planet or celestial body other than the earth, which, of course, with regard to the earth (or a point on it) is also moving (Table 11-1). In each case there is an element of motion between the point of origin and the point of reception.

[1] W. von Braun, "The Mars Project," University of Illinois Press, Urbana, Ill., 1953.

TABLE 11-1   *Uses of the Satellite for Communication*

Combination or signal route	Purpose of system	Remarks
Ground-satellite-ground	Improvement of terrestrial communications by passive (reflecting) or active (relay) transponders	Complete coverage requires high orbits; touchy problem of transmitter power vs. obsolescence of equipment
Ground-satellite-missile	Navigation reference for intercontinental missile, possible command-relay agency	Fairly low orbits used by such missile-assist satellites invite missile fire
Ground-satellite-space	Relay station to permit beams to "see" around earth, sun, target planets, or satellites; simple power boost for contact with ship in space	24-hr orbit used for earth relay may not solve all problems in space relay; translunar satellites and planets behind sun may require Trojan satellites; very expensive
Earth-ship-planet	Spaceship may be used for relay to target planet if colony is already there	Can be used only at certain times; ship's equipment may not be very powerful
Ship-satellite-ship	Signal boost for small transmitters on board spaceships; circumsolar satellites	Disadvantage that long orbital periods might demand a prohibitive number of satellites

In conventional terrestrial communications, as we have noted, the point of origin and the point of reception are fixed with regard to each other. Signal power here is important, but in terrestrial communications the main point of concern is the ionosphere, which strongly affects the possibilities of contact between the points in question. With contact between the surface of the earth and a body moving in space (as in any of the three major cases just mentioned), two factors immediately enter the picture. One is the necessity of penetrating the ionosphere (which in terrestrial communications is relied upon for reflectivity), and the other is the modification of procedure made necessary by distance and the fact that the two points are in motion relative to each other.

Planets also rotate as they move in their orbit. Combinations of these motions, or the simple motion of approach or recession of a spaceship, produces a Doppler effect which may change the nominal frequency of a signal by several hundred kilocycles. The general problem of space communication may be gleaned from Fig. 11-1, which, however, simplifies the situation a good deal.

In reflecting on the behavior of the planets, one is immediately aware of the fact that the rotation of the home planet changes the

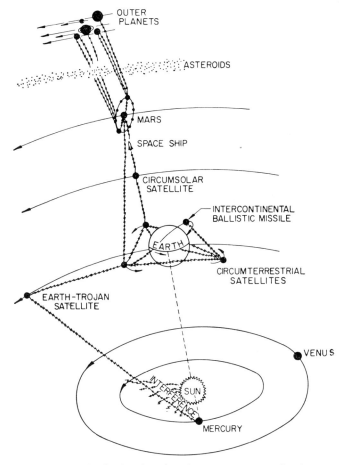

FIG. 11-1. The basic situation in space communications.

angle of a beam locked on, say, Mars, changing the angle at which the beam penetrates the ionosphere and thereby changing its characteristics. Also, continued rotation causes Mars to be completely invisible during half the day. This recommends the use of relaying stations which can make up for obstructions.

Satellite Transponders

It may be helpful to look at Table 11-1 to note the various possibilities that arise from the use of a satellite vehicle. There is no entry for simple earth-to-satellite, or satellite-to-earth. The former is covered within the meaning of the three major types, mentioned first, and assumes a manned satellite which does not answer—not very significant. The latter assumes that the satellite has information to send, of itself, which is largely telemetering and not communications in the conventional sense. Idea exchange between earth and a manned satellite is thus included in the concept of ground-satellite-ground.

Examining this proposition of a ground-satellite-ground system, we find that we have a variation of conventional radiocommunications techniques. A signal is sent aloft to be relayed in some fashion back down to the ground, which has the same net effect as the bounce off the ionosphere, but with better quality and reliability. Dr. John R. Pierce, of Bell Telephone Laboratories, has studied the matter of terrestrial communications, as assisted by satellites that could be built in the comparatively near future,[2] and has found that they may be able to compete commercially with cables under the oceans, though not with microwave relays across land, where it is necessary to add and drop hookups at many points. He proposes several possible solutions:

The first solution is the use of metallic spheres of 100 ft diameter in orbit at about 2,200 miles. Though not specified by Pierce, the satellite could be a capsule and a deflated balloon inside a folded mass of metal foil. Out in space, once ejected from the final-stage rocket, a pressurized gas cylinder holding, perhaps, helium, could be opened into the balloon. The balloon would inflate to 100 ft in diameter, requiring little gas at the near-total vacuum at

[2] J. R. Pierce, Orbital Radio Relays, *Jet Propulsion,* vol. 25, no. 4, pp. 153–157, 1955.

that altitude. Leakage would eventually redeflate the balloon, but no matter. There would be no air pressure to crush the delicate foil sphere.

A rectangular net of some wire of high tensile strength might be needed to ensure that overinflation did not burst the fragile foil, and that, once inflated, the surface presented would be rather even. The reason for this even surface would be that Pierce visualizes it (whatever it might ultimately be made of) as an isotropic reflector. That is to say, no matter what "face" the sphere turned to the earth, it would always be the same, and the same pattern of reflection (somewhat omnidirectional, but mainly down) could always be expected. Unfortunately, the satellite would be moving with respect to the ground, and as it moved more than a certain distance away from zenith, more and more atmosphere would have to be penetrated. Somewhat like light rebounding from a windowpane, the waves would finally reflect entirely from the ionosphere and never reach the satellite at all. Thus a number of satellites (possibly 12) would be needed so there would always be one reasonably close to zenith.

Since much of the power reflected from the sphere would go in directions other than toward the receiving point, the transmitter would have to be so powerful that even the small percentage reaching the receiving point would still be strong and clear enough, compared with natural interference noise, to be reliable for communications purposes. All communications must fulfill these basic requirements of readability and reliability. The power required for this is about 100,000 watts, a very powerful transmitter.

The number of satellites needed could be reduced if the orbit were higher, since the period would be longer and relative motion less. At 22,300 miles, only three would be needed, since they would be standing still with regard to any point on the earth and one of the three could always "see" the required destination. Unfortunately, the sphere would have to be bigger (1,000 ft in diameter), and the power of the transmitter would have to be increased to 50 million watts! This is a gigantic transmitter, and the cost of getting anything to 22,300 miles is certain to be extremely high.

On the other hand, as Pierce notes, if this reflector were a planar mirror, the increase in reflected energy would be tremendous; a modest transmitter of 50,000 watts could be used. But once the sphere with its isotropic-reflection advantage is abandoned, there is the problem of aiming the mirror and keeping it tilted at just the right angle so the beam will strike the ground just where it is wanted. A 10-cm microwave, 0.19° wide, would be only 72 miles in diameter at the target. It is obvious that the aim would have to be incredibly good, or the whole reflector, placed way out there at 22,300 miles, would be useless. This might also require odd locations for transmitters and receivers.

But, disregarding the cost of freight to 22,300 miles, another solution, the active repeater, presents itself. The active repeater, sometimes called a *transponder,* is a unit equipped with a receiver and transmitter which remains in a state of constant stand-by and operates only when a signal comes to the receiver. It then comes to life, so to speak, and the received signal is fed to an amplifier contained in the satellite and thence to the transmitter, where the same signal, now stronger, proceeds to the destination or to another active repeater.

The receiver in such a satellite would not be a receiver in the sense we usually think of for earth communications. In conventional receivers, a weak signal is impressed on an antenna lying in its path of movement, amplified, and then "detected" (or demodulated), a process which takes the significant information off the carrier and puts it on another circuit where it makes sounds audible to the human ear. These audio circuits are not needed in the active repeater. The radio-frequency signal from the earth, instead of being detected, would simply be amplified to a strength where it could drive another set of amplifiers called *finals.*

It turns out, on inspection, that the earthbound transmitter power requirements for an active repeater plunge to a mere 100 watts, a transmitter which could be run from the power available in an automobile. Antennas would be only 10 ft in diameter, and the power of the transmitter in the satellite only 30 milliwatts. This power is down in the range where, possibly, solar batteries could provide it. This is lucky, since trips out to 22,300 miles will not be made often, and the only other factors would be service life of components and traffic capacity.

Service life, with such low power requirements, would probably be very long, since equipment which operated so far below its normal load as to be under practically no strain at all could be designed. Traffic capacity (words per minute times the number of channels) would be of the volume and type built into it, but new developments in technique might make it obsolete too quickly to justify the original investment for so high a satellite. Passive repeaters, despite their disadvantage of high power, do not limit the development of new types of signaling, and, of course, in the active repeater the same problem of aiming will probably still be present.

The choices Dr. Pierce discusses were somewhat arbitrary and were intended to point up the problems of communications from the viewpoint of the electronics engineer. Orbits at 22,300 miles are out of the question for the near future, so it would seem that the 100-ft spheres, at 2,200 miles, passively reflecting signals from 100,000-watt transmitters, circumspectly, most nearly lie within our grasp.

Disregarding the logistics of the thing, however, it would seem that three active repeaters at 22,300 miles would be excellent if they could be built large enough to accommodate so many channels that obsolescence came slowly. Arthur C. Clarke, a prominent British writer on space flight, proposed this general idea about thirteen years ago.[3] He observed that, in view of the present cultural value of television, perhaps this use of the satellite vehicle was the best argument *against* space flight. Pondering the temper of the old school BBC, we may imagine that Howdy Doody coming in from America via outer space would have Englishmen saying within a few days that it was very unsporting of the Americans to use unconventional weapons, especially on their allies!

Speaking of weapons brings to mind the possibility that, in the communicative aspect, a satellite may be used for warfare. In the broad weapons sense, of course, action brings counteraction, and it may be supposed that any prospective enemies would seek to destroy it with ground-to-satellite missiles. Already, a satellite, grimly nicknamed Big Brother (renamed Pied Piper), after the omnipresent spying monitors of the state police of George Orwell's novel, "1984," is reportedly being studied by the United States govern-

[3] A. C. Clarke, Extraterrestrial Relays, *Wireless World,* October, 1945. See also his "Exploration of Space," p. 156, Temple Press, Ltd., London, 1951.

ment. The apparent object of this satellite is to serve as a mount for a television camera which will send back pictures taken while over an enemy country. This is almost a telemetering arrangement, but "gets in under the wire" of the communications satellite by being, broadly, a ground-satellite-ground system. It would avoid the major problems of Dr. Pierce's transponders by storing the pictures, taken at a relatively low altitude, until the satellite was traveling over the Western Hemisphere, at which time it would send down the series of pictures.

In another sense, the satellite may be used by missiles—notably intercontinental missiles—for navigational reference by sensing a beacon mounted in it. This perhaps would be controlled by commands relayed from the United States to the satellite and then to the moving missile. The introduction of a command function complicates the problem but is a logical consequence of such a use for the satellite.

Determination of missile position is possible in one, or a combination, of a number of ways. The missile "could ascertain its own position" for its autopilot, or other types of mid-course guidance, by the navigational fixes just mentioned. If there were only one satellite at low altitude, the missile would have to be launched when the satellite was in the proper part of the celestial sphere to be handy for reference (a limitation which might be serious with respect to timing). If there were a number of satellites, the missile could select the most convenient one and navigate by that. Remote control based on either tracking or double relay would be possible. Tracking could be done by triangulation from points on the earth's surface, by knowing the position of the tracking station and the distance, azimuth, and elevation of the missile from it, and by a progression of triangulations to determine the progress of the missile's flight. Double relay would use, perhaps, a television camera in the nose of the missile and comparison data from the autopilot, sent back to the United States by way of the transponder in the satellite.

Like all such devices, this satellite would be subject to jamming (intentional electrical interference) and destruction. It is electronically possible (though it would be very difficult) that the satellite could be "electrically" captured by the enemy and the wrong commands sent to the missile, so that the latter would either destroy itself in mid-air or be directed to some harmless spot in the world where it would detonate its warhead without destroying anything of value. Or it might conceivably be directed to a point over one of the cities of our allies. In some ways, the 22,300-mile orbit seems best here also. Counter-missile action would then be more expensive for the enemy and less damaging to us, since the command system would tend to remain intact even if a large number of our missiles were intercepted.

Thus far, the applications of the satellite for the purpose of communication have been only superficially astronautical, partly by virtue of the satellite's own location in space and partly because the intercontinental missile, if it happened to be ballistic, ascended high enough to enter space during part of its trajectory.

Interplanetary and Galactic Radio

Similar, though one may hope more peaceful, applications may be connected with a moving spaceship. Early ships may be "robot" craft, somewhat like missiles, designed to impact on the moon, or perhaps to orbit around it or around a planet such as Mars. This, as we noticed in Chap. 8, is called a probe, useful for preliminary survey, in any area where sending human crews is contemplated. Position fixing may be accomplished by triangulation, and commands issued to change course, or heading, prior to application of power, to adjust the transfer orbit.

Communication with a ship in space introduces some problems not encountered in terrestrial communications and not serious enough in the ground-satellite-ground systems to matter. Notable among these are distance and noise. Communications with the moon will not seem unusual to the casual listener, since the transit time for a signal is only a little over a second, but Mars or Venus, which may be anywhere from 50 million to 280 million miles away (depending on the relative positions of the two planets in their orbits), would require somewhere between 2¼ and 20 min each way, with radio signals traveling at light speed.

This is an irritating note to those of us who had become accustomed to the notion that radio is instantaneous, and it does not lend itself to rapid interchange of questions and answers in an emergency. This is serious enough, but interstellar spaceships would be much worse off. They would be immeasurably more isolated than the mutineers of HMS *Bounty* when they landed on Pitcairn Island, and, partly because of this, might enjoy a similar fate.

Another aspect of signal readability is noise. Noise ratios of 100:1 (the signal being 100 times stronger than the interfering noise) may obtain in earth-moon hookups, for example, because of the high directionality of the transmitting antennas and the fact that, traveling more or less vertically through the atmosphere, the signals go through less of it than do signals in terrestrial communications and, hence, "pick up" less noise. Even if they do not, the problem would appear to be less serious.

Several types of noise will be present: solar noise, galaxy noise, and thermal noise. The proportions affecting a signal at any one time will depend largely on the amount of sunspot activity then evident. Radiations from the sun will cause interference and, in bombarding the ionosphere, will change the amount of activity there, and so will affect beamed signals passing through. Galactic noise is the background of interference emanating from the general field of stars. Though distant, the nearer stars of the galaxy will probably produce enough interference to warrant allowance for them even in communications within the solar system.

Cosmic noise increases below 100,000 kilocycles, and receiver (circuit) noises increase above 200,000 kilocycles. Thus, purely from the aspect of signal-to-noise ratios, the range between 100,000 and 200,000 kilocycles seems most favorable. G. O. Smith[4] notes that spectrographic effects set in between 10 million and 30 million kilocycles, which should surprise no one—but a practical interplanetary radio system at these frequencies would. However, it is an aspect to bear in mind as the useful transmitting frequencies continue to climb.

Dr. von Braun, in his Mars Project, assumes a spaceship transmitter weighing three metric tons (6,613.8 lb) and considers a number of frequencies, such as 300,000, 600,000, and 3,000,000 kilocycles with various amounts of power. He shows that high power is not the whole story and juggles the various factors in order to use less power and convert the savings into increasing the

---

[4] G. O. Smith, Radio Communication Across Space—Ship-to-Ship and Ship-to-Planet, *J. Brit. Interplanet. Soc.*, vol. 12, no. 1, pp. 13–22, 1953.

band width. This, as every engineer knows, improves the information-carrying content of a signal and permits the transmission of speech and music.

Lower frequencies are also more convenient in respect to equipment construction. Von Braun came out with 300 megacycles (an easy frequency to use) and a power of only 1,000 watts (an easy transmitter to build if one is allowed three metric tons). This is close enough to the 100- to 200-megacycle band not to suffer very serious receiver noises. Three metric tons may seem, to radio amateurs, an extravagant weight allowance for a 1,000-watt transmitter, but it should be remembered that this includes also the power supply, radiotelephone modulators, several cabinets full of equipment associated with navigational computers, and a host of other components which must also be fed through the radio link to the base back home. It will still take some shrewd engineering.

In contacting the spaceship, we must remember that the earth rotates. Thus we will be fortunate if we have established the three transponders in the 22,300-mile orbit; one of them will always be visible to the beam from the spaceship. Reamplification of earth signals for the spaceship may not be urgent, but reamplification of comparatively weaker signals from the small shipboard transmitters may be helpful indeed in receiving messages on earth.

Signal strength and quality to the moon should be excellent, but there is a problem of contacting expeditionary parties on the far side of the moon, which is permanently invisible to the earth. For this, Arthur Clarke has proposed a circumterrestrial satellite 40,000 miles the other side of the moon. At this point, he says, it would traverse precisely the same number of degrees of arc per unit time as the moon, and, remaining in permanent eclipse, would be useful as a transponder for signals coming from the earth.

The matter of seeing around corners may be a frequent problem, at least on the earth end of any communications link. Another "corner" would occur when the planet at the other end was behind the sun from us. In the case of Mercury, this might not be too serious, as Mercury has a high orbital velocity; nevertheless, it is useful to examine the proposition.

In a line-of-sight problem, as would occur with radio beams, this is a matter of comparative circumferential velocities, so to speak.

Mercury covers 4.1° of arc per day (360° ÷ 88 days), and the earth 0.986° of arc per day (360° ÷ 365 days). The earth is moving at a slower rate, but still moving, and if Mercury is behind the sun, the motion of the earth has the effect of slowing Mercury by that much. Visually, the effect is the same as though Mercury traveled at $4.100 - 0.986 = 3.114°$ per day. The sun subtends an angle of 31.5 to 32.5″ of arc, as viewed from the earth. At 93 million miles the sun's disk just fills this angle; at another 36 million miles beyond, this same angle would include a larger distance, and in Mercury's orbit a larger subtended angle whose apex is in the sun.

If Mercury were directly behind the sun's equator, it would be eclipsed for something like eight hours. This, of course, does not happen every time. Usually Mercury "misses the sun completely" going both ways because of the inclination of its orbit. Otherwise it would go before the sun once in each revolution, and we would have possibly several transits a year.

Even so, the planet, on a line-of-sight basis, would be very close to the sun angularly, and a beam aimed at Mercury from the earth would pass close to the sun. An antenna aimed to pick up this beam (looking back at us) would be pointed very close to the sun and would thus pick up a storm of interference from the high activity in the sun's atmosphere. Allowing for this, there might be a period of a week when contact with Mercury was impossible.

To see around the corner, we might possibly be able to capitalize on the Trojan points of either the earth or Mercury. This is by no means certain. The Trojan asteroids of Jupiter are held in place by Jupiter's tremendous gravitation, but we also know that even they are agitated by the perturbations of Saturn and other planets. Theoretically, the useful Trojan position of earth and Mercury orbits would be as follows:

In Fig. 11-2, the earth (at A) and Mercury (at C) are placed on exactly opposite sides of the sun on a line between them which passes through the center of the sun. Trojan points, remembering the rules in Chap. 9, fall at E and B, for the earth, and at F and D, for Mercury. Since either can be used, only one set is shown, for simplicity. Looking at the right-hand set of possibilities, it would probably be more desirable from the Mercurian point of view to use a Trojan satellite-transponder at *D*, since the antenna on Mercury could be pointed about 60° away from the sun, achieving a great reduction in sun noise. Unfortunately, Mercury has only a feeble gravitation, and the satellite might easily be dislodged by the gravitational attraction of Venus the first time Mercury overtook that planet.

The other possibility is to place a Trojan satellite at *B*. Angle *ACB* would still be fairly favorable—something like 45°—and probably still quite free of solar interference. It is still subject to the perturbations of Venus, but perhaps less so, since the earth is

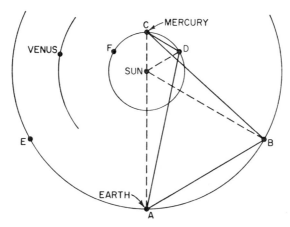

FIG. 11-2

about the same size as Venus. This may not be enough, since the maintenance of a Trojan point is a very delicate affair. If it should prove possible, however, an earth-Trojan satellite would have the further advantage that it could be used also for Venus when Venus was somewhere beyond *C* on the *AC* line. It would avoid the necessity of setting up Trojan satellites for each planet in the solar system, or at least for the inner planets.

For the outer planets, the earth at quadrature would still be rather close to the sun angularly, and it might be necessary to choose an orbit such that one of the Trojan points would always be more than a certain number of angular degrees away from the sun as viewed from the receiving planet.

For example, receipt of signals from earth by a station situated on Pluto might demand that the Trojan satellite be situated in the orbit of Jupiter. If so, this would be convenient, as Jupiter is most likely to be able to hold such a satellite transponder (this assumes that Trojan asteroids already present there would not scatter the signal beam or crush the satellite in the process of their physical oscillations). In such a situation either Jupiter or one of the Trojan points would always be visible from Pluto.

Establishing Trojan points is not as simple as it may appear from this brief glance. Finding the Trojan point, if there are not any asteroids already there, may prove to be quite a feat of navigation, and a question arises as to whether the launching of a retrograde satellite as the spaceship approaches the point would be precise enough to work. Possibly other adjustments could be made by remote control. As it seems in general practice to be more convenient to overtake celestial bodies, it may be that the satellite could be launched with near (but insufficient) velocity and gradually brought up to the correct orbital speed by the application of a series of carefully calibrated small bursts of power.

Figure 11-1 shows a satellite moving about the sun in an orbit between the earth and Mars. This is largely symbolic. Earth-Mars communication will probably not need it, and the satellite's orbital speed would cause it to lag behind the earth but move ahead of Mars. In time it would be more inconveniently located than Mars itself. The establishment of many of these might be prohibitive; on the other hand, maybe three, 120° apart, as with the Clarke-type of terrestrial transponder, would be enough.

Beyond Mars lie the asteroids. There are swarms of them, perhaps enough to produce serious scattering of a beam aimed, say, from Mars to Jupiter. They are probably not as dense as Saturn's rings, by any means, but signals passing through the asteroid belt may be obstructed by enough of them to warrant possibly a circumpolar set of three satellites around Mars. Tidal effect of Martian rotation would eventually turn the axis of the orbit away from the outer planets. Perhaps this may be combatted by establishing more satellites, say, as many as 12. The low escape velocity of Mars (only 3.1 miles/sec) simplifies the logistics of the proposition, and one of the satellites would always be far enough above the Martian poles to "see" Jupiter.

How far above the poles? The asteroids, as we noted in Chap. 9, are not in a nice flat ring as are those of Saturn. They are often inclined at high angles to the orbits of the planets; thus the net effect is rather untidy. To get an orbit around Mars high enough to miss all the asteroids, the satellite transponders might have to be located 100,000 miles or so away from Mars, and then the stability of the orbit, in view of the weak Martian gravity, might be open to question. The problem awaits an examination of the known asteroid orbits from this standpoint, and a decision as to what obscuration probability can be tolerated. As the likelihood of being faced with the problem is remote today, we may not expect the study to be accomplished with much of a sense of urgency or even seriousness.

Still further beyond lies the boundary of the solar system, and beyond that—at tremendous distance—the stars. Beyond that lies the boundary of our galaxy, within which most visible stars are situated. With increase in distance, signal strength will fade, and the ratio of galaxy noise will climb. Signals may be expected to travel at the rate of 8 min per astronomical unit, or a little over 11 million miles per minute. Table 11-2 is an approximation of

TABLE 11-2 *Minimum and Maximum Transit Times*

| Planet | LIGHT, MINUTES | | *Light, seconds* |
	Minimum	*Maximum*	Average
Mercury	4.88	11.12	
Venus	5.76	13.75	
Moon	. . .	. . .	1.28
Mars	4.16	20.16	
Jupiter	33.60	49.60	
Saturn	68.32	84.32	
Uranus	145.52	161.52	
Neptune	232.56	248.56	
Pluto	307.68	331.68	

minimum transit times (planets nearest each other) and maximum transit times (planets on the opposite side of the sun from each other) as viewed from the earth. A similar chart could easily be made up for any other planet. A quick multiplication shows that signal transit time from earth to Pluto is no less than five hours. If this is frustrating, recall that to the nearest star, Alpha Centauri, it is four years! To the other side of our galaxy it is about 100,000 years, and to the most distant known galaxies, several billion.

Now, a flight even to Alpha Centauri is so far in the future that the problem of communicating with it is not a serious one. Communication with a possible planet around that star, or to a spaceship well on its way there, will be a rather odd affair. Conversation in the conventional sense of query and response is out of the question, but continual tracking may be possible, and progressive information of some kind, which takes into account the long transit time, may have some usefulness to the interstellar ship making the trip.

Galactic intercommunication would not only be drowned out by local galactic noise but would have little meaning anyway. Ships traveling over these distances would be moving at very high velocities indeed, and Doppler effects would produce a very large frequency shift which would pose some weird design problems in the equipment. Furthermore, response to queries might arrive back on earth after such a long interval that those on earth may have forgotten what their own ancestors had in mind when they sent the queries!

For all practical purposes, then, it may be thought that interstellar and intergalactic communication presents such serious difficulties as not to warrant the effort of designing the radio equipment in the first place. Here again we are faced with the apparent upper speed limit of 186,000 miles/sec, if the provisions of Einstein's theory of relativity are truly ironclad.

Again we are beset by a feeling of technological inadequacy, but this may not be permanent. Since it may conceivably be possible for a ship to travel faster than light—if we should discover some now-unknown feature of relativity—it may also be possible to make signals do the same thing. Who knows? Science is yet young. Man's progress in science is largely a matter of doing the impossible because he refuses to accept that feeling of inadequacy or frustration. He may yet find a way out.

BIBLIOGRAPHY

Richey, J. R.: Are You There, Mars?, *The Sky,* pp. 20–30, September, 1938.

Tsien, Adamson, and Knuth: Automatic Navigation of a Long-range Rocket Vehicle, *J. Am. Rocket Soc.,* vol. 22, no. 4, pp. 192–199, 1952. Very technical; shows basis of flight on which a command system can later be based. The paper itself is largely ballistic.

Coupling, J. J., (J. R. Pierce): Don't Write—Telegraph! *Astounding Science Fiction,* vol. 49, pp. 82–96, March, 1952. Considerable detail in studying the problem of interplanetary communication.

Clarke, A. C.: Extraterrestrial Relays, *Wireless World* (England), pp. 305–308, October, 1945.

Merten, R.: Hochfrequenztechnik und Weltraumfahrt, S. Hirzel Verlag, Stuttgart, 1951 (see especially pp. 59–69 and 92–101).

ARS Space Flight Committee, On the Utility of an Artificial Unmanned Earth Satellite, *Jet Propulsion,* vol. 25, no. 2, pp. 76–78 (Appendix F, Orbital Radio Relays), 1955. [Essentially the same as the article of the same name appearing two issues later (see below)].

Pierce, J. R.: Orbital Radio Relays, *Jet Propulsion,* vol. 25, no. 4, pp. 153–157, 1955.

Smith, G. O.: Radio Communication Across Space—Ship-to-Ship and Ship-to-Planet, *J. Brit. Interplanet. Soc.,* vol. 12, no. 1, 1953. See also "Proceedings of the Second Symposium on Space Travel," American Museum of Natural History, New York, 1952.

Cummins, C. I., and A. W. Newberry: Radio Telemetry, *J. Am. Rocket Soc.,* vol. 23, no. 3, pp. 141–145, 1953. Shows the present philosophy of instrument packaging in small spaces such as rocket hulls.

Pierce, J. R.: Some Recent Development in Microwave Tubes, *Proc. IRE,* vol. 42, pp. 1735–1747, 1954.

Thompson, G. V. E.: Spaceflight Communications Methods, *J. Brit. Interplanet. Soc.,* vol. 13, no. 4, p. 198, 1954.

High Frequency Technique and Space Flight, (review of Hochfrequenztechnische, see above) *J. Brit. Interplanet. Soc.,* vol. 11, no. 3, p. 143, 1952.

Merten, R.: "Uber einige Hochfrequenztechnische Probleme der Weltraumfahrt, in Probleme aus der Astronautische Grundlagenforschung," edited by H. H. Koelle, pp. 239–244, Gesellschaft für Weltraumforschung, 1952.

Toth, R. C.: Toward Improved Missile Communications, *Astronautics,* vol. 2, no. 1, p. 54, 1947.

Paludan, C. T. N.: Redstone In-flight Telemetering, *Missiles and Rockets,* vol. 2, no. 6, p. 126, 1957.

Gaudillère, P. C.: Le Guidage des engins a grande distance, *Fusées,* vol. 1, no. 1, p. 45, 1956.

———: Le Guidage radioelectrique des engins, *Fusées et recherches aéronaut.,* vol. 1, no. 3, p. 219, 1956.

Canney, H. E., Jr., and F. I. Ordway, III: The Satellite Vehicle for Communications and Navigation, *Aero Digest,* vol. 71, no. 6, p. 40, 1955.

Stuhlinger, E.: Control and Power Supply Problems of Instrumented Satellites, *Jet Propulsion,* vol. 5, no. 26, p. 364, 1956.

Jensen, J.: Satellite Ascent Guidance Requirements, *J. Astronautics,* vol. 3, no. 1, p. 1, 1956.

———: Satellite Communication Problems, American Rocket Society Preprint, vol. 309, no. 56.

Webb, J. A.: Interplanetary Communications, *J. Astronautics,* vol. 3, no. 2, p. 29, 1956.

12

Destination One — The Moon

Background

Many theories have been propounded and many superstitions have evolved around the moon and its origin, but there is still no well-defined agreement on the matter among astronomers. Some point to the Pacific Ocean and suggest that, in the formative days of the earth, tidal effects of the sun, coupled with the natural elliptical shape of the earth (which was due to the centrifugal force of rapid rotation on its axis), produced a bulge which eventually separated from the earth and formed both the moon and the basin of the Pacific Ocean. This is known as the *tidal theory,* propounded by G. H. Darwin, an English mathematician, in the late nineteenth century.[1] Another explanation is that the earth at one time was surrounded by a ring of gases and minerals, similar to those of Saturn, which fused into a solid body.

Other astronomers have brought forward the theory that the moon was a separate planet captured by the earth and held in orbit by its relatively strong gravitational attraction. This point of view is supported by the fact that, when the moon's size is compared with the earth's, the moon is unique in the solar system, for it is one-fourth the size of its primary—almost a double planet.

There have been many such theories offered from time to time by the most learned astronomers, but conclusive proof has yet to

[1] P. Moore, "Guide to the Moon," p. 27, Eyre and Spottiswoode, London, 1953.

be found. Man's studies of the moon have been painstaking, and they have been conducted over many centuries, but there is no doubt that much must be learned before the final chapter on the subject is written.

As we know, the moon keeps the same face turned toward us at all times, the reason being that the moon's axial rotation and orbital revolution are of the same period. This has created an awkward gap in our knowledge of the moon's surface but is somewhat offset by a wobble or libration, which allows us to see a little around the edge, bringing our visual knowledge of the lunar surface up to about 60 per cent.

The ancients, awed and bewildered by the changing phases, beauty, and utility of the moon, worshipped it as a deity. Among the peoples so disposed were the Egyptians, the Africans (who continue to do so in some of the more remote areas), and the Druids of Britain. This custom of attaching supernatural importance to the moon resulted in some remarkable contributions in painting and sculpture from Greece and Rome in the centuries before Christ.

When Galileo trained his crude telescope on the moon and reported his observations to the world, they represented the first reliable pictures of a body which had been shrouded in a maze of confusion and mysticism. What he saw was not the Palaces of the Gods, but huge raised craters and great low-lying plains, which he thought of as *mares,* or seas.

Time has shown that the lunar plains are most certainly not seas, but whether the craters were formed by volcanic action, meteoric bombardment, or some other force is still a matter of hot debate. Likewise, it still remains to be established whether or not a tenuous atmosphere is to be found in the great cracks and gullies of the moon's surface.

From these early discoveries to the present day a great body of information has been amassed—so much, in fact, that it is doubtful whether much more can be disclosed to us with present observing equipment; and since building telescopes larger than those already existing would prove a tremendous and costly engineering feat, it is somewhat doubtful whether any such subject will be embarked upon. And there is another reason for not attempting to improve upon existing observation devices: we stand at the doorway to space travel.

The notion of a voyage to the moon has long entertained the minds of men. It has ranged from fantasy to speculation to organized scientific endeavor in recent years. Serious (though tentative) plans have been formulated, programs have been devised, and materials and resources have been surveyed.

The preamble of the moon voyage has been written in many different ways. Prominent engineers and scientists point out that the establishment of unmanned satellites reveals to us techniques of launch and recovery and the very necessary basic knowledge of cosmic rays, solar radiations, and meteor behavior. But beyond that, it is necessary to conduct practical research aloft on the habitability of spaceships. The establishment of a manned space station should be the first goal, some say.

The manned-station concept is contested by other authorities who advance the idea that it is more practical to investigate a suitable refueling orbit by manned flight first, and then to launch many smaller rockets containing fuel as the payload. They maintain that, with data from unmanned satellites, the necessary experiments can usually be done on the ground. To say that a manned orbiting rocket cannot also be a space station seems to be splitting hairs. It is in this line of thought that this chapter is written.

Moon Rockets

As explained in Chap. 4, a single-stage rocket launched directly from the earth and destined to land on, or circumnavigate, the moon would be so fantastically large as to make its design and construction impracticable. The moon rocket will be large, nonetheless, and still presents a logistical problem. What can be done? We know, for one thing, that manned flight into orbit close to the earth's surface presents no such unsurmountable problems, and *un*manned flight there has already been accomplished.

The construction of a moon rocket, then, can begin in space. This much at least is agreed upon by all authorities. Cargo rockets can carry into orbit the construction materials and supplies necessary to build the circumlunar rocket. Many such trips will have to be made for so tremendous a task before enough materials have been accumulated to complete the rocket. (It seems virtually certain that such a venture will have to be sponsored by a national government or, possibly, by an alliance of many governments. The expense involved in launching many multistage cargo rockets will be extremely high—utterly beyond the means of private industry. Moreover, vast support in men and bases will be required on earth to coordinate the operation.)

Upon completion, the rocket, an unmanned probe, heavily instrumented and carrying reconnaissance cameras (both conventional and radar), will be thoroughly inspected and launched. It should be remembered that the rocket will already have an orbital speed which will represent a rather large proportion of the velocity required for the journey.

The rocket will be accelerated from its earthbound orbit into an elliptic path which will "intercept" the moon, circumnavigate it, and return to the original orbit about the earth. This journey will take about five days, and it is possible that one trip will furnish all the basic information needed prior to the launching of a manned flight. Upon careful evaluation of this scientific and photographic information, a manned moon rocket can be constructed.

It has been suggested that an interim phase be adopted whereby an unmanned rocket would actually land on the moon. This rocket would then serve as an automatic radio beacon for the transmission of further data, indicating the solidity of the area chosen for landing and confirming the already anticipated landing techniques (these will be discussed later in the chapter). The design and construction of this type of vehicle would closely approximate that of the circumlunar vehicle, but would differ by the addition of landing gear and automatic equipment to perform the landing maneuver. Since the launching of Sputnik and Explorer, Russian and American scientists have repeatedly forecast that at least unmanned lunar probes will be developed within a relatively short time.

At this point, it is necessary to pause and recount the many advances made and to consider the magnitude of the next step. Assuming all ventures to this juncture have been successful, the amount of data collected, analyzed, and recorded will be immense. Basic information on cosmic rays, solar radiations, and meteor frequencies will be at hand for the scientist. The engineer's computations of flight path, control, structural integrity, rocket performance, propellant chemistry, and design will have been checked in practice, and if necessary, recalculated.

The astronomer's assessment of moon terrain will have been borne out or disproved by photographic surveys. Radar mapping and the physician's environmental chambers and space suits will have been tested and checked fully in practice. Photographic analysis will indicate, to the geologist, detailed terrain features of the proposed landing area, permitting calculations that will pin-point the exact spot for the manned rocket's descent.

Using a winged rocket orbiting about the earth as a base of operations, construction men will assemble prefabricated parts into the various components such as the crew sphere, the propellant tanks, the rocket-motor housings, the meteor shield, the solar mirror, and the many other units which make up the rocket. These construction materials and units will tend to drift away from the orbital site, because of small differences in orbital radius; and in order to prevent this, they will be tied to each other in some way and probably to the mother ship.

Conventional methods of construction and assembly will be used. Forces and temperatures expected to act upon the structure are considerably less than those which will already have been experienced in the launching. (Reentry of the winged rockets into the atmosphere will pose an aerodynamic heating problem, however.) Conventional materials such as aluminum alloys for the framework and alloy steels for the rocket motors may be used.

The moon ship in its final form (since there are no problems of aerodynamic drag) will not have the smooth lines and gently curving surfaces of modern high-speed aircraft, but may prove to be rather spherical in shape. A sphere is the most practical shape available as a pressure container and affords the optimum use of both volume and materials.

The selection of a crew to man the rocket should not pose too great a problem, since by that time trained scientists and engineers of high caliber should be available in rather large numbers and should be fairly well versed in the problems of space flight, because of their experience gained from flight into orbit. It is possible that a scientist prominent in one of the astronautical sciences will head the group. His responsibilities will be great, notably in his own particular science, but also in the same sense as being captain of an ocean liner.

A physician will be essential and a geologist will of course be included on all voyages requiring a landing and probably also on circumlunar trips. Rocket and mechanical engineers must be on hand to service and maintain the ship; a competent radio and radar specialist will also be needed. A surveyor and a physicist, preferably versed in cosmic-ray studies, will be necessary crew members. If the ship can carry only a limited crew, some men may have to be specialists in two sciences. The geologist, for example, might double as the surveyor, and so on.

The careful selection of the crew will be based on high psychological stability, as well as on physique and weight. It is virtually certain that the first landing party will make a geological survey to lay the basis for both future landings and the building of a lunar base. This is so important that many of the basic sciences may, unfortunately, not be represented on the first voyage.

Newton showed that all bodies in the solar system (and, indeed, the universe) move in strict accordance with the law of gravitation; Kepler pointed out that the flight path of any body obeying this law will be the same shape as one of the conic sections. In the case of a moon voyage, the path will be a long, slender ellipse, the major axis being a straight line intersecting the centers of both earth and moon. The length of the minor axis of the ellipse and the length of the flight path will be dependent on two factors: the orbital radius of the fueling satellite or construction base and the velocity and inclination of the rocket at cutoff speed.

Consider an orbital radius of 1,075 miles; circular velocity will be 4.39 miles/sec. An appreciable velocity will already have been attained by the moon rocket, and the additional velocity required for an elliptic ascent to the moon, as previously stated, will depend upon establishing the proper cutoff velocity and angle of launch. Since the moon rocket, like an earth-circling satellite, can be considered a celestial body, the means for calculating its path is readily available. Table 12-1 gives important quantitative information on the moon.

TABLE 12-1 *Moon data*

Diameter	2,160 miles
Volume *	0.02
Mass *	1/81.56
Density †	3.33
Gravity (surface) *	0.165
Escape velocity	1.5 miles/sec
Circular velocity	1.06 miles/sec
Orbital velocity	0.64 miles/sec
Sidereal period	27.32 days
Synodical period	29.53 days
Earth to moon distance, apogee	252,710 miles
Earth to moon distance, perigee	221,463 miles

* Earth = 1.
† Earth = 1 (density is 5.52 times that of water).

A problem arises of where to land on the moon. On reflection it will be apparent that the anticipated temperature gradients and the nature of the terrain in any proposed landing area must be closely studied.

It is probable that a walled plain will be selected in the general vicinity of the north or south pole, suggesting an intensive study of the craters Plato and Meton, in the north, and Schomberger and Stofler, in the south.[2] Some thought has also been given to Sinus Ronis and Palus Somnii, both in the north. Equatorially, Sinus Medii and Ptolemy are possibilities as far as terrain is concerned, but the intense heat at the moon's equator will probably preclude this.

Protagonists of moon-rocket programs have been heartened by the statement of the head of the Air Force Office of Scientific Research that, possibly within four years, an Air Force rocket will circle the moon. This statement was made at the AFOSR-Convair Astronautics Symposium, which took place in San Diego, in 1957. It was also revealed that moon-rocket study contracts have been let and that ICBM-type power plants would probably be used. It is known that the Rand Corporation has long been occupied with the problem, and one of its scientists presented a paper on the subject

[2] H. Wilkins, Where to Land on the Moon, *J. Brit. Interplanet. Soc.,* vol. 13, no. 2, p. 66, 1954.

to the 1956 satellite symposium at the Franklin Institute. This paper, subsequently published in the journal of the institute as "Monograph 2," assumed a 950,000-lb rocket, 175 ft long and 15 ft in diameter, made up of three stages and a payload section. One hundred pounds of scientific instruments and associated communication gear would be placed on its surface.

General Schriever, chief of the Air Force Ballistic Missile Division, has said that the "same guidance system that enables the warhead of a ballistic missile to reach its target within a permissible accuracy would also be sufficiently accurate to hit a target much smaller than the size of the moon, even at that increased range." The Army Ballistic Missile Agency is also entering the moon-rocket program, and a recent statement of Department of Defense philosophy suggests that the Army may be given the initial lunar flight task.

Round Trip to the Moon

Intensive observation by the largest telescopes would precede the voyage; later there should be a considerable amount of terrain detail data from the unmanned-probe exploration. But, even so, the final pin-point selection of the landing site would have to rest with the captain of the lunar vehicle.

The simplest part of the earth-moon journey, from the viewpoint of human effort, promises to be the mid-course flight. It will be as completely automatic as human ingenuity will allow. An automatic pilot will take charge of the controls at the earth orbital (or perigee) point, monitor the rocket acceleration to cutoff altitude, and then make any preliminary navigation corrections to establish the elliptic flight path. Extreme accuracy will be required at all times, because even small errors could prove disastrous.

Classically, the journey time has been estimated as five days, a figure that takes due regard of the amount of fuel expended at launch and deceleration and of the over-all size of the vehicle. It is theoretically possible to reduce this time considerably, even to the order of a few hours (if the human body can endure the accelerations), given better propellant efficiencies and high mass ratios. The latter involves the improvement of our present-day knowledge of materials and construction techniques; the former is a matter of genetics and training.

Communications during the voyage will be established by means of conventional radio and radar signals and will serve to correct the autopilot settings. During the entire voyage, the earth will be visible to the lunar rocket, presenting a superb view, colored where the sun strikes continent and ocean, and black on the right side—but not as pitch black as the background of space.

The moon, too, will be visible throughout the trip. Shortly after launch it will appear far off to one side of the flight path, because of the offset course the rocket must traverse in order to intercept the moon. At the beginning of the fifth day, the moon will loom ahead of the vehicle. The neutral point—or equating position—in the gravitational fields will have been passed, and the crew will prepare for the delicate and hazardous landing maneuver.

It should be noted here that the rocket ship will have lost a great deal of the initial velocity with which it began its flight,[3] since it will now be at apogee, but there will still remain a considerable velocity to be neutralized before a safe landing can be made. In order to accomplish this, the ship will be rotated through approximately 180° into its landing attitude.

Among the three cardinal axes of the vehicle, and at the center of gravity, will be positioned three flywheels. When any of these flywheels is rotated, the torsional reaction will cause the rocket to rotate in the opposite direction. The vehicle will be positioned with one or a combination of these flywheels.

At a predetermined altitude above the moon's surface, the rocket motors will start and the vehicle will begin to slow its rate of descent. The exact altitude will be known by means of a radar altimeter, enabling the braking rockets to vary their thrust and thus more closely control the rate of descent. The ideal landing will be made when the thrust of the motors and the weight of the rocket are precisely equal at the moon's surface and, hence, the moon ship becomes stationary.

This "hold-off" will be very critical, and it may be necessary to make last-minute adjustments or minute changes in course to avoid such obstacles as gullies, mounds, or rocks, which could quite possibly wreck the ship. It is also very essential that there be no

[3] Not through friction, of course, but because of Keplerian laws of equal area, etc.

horizontal component of velocity (sideward motion), since this would have the same effect.

Landing gear will be carefully designed and adjustable in all legs —probably four—to take up any small differences in the attitude of the landed ship. These legs will be extended, a minute or two before landing, to some median position and will be controlled, during the actual landing contact maneuver, by the ship's gyroscopes. It will be necessary that the legs have a sensitive device to measure the reaction of the ground beneath them, thus enabling the gyroscopes to "feel" the correct leg extension and settle the ship into the "absolute vertical."

A stark and forbidding world will be revealed to the first explorers to view the lunar landscape. With great mountains and dust-covered plains rolling away to a short horizon (about two miles from an average elevation), the curvature will appear very pronounced compared with that seen on the earth, a body four times the size of the moon.

Color, as we understood it, will be virtually nonexistent—only the jet black of space forming the backdrop to a brilliant white, where the sun strikes the ground, relieved only by dead tones of brown and gray.

There will be no clouds to break the monotony, no wind to ripple or move the lifeless dust, and not a sound to break the intense quiet—an eerie, dead world, devoid of movement, sound, or color because of the lack of atmosphere. Gravity will be about one-sixth that on earth and will produce a strange assortment of phenomena in the physical movement of samples and specimens of the moon's surface as they are mined and loaded.

Two weeks will be allowed for exploration, because, first, this is the period of day or night on the moon and it is likely that the first expedition will not be equipped for a longer stay; and second, the earth and moon are in favorable position for the return at this time. Hence, the ship's crew will need to apply themselves immediately to their various tasks, working against the clock.

Solar mirrors will be erected to furnish the necessary power to replenish the lunar ship's batteries and to drive the small machines and mechanisms to be used for obtaining geological samples. Space suits, to provide the necessary human environment and protection for individuals (to a lesser extent, from micrometeorites), will be worn at all times while the men are outside the ship.

It seems certain that the time chosen for the landing will be during the two weeks of sunshine, since there is no apparent reason why the subzero temperature of the long moon night should be endured unnecessarily.

The explorers will not venture far from their home base (the rocket ship) because all the preliminary studies that will have to be conducted can be carried on within a very short radius. Sampling the various strata will absorb many days, and it can be reasonably assumed that the geological aspect of exploration will be the most fruitful. Mineralogical specimens, labeled and identified as accurately as the laboratory facilities on the ship will allow, will be carefully packaged and stowed in the cargo space.

Many more clues to the origin of the universe will undoubtedly be disclosed. Prospecting for traces of frozen air and water in crevasses [4] will have high priority, since these two fundamentals, together with food, form the basic necessities for life as we know it. Any lunar base of the future would be primarily concerned with "living off the land," because continual transportation of supplies brought from earth to provision the base would be extremely costly. Rather detailed attention has already been given to extraterrestrial mining on an airless body,[5] with emphasis on constructional materials, life-maintaining materials, and propellant materials.

One of the most interesting results of the trip will be the possible disclosure of how the great craters of the moon were formed. Much other information concerning such factors as the abundance of raw materials and valuable minerals will be sought, and there will be findings from such research as can be conducted with a minimum of equipment. Also important will be the assessment of the intensity of cosmic rays and the frequency of meteorite hits. Measurements of the magnetic flux (if one exists) on the moon may help solve the riddle of our own magnetic variations in both magnitude and direction. This is not intended as a complete survey of all

[4] A. C. Clarke and R. A. Smith, "Exploration of the Moon," Frederick Muller, Ltd., London, 1954.

[5] A. J. W. Rozelaar, "Extraterrestrial Mining," *J. Brit. Interplanet. Soc.,* vol. 15, no. 6, p. 308, 1956.

of the scientific probing that could be accomplished by the first explorers, but only as an outline of problem areas. Human ingenuity can and will accomplish much. Scientific establishments and research laboratories of the earth will be occupied for years evaluating the data supplied by even a single exploratory venture of this nature.

Toward the end of the two weeks during which this feverish exploration and study has been going on, the sun will begin to set and the earth, which, at the time of landing, appeared dimly lit apart from a "new moon" crescent, will present a picture similar to that seen on earth at full moon—the "full earth," so to speak. (The difference will be that the earth will be four times larger.) This will mark the time for departure.

The moon's gravitational attraction, being only a small fraction of that of the earth, will not pose a serious problem to the escaping rocket; thus the return voyage to the refueling orbit should be relatively simple. Loosely speaking, the navigational or maneuvering procedures will be the reverse of the first part of the trip.

In orbit, at the original refueling site, will be one of the winged rockets (first used to transport construction materials up to the growing lunar vehicle) waiting where it was left to return the precious data accumulated in the two weeks of exploration to the earth. It may be that no other event in history will have rendered so much to man's knowledge in so little time.

In general, colonization follows exploration, and it is not unreasonable to assume that, some time after the initial flights are made, men will ponder what they have found and weigh the merits of setting up a permanent lunar base. This is no idle dream. Some serious studies have been made on the construction of a lunar city on the barren surface of our satellite, and it has also been suggested that food can be produced, given reasonable attention and a closed environment. Since it may tentatively be assumed that all the elements present on earth are also present on the moon, no shortage of raw materials should exist. The problem is one of collecting and assembling the machinery and equipment to utilize these resources.

An article appeared in the *Journal of the British Interplanetary Society* (January–February, 1956) on the possibility of utilizing soilless cultures to produce crops on the moon. The author shows that hydroponics will have to be used on a large scale and suggests that plants will grow much higher than on earth, because of the low gravity. The author assumes no water in the liquid form on the moon, a "virtually negligible" atmosphere (reported elsewhere as not more than a million-millionth as dense as earth's at sea level), optimum sunshine conditions (the lunar day is 14 earth days long), surface-crust temperatures of about 216°F at noon, a long night when temperatures drop to —243°F, adequate mineral salts derived from crushed rock, and total absence of humus and soil bacteria.

The difficulties in establishing such a colony are tremendous and must first be outweighed by the need. There is little doubt that the construction of a moon ship would be underway today if funds were made available. Technologically we are ready.

Based on predictions of Air Force and Army experts, it may be that funds are, or soon will be, ready for the enterprise. The Russians, in the meantime, are apparently having less trouble raising money for a moon-circling rocket, and government approval seems certain there. Scientists have spoken about automatic rockets going around the moon for observation purposes, approaching to within about 17,932 miles of the surface. The total flight time works out to be 10 days, including 60 hours of close observation time. Parachutes and gliders would bring the rocket back to the Earth.

It is apparent that two rather unfriendly powers are planning on the conquest of the earth's satellite, and it is hoped that the exploration and colonization of the moon will be prompted not by the ancient motives of war or greed, but by the concentrated efforts of these nations acting in harmony. It would be a welcome novelty for the effort to be dedicated to one of the highest aspirations of humanity: knowledge for its own sake.

BIBLIOGRAPHY

Baker, R. H.: "Astronomy," D. Van Nostrand Company, Inc., Princeton, N.J., 1957.
von Braun, W., F. Whipple, and W. Ley: "Conquest of the Moon," The Viking Press, Inc., New York, 1953.
Kahn, F.: "Design of the Universe," Crown Publishers, Inc., New York, 1954.

Clarke, A. C., and R. A. Smith: "Exploration of the Moon," Frederick Muller, Ltd., London, 1954.

Moore, P.: "Guide to the Moon," Eyre and Spottiswoode, London, 1953.

Clarke, A. C.: "Interplanetary Flight," Harper & Brothers, New York, 1953.

Firsoff, V. A.: "Our Neighbor Worlds," Philosophical Library, Inc., New York, 1953.

Ley, W.: Rockets, "Missiles and Space Travel," The Viking Press, Inc., New York, 1957.

Clarke, A. C.: "The Exploration of Space," Harper & Brothers, New York, 1954.

Opik, E. J.: The Origin of the Moon, *Irish Astron. J.,* vol. 3, no. 8, 1955.

Ehricke, K. A., and G. Gamow, Rocket Around the Moon, *Sci. American,* vol. 196, no. 6, p. 47, 1957.

Moore, P.: What we Shall Find on the Moon? *J. Astronautics,* vol. 2, no. 2, p. 47, 1955.

Bergaust, E.: The Conquest of the Moon, *Missiles and Rockets,* vol. 2, no. 3, p. 82, 1957.

Egorov, V. A.: "Some Questions of Dynamics of Flight to the Moon," Casebook on Soviet Astronautics, Part II, Rand Corp., June, 1957.

Ordway, F. I., and R. C. Wakeford: Man on the Moon—Probes Due First, *Missiles and Rockets,* p. 69, April, 1958 (a very complete bibliography is appended).

ARTICLES IN THE *Journal of the British Interplanetary Society*

Moore, P.: What We Know About the Moon, vol. 11, no. 1, p. 19, 1952.

Wilkins, H. P.: The Other Side of the Moon, vol. 12, no. 1, p. 1, 1953.

————: Where to Land on the Moon, vol. 13, no. 2, p. 65, 1954.

————: Recent Research on the Moon, Part I, vol. 13, no. 6, p. 313, 1954; Part II, vol. 14, no. 3, p. 133, 1955.

————: Light and Shade on the Moon, vol. 15, no. 2, p. 101, 1956.

Douglas, S.: Farming on the Moon, vol. 15, no. 1, p. 17, 1956.

Rozelaar, A. J. W.: Extra-terrestrial Mining, vol. 15, no. 6, p. 308, 1956.

Sowerby, P. L.: Structural Problems of the Lunar Base, vol. 13, no. 1, p. 36, 1954.

13

Navigation in Space

Space, Time, and Gravity

Before attempting to discuss the movement of man-made space craft across planetary distances, we may well briefly recall a few facts about the solar system noted in Chap. 9. The mean distances of the planets from the sun, in millions of miles, are as follows:

Mercury	36
Venus	67
Earth	93
Mars	142
Jupiter	483
Saturn	886
Uranus	1,783
Neptune	2,794
Pluto	3,616

The planets follow paths of roughly circular shape, except for Mercury and Pluto, which orbit in ellipses of considerable eccentricity. Only the orbit of Pluto inclines to the ecliptic by more than 7°. Orbital velocities range from 29.7 miles/sec, for Mercury, to a mere 3 miles/sec, for Pluto. Escape velocities vary from 2.6 miles/sec, for Mercury, to 37 miles/sec, for Jupiter. All the planets revolve from east to west, with sidereal periods as shown in Table 9-4 on page 228 and presented in terms of days or years on page 314.

Planet	PERIOD OF REVOLUTION (SIDEREAL)	
	Days	Years
Mercury	88	
Venus	225	
Earth	365¼	
Mars	687	
Jupiter		12
Saturn		29
Uranus		84
Neptune		165
Pluto		248

The motions of the planets around the sun are known today with great accuracy, and this knowledge permits a discussion of interplanetary navigation to maintain a close contact with reality. Kepler's laws state:

1. Each planet orbits in an elliptical path with the sun at one focus (elliptical law).

2. Each planet so moves that a line connecting it and the sun will sweep over equal areas in equal time intervals (area law).

3. The squares of the periods of revolution of any two planets are in the same proportion as the cubes of their average distance from the sun (harmonic law).

With these laws as tools, the motions of the planets (or satellites or spaceships) can be predicted accurately, corrected only for local perturbations.

The orbits of any two celestial bodies are not influenced by any motion of the center of mass of the system. Furthermore, in considering two-body problems, both bodies are known to revolve around a common center of mass, the size of the orbit of each varying inversely with the mass. These orbits are what interest the space navigator, since his vehicle will act like any celestial body and will describe one of several forms of curves through space.

Kepler's first law mentions only the ellipse, which is one of the several conic sections and is represented by the intersection of a plane with a cone when the intersecting plane is not parallel to the base of the cone. (A circle is formed when the plane *is* parallel to the base. A parabola is formed when the cone is intersected by a plane parallel to one of its sides, and a hyperbola when the intersecting plane is parallel to its axis. A parabola is often thought of as a sort of ellipse that does not close, though this should not be taken literally.) Newton later showed that bodies influenced by central masses must move in conic sections, the curve followed depending on the velocity of the object in the particular situation.

We have noted perturbations, disturbances of orbit produced by celestial bodies other than those responsible for an object's regular motion. The moon, for example, would perturb an artificial satellite orbiting around the earth. To a greater or lesser extent all bodies in the universe perturb all others, though it is very strongly suspected that, for practical purposes, all but the perturbation by the closest bodies may safely be disregarded for most navigational purposes.

In space navigation it is obviously very useful to know the velocity of a body (traveling according to a conic section). In order to determine the conic along which a body or object will travel, two things must be known: the principal attracting force and the speed at which the body or object is *started*. It is quite obvious that the curvature of the orbit will depend on the major attracting force (the force that causes its deflection) and the distance it can move along this orbit. From the equation of energy we have

$$V^2 = G \ (m_1 + m_2) \left(\frac{2}{r} - \frac{1}{a} \right) \tag{13-1}$$

where V = velocity of revolution at distance r
G = gravitational constant
a = semimajor axis
m_1, m_2 = masses involved

It can be seen that a will increase as V increases. If the orbit is circular, a equals r, making V^2 proportional to $1/r$, whereas if the orbit is parabolic, a is infinite and V^2 is proportional to $2/r$. If we multiply the velocity of a body moving in a circular orbit by $\sqrt{2}$, the orbit will henceforth be parabolic. Parabolic velocity is escape velocity, and any body transferring from circular to parabolic velocity will leave the system. Whether velocities are circular or parabolic depends on the planet involved.

A body just beyond the earth's atmosphere will maintain itself in circular orbit if a velocity of 4.9 miles/sec is imparted to it. If the speed exceeds this, the result will be an elliptical orbit whose eccentricity (half distance between foci divided by semimajor axis) will increase with the speed of projection. At 6.9 miles/sec (escape velocity), the ellipse becomes parabolic, and any space vehicle moving along a parabolic path will permanently leave the earth system.

A spaceship traveling at speeds faster than 6.9 miles/sec will enter a hyperbolic orbit, which, as velocity reaches toward infinity, will become nearly a straight line. We shall see that hyperbolic routes to the planets are very rapid ones, but outrageously expensive. Conservative elliptical routes take a long time, but in terms of propellant expenditures and foreseeable velocities, they are the only paths to the planets that appear feasible today.

The conic along which a body moves depends on the united mass of the two bodies, the distance between them, and the relative velocity. When V is less than the critical velocity of escape, we find that the orbit is elliptical. When V reaches a critical point, we have parabolic or escape velocity; above this, movement occurs along a hyperbola. *It is extremely improbable that a body will travel at exactly the critical velocity required for a parabola; thus when planning a space voyage, we shall only consider elliptical and hyperbolic paths.* It is interesting to note that, relative to the sun, the velocity of an object following a parabolic path, at every distance, would be exactly that which it would attain at the given point were it to fall from infinity toward the center of the sun.

Newton stated that the force which determines the orbits of the planets is directed toward the sun (a fact that space navigators must never forget); that the force acting on any given planet varies inversely, at different points in the orbit, with the square of the radius vector (the line connecting the sun and any planet (or body) at any point in the orbit); and that the attractive force depends only upon the mass and distance of the bodies under consideration and is independent of their physical condition. That is to say, the gravitational force depends only on distance and mass.

To work out the major problems of celestial mechanics and space travel, we can use the two-body method of calculation. This means that we can consider the movement of the earth only in terms of the sun, of a space station revolving around the earth in terms of the earth, and of a spaceship in terms of either the sun or of the planet whose proximity in space is most likely to influence it.

Newton presented the problem thus: Find the motion of any body now, and determine its position for any future time. To do this we are given the knowledge of the law of gravitation (each particle of matter in the universe attracts each other particle with a force proportional to their masses and inversely proportional to the square of the distance between them), or $F = Gm_1m_2/r^2$, given the masses of the two bodies and their positions and motions in space at a specified time. In planetary astronomy and space navigation we can think in terms of the relative motions of the small body around the larger (actually, both bodies revolve around their common center of gravity, found, in the case of the sun and planets, only a few hundred miles from the sun's center). The orbit that a planet, satellite, comet, or spaceship describes will be, as we have seen, a conic.

We normally like to treat space navigation and planetary voyages by thinking of only two bodies: the planet, satellite, or sun involved and the spaceship. It is impossible, however, to ignore the influences of third bodies, which will always act to perturb the motions of spaceships. The mathematical treatment of three-body problems is most difficult,[1] although given the required data (masses, positions, and motions of three bodies at a given *instant*), a solution, for a particular instant, can be calculated. Mathematical limitations show up when we attempt to plot the perturbations of a continually moving spaceship over a period of time.

We generally find that the disturbing force of the third body will act on a spaceship with only a minute fraction of the whole attractive energy available; that is, this disturbing force will depend on the difference of the two attractions exerted by the third body upon each of the other two bodies whose relative motions it disturbs (intensity, direction, or both).

In recent years the general subject of astronautics has become tied in with guided-missile development, and it is for this reason that one tends to forget that space flight is essentially an astronomical problem. The launching and tracking of Sputnik, however,

[1] Herrick has written, "The 'three-body problem' is more celebrated for what is not known about it than for what is."

quickly brought the astronomers into the limelight. The tried methods of analytical mechanics and theoretical astronomy are applicable to treatment of the navigational problems associated with a vehicle describing an orbit through space.

Flight to Mars—Orbits

In taking off from the earth (or from a satellite orbit around the earth) and traveling toward a destination such as Venus or Mars, we must choose a route that requires the minimum expenditure of energy. We shall see that some of the paths toward the planets are much more economical than others, and while we are most interested in exploring these economical routes, we nevertheless shall mention the others for completeness and as a matter of academic interest.

Probably the best way to cover a subject as complex as interplanetary navigation is to take a specific case, say a trip from earth to Mars, and examine as many ramifications as possible. A trip of this sort will involve either take-offs from and landings on the planetary surfaces or a simple orbit-to-orbit voyage. A navigator will, at all times, be interested in measurements of distance, time, acceleration, direction, and radial velocity. Radio-chronometer combinations and ammonia and crystal clocks have all been suggested as timepieces for space flight.

If we assume take-off from a satellite orbit around the earth and termination in satellite orbit around Mars, we shall consider the trajectory of the trip as being made up of three distinct arcs or orbits. The rocket will transfer from an elliptical orbit with earth as a focus into an elliptical path under the influence of the sun and finally will enter an elliptical orbit with Mars as one of the foci, from which the rocket could drop to circularity. Space navigation, then, is essentially concerned with orbital transfer.

In the interest of obtaining the maximum economy of propellants in a trip of this sort, we must use a trajectory following these elliptical paths, applying thrust at the transfer points where one center of attraction substitutes for another. Thrust may also be employed to make corrections en route (following their detection and the computation of a new orbit), but in general only two basic thrust periods may be expected. These would be (1) to transfer from orbit around earth, entering the earth-Mars trajectory, and (2) to enter into orbit around the target planet.

The physical motions of a spaceship are chiefly in the realm of celestial mechanics, and it may be said that a spacecraft will obey its laws at all times *except* during those relatively brief periods when the rocket motors are functioning. Furthermore, a distinction must be made between flight from a planet to a moon belonging to that planet and flight from one planet to another. In a trip to a moon, a rocket operates within the planet-moon system. In a trip to another planet, it operates for the major part of the time in an orbit determined by the sun. In true interplanetary flight, the sun looms large gravitationally, and a rocket must perform work to move toward or away from that powerful center of attraction.

It should be remembered, incidentally, that the planetary orbits all lie in different planes and that "up and down" corrections will have to be made lest errors of millions of miles result. Thus, no flight completely along the orbital plane of the earth can be expected. Venus, for example, inclines 3.4°; Mars, 1.9°. Furthermore, a rocket attaining exact escape velocity from earth will, at about one million miles, have its relative velocity brought down to about zero and will consequently move in a heliocentric orbit nearly identical to that of the earth. Very little velocity would then be needed, however, to transfer outward to the orbit of Mars.

While of no practical importance, it is interesting to know that the escape velocity at the sun's surface is about 384 miles/sec. This is formidable, but no one will be faced with the problem of taking off from the sun, and furthermore, even at the orbit of Mercury, the amount of energy required to move outward to infinity has greatly reduced. This is very fortunate, and we shall see that relatively little energy is needed to travel from orbit to orbit in the solar system but that a relatively great amount must be expended in merely escaping from a planet. It is far harder to escape from the earth, for example, than for a rocket to transfer from earth's orbit to Mars's orbit, millions of miles away.

At all times we must know the velocity of escape to infinity from the sun's attraction at points on the orbits of the planets. Thus, to escape from a point on Mercury's orbit, but not from Mercury itself, a speed of slightly more than 42 miles/sec will be necessary.

If a rocket has the orbital speed of Mercury (nearly 30 miles/sec) as a boost, as it will have if it moves in Mercury's orbit, an additional 12 miles/sec will be required to drive the rocket to infinity. Compare this with the figure of 37 miles/sec required to escape from Jupiter, a much tougher dynamical problem than not only to escape from Mercury, the planet, but to attain a heliocentric parabolic velocity.

It is known to be easier to escape from a circular orbit around a planet by applying one tangential impulse than to fire the motor a number of times in transferring outward. This statement probably would not be true in the case of a vehicle escaping through a satellite system such as that possessed by Jupiter, since then, at least, third-body perturbations would exert appreciable influences.

With these ideas in mind, we can consider the earth-Mars trip, typical of any that could take place between planets in the solar system. The first thing that we must know is the value r, the distance from the center of the earth to the orbit.[2] We can then calculate the velocity of a rocket or satellite vehicle in the selected orbit, i.e., the circular velocity. We should next calculate the velocity of escape at this level and find the difference between it and the circular velocity. The resultant figure will tell us the velocity increment needed by the rocket to escape from the earth's pull at the orbital distance.

Once the rocket has escaped from the earth, it will move on the transfer orbit toward Mars, under the sole influence of the sun. We first find the velocity of the escape rocket relative to that of the earth in its orbit. This velocity is vectorially added to the orbital velocity of the earth. It is quite obvious, here, that we must know two things: (1) the relative velocity of earth with respect to the rocket and (2) the angle of rocket motion with respect to the orbital path of the earth. On entering its transfer orbit, the rocket will be one astronomical unit from the sun; that is, it will be at some point approximately on the earth's orbit. This transfer orbit will be elliptical, with the sun at one focus. The character of the orbit can now be determined by finding the major axis. The rocket will move

[2] It is assumed that orbital refueling techniques will be employed in all cases.

outward toward Mars on this path, and will intersect at a point on the orbit of Mars. If the computations have been correct so far, and if no new and undetected errors have crept in, the point where the rocket intersects Mars's orbit will be very close to the point occupied by Mars at the time of the rocket's arrival.

On arriving, the speed of the rocket will be known. The angle made by the rocket's arrival path with the orbit of Mars must then be determined, as well as the relative velocity of the rocket in terms of that of Mars. The rocket is now at the "other end" of its earth-Mars transfer orbit. As in the case of the earth, we vectorially add the rocket's relative velocity to Mars's orbital speed, yielding the velocity of the rocket in terms of the sun (remember that until now we are still on the elliptical path governed by the sun and not by Mars). Once we know the velocity of the rocket relative to the sun, we can easily learn the speed at which the rocket is approaching its target.

The rocket now can enter Mars's *field of influence*. The characteristics of the motion of the rocket will cause it to approach along a hyperbolic path, the exact slope of which will naturally depend on the approach made by the rocket in relation to the location of Mars. The rocket will now merely descend this conic arc until it reaches the point at which it is desired to enter into circular orbit. The application of thrust is then made by firing the motors, and the rocket's velocity is reduced to a value consistent with the calculated circular velocity for the distance r chosen.

The only thing we have to do now is apply the escape velocity at the level of the orbit around Mars and the velocity of maneuver of the rocket transferring into its circular path, so that figures for the final elements of the trip can be known. The rocket is then in a position to transfer down from its orbit to the surface, although it must be considered that less energy will be used in doing this than would be needed for arrival on an airless world of identical attraction. That is, some form of aerodynamic descent may be supposed.

With an idea of the elements necessary to make an earth-Mars voyage, we can now look at a few details eliminated from this rather sweeping picture. We noticed that the earth, Mars, and, for that matter, all the planets move at speeds greater than the transfer-speed increments between individual orbits. We saw that the most economical routes are ellipses such that the arcs just graze the orbits of the take-off and target planetary orbits. Such ellipses are sometimes called *tangential transfer ellipses* or *cotangential orbits*.

We cannot leave a planet such as the earth at any time we desire and expect to arrive correctly at the destination planet. The path and time will have to be computed with great precision. In the case of our Mars trip, take-off from the earth when this planet is at perihelion and landing on Mars when at aphelion will allow the maximum propellant economy. On the basis of distance this looks wrong, but it should be recalled that the earth moves faster when at the perihelion point of its orbit, and Mars moves slower when at aphelion (Table 13-1).

TABLE 13-1   *Useful Mars and Earth Data*

	Mars	Earth
Period, days	686.98	365.25
Period of axial rotation	24ʰ 37ᵐ 22ˢ	23ʰ 56ᵐ 04ˢ
Distance from sun, astronomical units *		
Mean	1.524	1
Perihelion	1.382	0.984
Aphelion	1.667	1.03
Orbital velocity, miles/sec		
Mean	15	18.5
Perihelion	16.4	18.8
Aphelion	13.6	18.2
Diameter, miles	4,215	7,927
Acceleration of gravity, ft/sec^2	11.2	32.12
Escape velocity at surface, miles/sec	3.1	6.95
Volume, Earth = 1	0.15	1
Mass, Earth = 1	0.108	1
Inclination of equator to orbit	24° 10′	23° 26′ 59″
Oblateness	0.0052	0.0034
Longitude of perihelion	334° 34′ 12″	101° 33′ 53″
Mean density, water = 1	3.85	5.52
Orbital eccentricity	0.093	0.017
Orbital inclination	1.9°	0°
Maximum surface temperature, °F	85	140
Minimum surface temperature, °F	−150	−105

* An astronomical unit is taken as the mean distance of the sun to the earth and is equal to 9.3×10^7 miles. Actually, the mean distance sun to earth is slightly less, 9.29×10^7 miles, but the larger, rounded-off value is more convenient.

The problems associated with escape from the earth can generally be applied to escape from any body, except that there will be no aerodynamic drag where the body has no atmosphere. Observing limitations imposed by thermal barriers, it is advisable to apply a thrust as strong and soon as possible following take-off. This initial application of thrust may have to be supplemented later in order to correct for errors.

Interplanetary Orbits—Navigation

The problem of correcting interplanetary orbits has not been overlooked, and one of the most valuable papers on the subject was published in Great Britain by Derek Lawden four years ago.[3] Recognizing that transfer routes to the planets will be calculated long before a rocket ship takes off, it is nevertheless necessary to develop methods to correct all errors that may creep in en route. The astronavigator cannot be content with errors measured in mere hundreds or thousands of miles. A small, uncorrected error arising at one point of flight can produce a very large error later. Lawden emphasizes that, once a rocket departs from the computed trajectory, a *new* situation must be recognized and calculations must be performed to set up the path from the instantaneous position at time of discovery of error to the destination.

The original path and all corrected paths must be aimed at optimum conservation of propellants. Lawden suggests that, if an error is observed, the rocket's velocity be so altered that the rocket will move into an orbit passing through the precomputed terminal junction point at the *same* time it *would* have arrived on the original (optimum) route. It will remain only to apply a small velocity correction, when the rocket reaches the junction point, to "achieve agreement with the optimal programme." Such a correction will have to be consolidated into whatever velocity increment was established to occur at the point of juncture.

Ehricke has developed the concept of the "Instrumented Comet" (cf. *Interavia,* December, 1956) for one-way exploratory missions out into space. The one-way trip would offer a great fuel savings, and the weight gained could be used either to reduce the vehicle

[3] D. F. Lawden, Correction of Interplanetary Orbits, *J. Brit. Interplanet. Soc.,* vol. 13, no. 4, 1954.

size or to increase the instrument payload. (Hyperbolic orbits are assumed.) Such a probe could explore the solar surroundings that no manned ship could possibly ever approach—shown by Ehricke to be a distance halfway between the sun and Mercury. Here the radiation equilibrium temperature would be up to 1000°F, so a satisfactory emission-to-absorption ratio would have to be provided. His solar probe would investigate the corona, solar emitted material, magnetic fields, zodiacal light, solar cosmic radiation, and so forth.

For planetary exploration a planetary probe, which would be simpler from an energy-expenditure point of view, would be employed. Optical exploration of Mars and radar probing of Venus could be carried out; data could be transmitted to a space-borne transponder and then relayed to earth. To help locate the comets in the depths of space, small nuclear bombs (which would allow for optical acquisition and then electronic lock-on) would be detonated. The probe concept is nicely developed by C. A. Cross in the July–September, 1957, *Journal of the British Interplanetary Society*.

The French astronomer, De Vaucouleurs, speaking at Harvard in 1957, suggested determining the mass of Venus by satellite techniques, since the planet has no natural moon. Radio-ranging could be employed to find not only the depth of the atmosphere, but the diameter of the planet.

As for Mars, a probe could help work out details of the oblateness and internal structure, discrepancies between present optical and dynamical determinations, fine structure of surface markings, and continuous strip-mapping surveying. If two vehicles were used, they could conduct spectroscopic tests of the atmosphere between them. Alternatively, one vehicle could extend a reflecting mirror. Variable-frequency soundings for the detection of ionized atmospheric layers, ring-current investigations, and magnetometer and radio surveys would be other areas of study. Such techniques should permit the partial exploration of the solar system before man leaves his terrestrial control stations.

Suppose we are aboard a spaceship somewhere in outer space, but within the solar system, and radio failure occurs. How, then, will we be able to determine, by optical means, our position in

space? An interesting attempt to answer this question was presented at the Institute of Navigation, in 1950.[4] One way of fixing
position would be to take three observations of a planet in much
the same way we do with a comet. This would be efficient and
accurate, but the complexity of the computations would stagger the
limited facilities of an interplanetary rocket. It would be far simpler
to plot the spaceship's position from simultaneous observations of
two or more planets. To do this with sufficient accuracy, a photoelectric means of locating the planets' apparent positions has been
suggested. If a very accurate fix is required, one would merely
increase the number of planets under observation to three, four, or
possibly even more.

How do we orient a spaceship? We shall probably see some sort
of gyro mechanism inside connected with photoelectric equipment
outside the ship. If an accuracy of 0.1' of arc can be maintained,
Atkinson feels that the "error of a fix would be about 5,000 miles
in each of the two tangential coordinates at the distance of Mars."
This is quite respectable. He shows that it will be necessary to keep
a specified axis pointed always to the sun; "the direction of this
fundamental axis could . . . be used exactly as the direction of
gravity is used in surface navigation; the angles made with this
direction by the lines of two or three stars would yield the ship's
heliocentric latitude and longitude."

We could work out latitudes and longitudes by observing the
angular positions of stars, and, as on earth, this would mean
spherical trigonometry. If our ship were on the ecliptic, we could
handle only plane triangles, provided, of course, the longitudinal
observations were made with stars on or very near the ecliptic and
that latitude was taken from polar stars. In this connection, the
space navigators will surely find it useful to know the radial distance from the sun, which can be determined by photographic
measurement of the apparent diameter.

Pin-pointing a ship in three-dimensional space with an accuracy
of several thousand miles will probably be sufficient for the major
part of a space voyage, but it may often be desirable to determine
roughly how far from a planetary body the ship is. There are a number of direct ways this can be done; two which promptly come to

[4] R. d'E. Atkinson, Some Problems of Interplanetary Navigation.

mind are the use of radar (as the Army Signal Corps has already illustrated in the case of the moon) and the determining of apparent diameters. Since we know the real diameter, once we can measure accurately the apparent diameter of a planet, true distance will be calculated simply. Both these techniques will undoubtedly be employed only when the rocket is a million miles or less out from the target planet.

An interesting article on orientation in space appeared in the *Journal of the British Interplanetary Society,* November–December, 1956, by Vertregt. The author sets up a system of coordinates and shows that a spaceship position can be determined by "its heliocentric longitude and latitude according to the frame of reference [described in the paper] and its distance from the sun." To get the necessary data, the spaceship observes the apparent latitude and longitude of the sun among the stars, and, knowing a given planet's heliocentric latitude and longitude and distance from the sun at any instant together with the apparent longitude as seen from the spaceship, it can position itself rather accurately. An astronautical almanac will of course be essential.

Castruccio, writing on navigation in interplanetary space (*Missiles and Rockets,* December, 1956), points out that seven things must be known to properly navigate a ship: (1) position with respect to some frame of reference, (2) direction of travel with respect to the same frame, (3) velocity, (4) position of body toward which the ship is moving, (5) direction of travel of body, (6) speed of travel of body, (7) any predictable deviation from a straight-line course of the body. Castruccio suggests that navigational systems such as space Loran (or variations), broad-beam or omnidirectional radiators on destination planet, and beams between planets forming polygons or variable legs be employed. In the latter cases the spaceship would merely tune in to the frequency, allowing automatic devices to bring the ship to the destination. The author thought that, theoretically, a beam-rider system could bring a ship to Mars within an accuracy of 10,000 miles if a 30-ft-diameter antenna at a 3-cm wavelength were used. As for Loran, it would enable a fix to be made, following which the pilot would work out and follow a course.

Von Braun, Herrick, Lawden, Thompson, Clarke, Richardson,

and others (see bibliography) have treated earth-Venus and earth-Mars flights mathematically, generally relying heavily on factors that lead to economy of fuel rather than economy of time. Thompson discusses the principles of fast orbits as applied to earth-Mars flight. He assumes a take-off from earth's satellite orbit at 5,000 miles and arrival at Mars's satellite orbit at 3,000 miles, from the respective centers. His ship accelerates so that "its path will become hyperbolic with respect to the earth." At present it is only of academic importance to consider a straight-line approach to a planet, wherein a rocket would not only have to achieve escape velocity of the earth but would have to counteract the earth's orbital velocity of over 18 miles/sec.

Professor Samuel Herrick, of the University of California, has made a number of interesting calculations based on the earth's orbital velocity at 18.5 miles/sec and escape velocity at 6.9 miles/sec and Mars's perihelion velocity at 16.4 miles/sec and escape velocity at 3.1 miles/sec. His rocket travels along a two-body orbit at a perihelion velocity of 19.8 miles/sec and an aphelion velocity of 14.3 miles/sec. The rocket trajectory is tangent to the perihelion of the orbit of Mars. By subtracting the velocity of the earth from the perihelion velocity of the rocket, we get

	Miles/sec
Perihelion velocity of rocket	19.8
Velocity of earth	−18.5
Velocity of escape rocket	1.3

This is the velocity that an escape rocket will have once it has reached a point roughly a million miles from earth where the sun exerts by far the major influence.[5] By the time it reached Mars's orbital intersection point, we would find that Mars would come up on the rocket with a relative velocity of 2.1 miles/sec:

	Miles/sec
Orbital velocity of Mars	16.4
Rocket velocity of aphelion	−14.3
Relative velocity of Mars	2.1

[5] The heliocentric velocity following escape from earth will be 18.5 + 7.1, or 25.6 miles/sec (in same direction as earth orbits, of course), which, a million miles out, will reduce to 19.9 miles/sec and, at aphelion of its trajectory (perihelion of Mars), will be 14.3 miles/sec.

Suppose, now, that we wish to leave the earth with just enough velocity to assure us of the 1.3-miles/sec velocity the rocket is to assume relative to sun. Calculations show this to be less than 7.1 miles/sec, only slightly greater than parabolic, or simple escape, velocity. Herrick, here, goes on to assume that a rocket arriving at Mars will have to apply thrust to neutralize or check a 3.35-miles/sec velocity increment.[6] Adding this to the departure velocity from earth, we have

	Miles/sec
Departure velocity from earth	7.1
Velocity increment	3.35
Characteristic velocity of	10.45

or the total characteristic velocity of the maneuver that must be generated by ejecting mass from the rocket. All other movements are celestial in nature, and the rocket responds only to gravitational fields.

Elsewhere, discussing a trip to Venus, Herrick writes that

if the "initial" geocentric or relative velocity of a rocket is 7.12 miles/sec (i.e., at the end of a short thrust period), and if it is directed away from the center of the earth and in the direction opposite to that in which the earth is traveling, its geocentric velocity at a distance of about a million miles will be about 1.5 miles/sec.

This means that the heliocentric velocity will be

	Miles/sec
Velocity of earth	18.5
Geocentric velocity	−1.5
Velocity in direction of earth	17.0

Since the rocket is moving, relative to the sun, at a velocity less than circular velocity at the distance earth-sun, the rocket will immediately tend to drift inward toward the sun. After a trip of 146 days and 250 million miles, the rocket will reach its perihelion point with a velocity of 23.5 miles/sec at a position on the orbit of Venus. There it will have a velocity of about 1.5 miles/sec above

[6] In one paper he assumes a figure of "not more than 3.7 miles per second."

that of Venus, which the pull of Venus will increase by an additional 5 miles/sec. A combination of thrust and aerodynamic-descent techniques will allow for a landing on the surface.

We have mentioned quite a few velocity figures. What, exactly, could a space navigator do to ascertain the velocity at which his vehicle travels? This is an intriguing question, one that has been only partially answered. We might find the radial velocity by observing the Doppler shift of the sun's spectrum, but this technique would require some fairly good photographic equipment and, of course, a rather large slit-type spectroscope. The Doppler principle refers to the fact that the spectrum of an approaching body will be displaced toward the violet, while that of a body in recession will be shifted toward the red end. The following relation would obtain:

$$\text{Radial velocity} = \frac{\text{change of wavelength}}{\text{normal wavelength}} \times \text{velocity of light}$$

This method would allow us to compute the relative velocity of approach to, or recession from, the sun.

A second astronomical technique, useful perhaps only at the tremendous speeds of galactic flight, concerns the apparent displacement of stars toward the apex of the rocketship's way. This would be due to the inevitable aberration occasioned both by the ship's motion and the noninstantaneous transmission of the light waves. The technique would be very similar to the method used to determine the motion of the sun, wherein the stars in the direction toward which the sun moves appear to open out, while those behind close in.

Returning, now, to the solar system, we note that some investigators set up what they call "velocity burgets" to the planets. For example, Clarke [7] arrives at the figure of 16.7 miles/sec as the total of various velocity increments necessary to accomplish a Venus trip, although he assumes the figure will go over 18.5 when gravitational losses and navigational corrections are incorporated. The velocity budget for the trip, lasting nearly 150 days, would break down as follows:

[7] A. C. Clarke, The Dynamics of Space Flight, *J. Brit. Interplanet. Soc.,* vol. 8, no. 2, 1949.

	Miles/sec
To escape earth	6.95
Earth orbit to voyage orbit	1.55
Voyage orbit to Venus orbit	1.68
Descent to surface of Venus	6.45
Characteristic velocity of trip	16.64

A 237-day Mars trip would look something like the following, with figures rounded off in conversion from kilometers:

	Miles/sec
To escape earth	6.96
Earth orbit to voyage orbit	1.80
Voyage orbit to Mars orbit	1.68
Descent to surface of Mars	3.11
Characteristic velocity of trip	13.55

This would probably run around 15 miles/sec when navigation corrections and random gravity losses are included. The amount of time the trip will last can be readily calculated from Kepler's third law, knowing that the period of an elliptical orbit is proportional to the three-halves power of the semimajor axis.

These figures vary somewhat according to assumptions and positions of planets at take-off and landing. Richardson, in his book "Exploring Mars," has prepared velocity budgets for Venus, Mars, and Mercury trips, the last of which would take 96 or 115 days, depending on whether contact was made at aphelion or perihelion. In addition, he lists transfer velocities and times of transit for the planets, assuming travel along the most economical routes. Thus a trip to Pluto would require 7.5 miles/sec and last 10,972 days (30 years), against his figure of 1.4 miles/sec and 237 days for Mars.

Richardson speculates on the use of high-speed hyperbolic orbits, and compares them with the economical, but slow, elliptical routes. Transfer time to Mars would be 29 days at 40 miles/sec, 22 days at 50, and only 10 days if the figure of 100 miles/sec could be achieved. Even Pluto, approached at this latter speed, would lie but 330 days away.

There are a number of specialized aspects of both navigation and communications in space. Assuredly, among the astrionic equipment aboard a ship where any sort of navigation is to take place, semiconductor devices will be found. The highly uniform crystalline structure of the semiconductor would almost definitely be affected by primary cosmic radiation and by radiation not properly shielded from any nuclear reactor that might provide on-board power. Both fast neutrons and gamma rays would do the damage, and it seems hard to visualize a means of affording complete protection. The question of whether or not transistors and diodes could operate in space might be crucial to any astronautical venture. Temperatures, radiation, and pressures would all affect electronic equipment and batteries. For example, batteries become rapidly inefficient below about 20 to 30°F, and transistors operate poorly above 140°F. We shall therefore have to maintain an internal temperature within rather narrow limits.

It will have to be determined whether equipment should be hermetically sealed, whether tubes should be constructed to profit from hard-vacuum conditions, etc. If we pressurize the electronic package, what would pressure loss due to a meteor hit entail? Micrometeoric erosion of vehicle and optical parts might be catastrophic. The Vanguard and Explorer programs include, as we have seen, experiments that will tell us about temperature and pressure conditions of the instrumented package and micrometeor incidence, and in the meteorological experiment optical equipment will be carried. In this light, they are certain to be of immense help in paving the road toward unmanned navigation in space.

Remote-controlled research probes may well be the first man-made vehicles to accomplish lunar and planetary exploration. Man, and devices and materials capable of sustaining him, may just be too heavy to carry aboard the minimal vehicles we shall have to put up with during the early exploration years. Vehicle instrumentation and surface control techniques available today might be sufficient to make the first try. Much as with the current Explorer and Sputnik programs, data could be telemetered back to earth. Techniques would be the same, though power requirements and other factors would have to be scaled up. Television cameras might give us the aspect of the other side of the moon, years before man himself could get there. All guidance and control operations could be monitored by the types of electronic computer we have now, or by moderate variations. The philosophy of this approach is obvious: Know well your ocean before setting sail on it yourself. This is something we can do now, but could not do in Columbus's day. Experts seem to agree that we should take advantage of it. In effect, this is what we are doing with Explorer and Sputnik, and instead of going right ahead and making the manned station in 1958, we are first sending out our instrumented probes.

The system to be used would be some sort of closed-command data-control loop, links being provided by radio. The output would be not only the measurements effected by the on-board instrumentation, but data on the space position, or trajectory, at any given time. Such a huge radio link reaching out into space and back would provide input and output channels for commands, data transmittal, and corrective signals.

Radar installations of very high power would track the instrumented probe, using pulse coding for range data and command coding. Large computers would be used to determine and compare the position of the probe with the predetermined trajectory, and command corrective changes. All outgoing signals would be voltages which could be received and decoded on the vehicle.

Not only would the position and orientation of the probe have to be continually watched and monitored, but accelerations and rates of position change would also have to be considered. Operating frequencies of between 100 and 3,000 megacycles would be employed. Ground-transmitter powers would depend largely on the size of the antennas used on the probe.

The probe would have to be careful in traversing the earth's atmosphere on its way into space. Not only would heat-resistant materials have to be used to cope with aerodynamic heating, but vibrations covering a wide range of frequencies would necessarily have to be provided for. And in space itself the heat generated by the electronic gear would have to be dissipated continually.

We have purposely attempted to bring the reader, so to speak, "back to earth" by presenting, at the end of the chapter, a rather unimaginative concept of sending instrumented probes out to navigate space long before man himself dares leave his planet. Surely, after following hyperbolic orbits to Pluto, an instrumented gadget circumnavigating the moon seems dull. Yet we must continually remind ourselves that planetary travel is a long way off and that dozens of techniques must be tried and proved before we even step on the moon. If man can get a 10-lb instrumented payload around the moon, he will later get 100 lb on it. And then, inevitably, he himself will follow.

Now, to end up once again in space, let us summarize what this survey has shown us. The nearest planets can be attained, along elliptical routes, in travel times that can be measured in days, while the outer planets will take years to reach. Trips to Jupiter, Uranus, or Pluto will become feasible only when very high-powered propellants come into the picture. But this need not discourage us. We may have to be content for a while with our friend, the ellipse, but some day, as the interplanetary age advances, we may succeed in "taming" the hyperbola. Science has a habit of fooling the pessimists.

BIBLIOGRAPHY

The literature purely on space navigation is understandably small, but many books have chapters devoted to the subject. Professor S. Herrick is working on a book on astrodynamics, and he has written numerous articles on all phases of space navigation. In the periodical literature, many of the recent contributions in the subject appear in the German language, as well as in English.

ARTICLES IN THE *Journal of the British Interplanetary Society*

Preston-Thomas, H.: Generalized Interplanetary Orbits, vol. 11, no. 2, p. 76, 1952.
Lawden, D. F.: Correction of Interplanetary Orbits, vol. 13, no. 4, p. 215, 1954.
————: Escape to Infinity from Circular Orbits, vol. 12, no. 2, p. 68, 1953.
————: The Calculation of Orbits, vol. 14, no. 4, p. 204, 1955.
————: Fundamentals of Space Navigation, vol. 13, no. 7, p. 87, 1954.
Forbes, G. F.: Powered Orbits in Space, vol. 14, no. 2, p. 85, 1955.
Porter, J. G.: Interplanetary Orbits, vol. 11, no. 5, p. 205, 1952.
————: Navigation without Gravity, vol. 13, no. 2, p. 68, 1954.
Herrick, S.: Space Rocket Trajectories, vol. 9, no. 5, p. 235, 1950.
Cashmore, D. J.: Some Problems of Interplanetary Navigation, vol. 10, no. 2, p. 71, 1951.
Leitmann, G.: On the Equation of Rocket Motion, vol. 16, no. 3, p. 141, 1957.

ARTICLES IN OTHER JOURNALS

Herrick, S.: Rocket Navigation, *Navigation,* vol. 2, December, 1950.

Lawden, D. F.: Minimal Rocket Trajectories, *J. Am. Rocket Soc.,* vol. 23, no. 6, 1953.

Herrick, S.: Interplanetary Navigation, *Navigation,* vol. 3, September–December, 1951.

Tsien, H. S.: Take Off from Satellite Orbits, *J. Am. Rocket Soc.,* vol. 23, no. 4, 1953.

Castruccio, P.: Navigation in Interplanetary Space, *Missiles and Rockets,* vol. 1, no. 3, p. 98, 1956.

Vertregt, M.: Orientation in Space, *J. Brit. Interplanet. Soc.,* vol. 15, no. 6, p. 324, 1956.

Thompson, D. I.: Interplanetary Flight Calculations, Simplified, *Missile Away!,* vol, 4, no. 4, p. 30, 1957.

Parker, N. F., and C. P. Greening: La Navigation par inertie, *Interavia,* p. 575, June, 1957.

Cole, D. M.: Times Required for Continuous Thrust Earth-Moon Trips, *Jet Propulsion,* vol. 27, no. 4, p. 416, 1957.

Leitmann, G.: Rocket Trajectories, *Ordnance,* vol. 41, no. 221, p. 916, 1957.

Cole, D. M.: The Earth-Mars Constant Thrust Brachistochrone, *Jet Propulsion,* vol. 27, no. 2, p. 176, 1957.

Books of special interest on the subject are listed below. In addition, books on general astronautics almost invariably treat space navigation, as do some books on astronomy.

Richardson, R. S.: "Exploring Mars," chap. 5, McGraw-Hill Book Company, Inc., New York, 1955.

Hohmann, W.: "Die Errecichbarkeit der Himmelskörper," R. Oldenbourg-Verlag, Munich, 1925.

von Braun, W.: "The Mars Project," University of Illinois Press, Urbana, Ill., 1953.

Clarke, A. C.: "Interplanetary Flight," Temple Press, Ltd., London (Harper & Brothers, New York), 1950.

14

Interstellar Flight

Light Speed and Relativity

So ambitious a title as "Interstellar Flight" may seem out of place in a book purporting to give an accurate, realistic presentation of the space flight and allied sciences. We saw, in the chapter on human factors in space flying, that the total concept of interstellar flight is fraught with seeming impossibilities. Later, in our discussion of navigation in space, we saw what was involved in voyages to the planets. In Chap. 7, in a moment of enthusiasm, we looked into the problem of escape from the solar system, although there we did not go into what we would do after we had escaped from the sun's attraction permanently.

Needless to say, the problems involved in any space voyage are titanic. We have not yet reached our own moon, nor have we even established a manned satellite. What does it mean, then, to devote even a short chapter to flight to the stars, or perhaps to exterior galactic systems? The why is as elusive as the how but is fortunately somewhat easier to grasp once the ingredients that go into it are delineated.

First of all, our world is small, and population pressure may eventually force man to seek less hospitable worlds in our own solar system. If he is forced from his own planet for this reason alone (neglecting such intangibles as adventure and curiosity or such tangibles as war, colonization, and search for new resources), he can ultimately rationalize trips involving stellar distances. This

335

would be all the easier were none of our neighbor planets to offer even a semihospitable abode to future pioneer settlers.

Strange as it may seem, if we can ever accelerate our rockets to high suboptic speeds, we are likely to be able to visit many of the stars in our galaxy without unsurmountable difficulty. As we approach the seeming limit, the speed of light, it will become possible for man to travel even to the galaxies and return to his home coordinate system (or frame of reference) within his lifetime. The concept of generation travel (Chap. 10) will become significant only if man attempts interstellar travel before such time as he enjoys the means of roving at high fractions of the speed of light. The question that arises in any consideration of generation travel is: What is the maximum feasible time span? An answer of 100, 1,000, or 10,000 years would depend on so many subtle factors that any assessment today is made a totally academic proposition.

In the light of this, it would be extremely hazardous to make any estimates of what interstellar travel will mean or what impact it will have on future civilization. Certainly new philosophies, sociologies, and a more advanced understanding of time and the universe will be available, as well as a deeper knowledge of the biological sciences.

Flight to the stars will depend on transit times and the distance to the destination star or system. Energy considerations will dictate ultimate speeds, whether 100, 1,000, 10,000, or 100,000 miles/sec, and power levels attainable will tell us what accelerations will be produced to reach eventually such high speeds. Without speculating further, one can only add that it is unlikely man will ever embark on a voyage to a star unless he knows it has a planetary family, or unless he has almost unlimited energy sources at his command and is willing to pay some of the prices that will become apparent shortly.

Unless we are willing to undergo the ordeal of generation travel, it is impossible to think of interstellar flight in terms other than those involving velocities approaching the velocity of light. All discussions are based on the assumption that the velocity of light is an upper limit (i.e., nothing can go faster), that its velocity through a vacuum is constant, and that the relative motions of all bodies in the universe have no influence on it.

Once we enter the realm of near-optic speeds, we find that relativistic dynamics begin to govern the motion of any moving body. A rocket traveling at 0.95 c, for example, would force us to consider problems in the precincts of special relativity, and these problems would remain with us as long as we chose to maintain such speeds. Classical theory holds that, if a rocket ship moves at a constant velocity V and receives an additional velocity increment V', it would have a resultant $V + V'$. Relativistic laws, on the other hand, provide the following situation:

$$V_f = \frac{V + V'}{1 + VV'/c^2} \tag{14-1}$$

where V_f is the resultant final velocity. (In all cases observations are made from a given stationary point of reference of a coordinate system.)

Taking the case of a vehicle moving at 0.95 c, we could assume that a relative increase of 0.05 c is made. The vehicle, however, will not travel at light speed c but, according to the above formula, at some lesser speed. This works out to be 0.9546 c by

$$\begin{aligned}
V_f &= \frac{0.95 + 0.05}{1 + (0.95 \times 0.05)/1^2} \\
&= \frac{1}{1.0475} \\
&= 0.9546
\end{aligned}$$

In this example, the space rocket fails by 0.0454 c to reach the ultimate or limiting speed of the universe.

While we apparently cannot reach light speed, we may conceivably someday accelerate a rocket to 50 or 75 per cent, or more, of that velocity. As the speed of light is approached, a number of things are likely to happen. One involves the so-called Lorentz transformation; the other, time-dilation effect (or, as it is sometimes called, "the time paradox").

Lorentz-Fitzgerald Contraction Theory

Hendrik A. Lorentz, a famed Dutch physicist, investigated what would happen to the dimensions of a rigid body moving at extremely high uniform speed in terms of a given fixed system. He established a formula, basing his reasoning on the laws of magnetism and electricity, such as that the initial length of a body would decrease as the velocity increased, or

$$L = L_o \sqrt{1 - V^2/c^2} \qquad (14\text{-}2)$$

where $L = $ *relative* length when the object (rocket for us) is in motion

$L_o = $ object's length at rest

$V = $ velocity of object in question

$c = $ velocity of light

For an object at rest, V would equal zero, so L would equal L_o; and if V reached c, L would become zero, an obvious limit in terms of this equation. This ties in with Lorentz's relativistic mass equation, in which he made the assumption that the mass of an electron will increase with velocity. That is,

$$m = \frac{m_o}{\sqrt{1 - (V/c)^2}} \qquad (14\text{-}3)$$

where $m_o = $ mass of electron at rest

$m = $ same mass traveling at velocity V

If V equaled c, m would become infinite. Another matter that must be taken into account is the amount of force necessary to change the direction of motion of a mass traveling at velocities close to the velocity of light. The mass of any body at rest may be termed "rest mass." Classical mechanics tells us that the greater the mass the greater the resistance to change in motion, and vice versa. But once we get into the realm of relativistic motion, we find that velocity enters into the picture as well as rest mass, and that the resistance to change "becomes infinitely great as the velocity approaches that of light." [1]

Summing up Eqs. (14-2) and (14-3), if a rocket accelerated to the velocity of light (assuming it to be possible), it would have zero length and an infinite mass. One might wonder just what the crew would think about this bizarre state of affairs!

Time-dilation Effect

As our hypothetical space traveler accelerates his interstellar rocket to higher and higher velocities, he will find that time be-

[1] A. Einstein and L. Infeld, "The Evolution of Physics," chap. 3, pp. 205ff., Simon and Schuster, Inc., New York, 1952.

haves according to points of reference. Suppose we take two points in space. We then establish an observer at a fixed reference point (coordinate system) with a time-measuring device and request that he clock a rocket voyaging at a substantial fraction of c. He will find that the elapsed time in the other special point (the rocket) will be greater from his point of view than from that of an observer moving inside the rocket. In other words, time is directly dependent on velocity and the relative motion of the observer. This has been experimentally verified by watching mu-mesons passing through the atmosphere (where they are able to travel further than their lifetimes should permit, even assuming that they could attain the speed of light).

We are brought to Einstein's special theory of relativity when we consider bodies that are moving at a constant velocity, and to the general theory when we consider bodies that are being accelerated. As we can now see, both space and time are relative, requiring us to specify all events in time as well as in space. Furthermore, everything must be compared with an established frame of reference or coordinate system "constructed of rigid unchangeable bodies," to which all observations are referred. In general, we consider the earth as our coordinate system.

Light, so far as we know, is the cosmic limit to our velocity aspirations. But fast as it is, it is still finite. When we gaze out at a star on a clear night we see it as it *was,* not as it really *is,* for its light has spent many years in reaching us. In effect, we are looking backward into time. If time is relative, there must be some expression to tie it in with the relative velocity on which it depends. The expression we want is called the relativistic time equation:

$$t = \frac{t_o}{\sqrt{1 - (V/c)^2}} \tag{14-4}$$

where t_o = interval of time experienced by an observer in the coordinate system (at rest)

t = time recorded by a clock moving in the rocket at a constant velocity V across space

c = velocity of light in a vacuum

A clock in a very fast space rocket will, to an observer in the coordinate system, appear to run slowly. It is further evident that, if the clock recedes from the coordinate system at V equals c, then no change in time would occur, that is, any point in the universe would seem to be attained instantaneously. Any such concept as *now* is purely local, invented to satisfy a local point of view in time reference.

It becomes apparent that, if we could bring a space vehicle to speeds close to the speed of light, we could tour the universe within the lifetime of a human being. Yet if this hypothetical traveler should return to his original coordinate system (the earth), he might find (depending on how near to c he managed to get) that thousands, millions, or even billions of years had passed. Conceivably, the earth upon which he was born might have long since ceased to sustain life. Even the galaxy might have changed beyond recognition.

In this context (and only in this context) time travel can be lifted from the pages of science fiction and placed into reality. Theoretically, man can travel almost anywhere in the universe, provided, of course, he will (1) intellectually accept the possibility of having eons elapse within the coordinate system from which he started, and (2) be able to devise some way of generating the tremendous velocities an interstellar rocket would need to enter into relativistic motion.

A good deal of fuss on this matter has been stirred up, particularly by letters appearing in the British journal *Nature* (McCrea, vol. 167, p. 680, 1951; Dingle and McCrea, vol. 177, p. 782, vol. 178, p. 680, 1956; Singer, vol. 179, p. 977, 1957). These letters show, with remarkable clarity, that there is considerable disagreement about the Einstein clock paradox. The major problems have been neatly summarized by Stehling in *Jet Propulsion,* December, 1956, and it would wander from the main purpose of this book to discuss the controversy in detail here.

Matter into Energy

Recent progress toward harnessing atomic power for submarines has led to accelerated atomic-airplane development programs in both the United States and Russia. Atomic-reactor progress at Idaho Falls has been steady, and the so-called "frozen atom" break-through hints at missile applications in the not too distant future. Project Rover and other programs are being watched carefully.

It was discovered, as a result of World War II research, that both slow and fast neutrons could cause uranium fission, but that intermediate-velocity neutrons were quite useless. This was understandable when it was realized that intermediate neutrons have an "ideal" quantity of energy and can more or less slip into the nucleus; while the slow variety cannot penetrate the normal uranium nucleus, but are able to split the U^{235} isotope. U^{235} exists in very small quantities in normal U^{238}; about 1 atom in 140. The fast neutrons directly split the U^{238} isotope, releasing tremendous energy.

We get more than just energy, however, for new neutrons are now released and may split other nuclei, causing fission and subsequent release of more energy and more neutrons. A chain reaction has occurred. It is obvious that, to sustain a chain reaction, we must ensure that more neutrons are created than are lost (loss can occur by nuclear capture without fission, capture by an impurity, or escape from the system). By keeping the surface area-to-volume ratio as low as possible and by using a neutron-reflecting material, at least partial control of neutron escape is possible, with consequent savings.

Now, what should be done to help prevent neutrons from being captured by nuclei? Recalling that U^{235} fission is brought about by slow neutrons and that fission-produced neutrons are of the fast variety, it would seem logical to somehow slow up the latter type. This is what is done, and a moderator generally made of graphite is the instrument employed. This slowing-down action will greatly increase the chances of U^{235} fission and, at the same time, reduce the probability of nonfissile U^{238} capture.

If we want to make an atomic bomb, we use a "fast" type neutron pile; but should we desire to keep on the safe side, we find that a "thermal" pile is more useful. Here, much graphite moderating material is employed to bring down the available neutron energy by elastic scattering. Sooner or later the neutrons will have their energies so reduced that they enter into thermal equilibrium in the system. To pay for safety we must accept increased weight and bulk.

A few other points should be mentioned. To have a successful atomic reactor or pile both the uranium and graphite must be very pure. Furthermore, we are not necessarily hampered by the fact that U^{235} is extremely rare, since we can merely bombard the U^{238} to produce an artificial element, plutonium, offering the same fission qualities as U^{235}.

Before we could envisage practical applications of atomic energy, it was necessary to know how to control the reactor output. Neutron-absorbing rods were developed, and, depending upon the extent to which they are inserted in the pile, neutron activity is thus controlled by simple absorption. With continuously variable control possible, a reactor can theoretically be tamed to whatever requirements are imposed.

When working with a nuclear reactor we must at all times, as noted above, ensure that the supply of neutrons is greater than the loss; that is, a chain reaction must continually occur. No discussion of atomic rocket propulsion is possible without at least a rudimentary knowledge of these nuclear reactions.

Atomic Rockets

The nuclear-reactor–powered rocket would be similar to the chemical rocket in that matter would be exhausted as the reaction mass. The two would differ, however, because in the former the source of energy and the source of the exhaust gases would be different, while in the latter the two are one and the same. Some authorities on atomic propulsion prefer to think of the propellant as being the "working fluid" which is expanded and ejected, reserving the word "fuel" for the fissile products employed in the reaction. Nuclear rockets, as conceived today, will essentially consist of a nuclear reactor and an inert working fluid (possibly hydrogen, methane, or even water).

Generally, a nuclear reactor will consist of alternate uranium and graphite blocks, although a liquid moderator such as heavy water can be employed. Resulting from the reactions that take place are dangerous gamma radiation and the production of neutrons, protons, and other basic particles. It will probably be impractical at first to utilize these particles directly, so nuclear-reactor engineers will no doubt use only the heat released, transferring it to a working fluid.

Heat derived from U^{235} neutron reactions is immense; it is said to be of the order of 200 million electron volts for each uranium atom, or, put another way, about 20,000 kilowatthours for each gram of uranium used. Apparently, the quantity of working fluid that a spaceship could carry would be the limiting factor, rather than the energy supplies available. Mass ratios are apt to be much the same as in chemical rockets, since both types achieve their momentum from the discharge of appreciable portions of the original mass. Once we are in a position to use the fission products directly, however (an idea we shall examine shortly), we shall find that very different conditions result.

Power requirements are high; in one theoretical case, 32 kilowatts per pound of thrust for a hydrogen working fluid under 300-lb/sq in. pressure and a specific impulse of 750 lb-sec/lb would be needed. Chemical equilibrium at nearly 50,000°F is assumed here; it is probably far higher than we shall be able to work with conveniently. The effective handling of extremely high temperatures will assuredly be one of the major problems to be overcome in applying atomic energy to rocket propulsion. Perhaps the other great problem will be to transfer efficiently the heat generated in the reactor to the fluid that is to provide the rocket's exhaust stream. Selecting the correct fluid, developing the low-critical mass reactor, handling the high temperatures sure to be involved, and developing a satisfactory shield are all problems that plague the engineer as he works to marry the atom to the rocket for tomorrow's propulsion systems.

Types of Nuclear Reactor

Most experience gained to date has been from *solid* reactors, which are the type commonly under development for industrial purposes. By the well-known heat-transfer methods of conduction, convection, and radiation, a working fuel is heated up by passing it through the reactor. While simple in theory, engineers have been unable in practice to obtain this transfer without generating excessive wall temperatures. It must never be forgotten that here the heat is transferred from the reactor to the fluid, just the reverse of what we have in chemical rockets, where temperatures are passed from fluids to the walls.

Before moving on to the second type of reactor, the gaseous reactor, we should first review rapidly what is required in the design of an acceptable conventional atomic reactor. First, resistant materials are needed to survive the intense particle bombardments and temperatures. Materials will also have to be developed to protect passengers and crew from dangerous power-plant radiations. Second, while high temperatures produce many problems, they are vital in an efficient reactor, since we desire to raise the gas temperatures as much as is feasible. Finally, in order to create as much area as possible for heat transfer from the reactor walls to the working fluid, long tubular passages will undoubtedly be used. Typical problems cropping up in this connection include large pressure drops across the reactor, material stress, and novel pumping needs.

A gaseous reactor solves some problems but produces others. By mixing gaseous propellant products with a nuclear fuel in a suitable rocket thrust chamber, superb heat-transfer characteristics would result. This would immediately suggest that wall temperatures could be lowered, solving, at least partially, critical material problems. Gas temperatures, pressures, quantities of working fluid and fissile materials, system size, and geometry would all enter into gaseous-reactor design and would indicate the feasibility of maintaining the critical chain reaction.

As in the case of the solid reactor, the gaseous scheme introduces a number of important dilemmas. For example, if nuclear fuel is used in the exhaust, it will deplete rather rapidly, requiring larger supplies than are now feasible. And, of course, once we add nuclear particles to the efflux, the radiation hazard will sharply increase. The questions of proper chamber geometry, temperatures, and pressures seem hard to solve, and the question of how to properly control the exhaust stream has yet to be answered in terms of the introduction of nuclear fuels into the chamber. Finally, just how simple it will be to prevent excessive neutron capture and maintain the chain reaction has still to be determined.

The materials problem is most likely to be a limiting factor that will continue to haunt us. Let us say that we can use a hydrogen working fluid at an 8000°F temperature and 1,000 lb-sec/lb specific impulse. Assume that fission and rate of heat removal can be controlled. Does this sound feasible? Today we work with materials of 3000°F, and it is possible that some day we can learn to handle 5500°F. Above some 6000°F, materials change into the gaseous state, so unless we get to the point where we can effectively modify the atomic binding structure, we are not going to proceed very far. Today, one reactor is reported to operate in the range of 3500°F, though most run at 2000 to 3000°F. Surely nuclear-powered rockets are not just around the corner.

Even less likely is the use of nuclear particles themselves, as opposed to the heat provided by reactors. The power-dissipation problem alone is titanic, and we have very few concepts of how we might practically control the direction of the efflux.

Fusion reactions are the well-known thermonuclear reactions that take place in the stars and in hydrogen bombs. Some scientists think that controlled fusion may be with us in 20 years or so, and if so we may completely bypass fission. Waste disposal, for example, would be greatly eased, but energy generation would be enormously increased. Work in plasma physics will have to be carefully watched, and it is through research in this area that eventual success is expected. Reports from a recent joint British-American thermonuclear power conference suggest controlled reactions have already been achieved in the laboratory.

Thermonuclear reactants are hydrogen isotopes, deuterium or deuterium and tritium. When they are ionized, they evolve into the plasma state. (When a light element like hydrogen fuses, great amounts of energy result.) A fusion reactor would probably be of toroidal form, magnetic lines of force maintaining in position the very hot plasma. This would be done to assure that no direct contact was made with the walls, to prevent vaporization. As the plasma became fused, X rays and neutrons would result, their energy appearing as heat when contact was made with the walls of the reactor. A reaction would become self-sustaining at 900,000,000°F.

One of the great current developments is Princeton's stellarator, which was designed to study methods of slowing the rate of nuclear fusion to practical values. Expected to be ready within three years, it will consist of a hollow tube that will contain the plasma maintained by a magnetic field produced by external coils. Temperatures will rise into the millions of degrees.

Because of radiation hazards and other factors, we may find that future atomic rockets will not be used for take-off from the earth, but rather as second or third stages only, with reliance on chemicals to do the initial boosting through the atmosphere. For travel between satellite orbits and for crossing interstellar space, where accelerations measured in fractions of 1 g would be acceptable, some scientists have suggested the ion rocket.

Other Power Plants

The *ion-rocket* principle is identified with low thrusts and acceleration, but with very high exhaust velocity, and involves a system wherein ions are accelerated in a controlled direction by an electrostatic field. In such a case, we would rely on voltages to replace heat employed in conventional and atomic engines, although it will be no easy matter to provide for the necessary generation of power and, at the same time, keep within realistic weight limits. High-frequency electromagnetic devices and electrostatic generators have been suggested to replace conventional low-frequency electrical generators. To ensure that the space rocket using the ion drive remains uncharged, electrons will have to be emitted from heated cathodes to compensate for ion discharge.

In a series of electrical spaceship proposals by Stuhlinger,[2] both nuclear reactors and solar energy have been forwarded as likely power sources, to be employed in conjunction with turboelectric generators. Atomic or solar energy would be transformed into first mechanical and then electrical energy. Both rubidium and cesium have been considered as the propellant for the ion drive, the former being the more readily available, but the latter the more desirable. The power plant would operate by vaporizing and ionizing the

[2] E. Stuhlinger, Possibilities of Electrical Space Ship Propulsion, "Bericht über den V. Int. Astronautischen Kongress," Springer-Verlag, Berlin, Vienna, pp. 100–110, 1955. E. Stuhlinger, Electrical Propulsion System for Space Ships with Nuclear Power Source, *J. Astronautics,* Winter, 1955; Spring, Summer, 1956. E. Stuhlinger, Outlook to Space Travel, *The Space Journal,* Summer, 1957.

propellant on numerous incandescent platinum surfaces and by providing voltage to accelerate the resulting particles in a given direction to produce useful thrust.

A number of firms are working in the ion field under Air Force contract; they include North American Aviation, Avco Manufacturing, and Giannini Research. North American has a feasibility study of ion propulsion under way, and company scientists have come up with what is called Project Snooper. This would have two ion motors designed to accelerate charged particles resulting from vaporized cesium. Thrust would be $\frac{1}{3}$ lb, acceleration 0.0001 g. The vehicle would weigh 3,300 lb, would have a sodium-cooled, unshielded nuclear reactor; heat exchanger; turbogenerator; and electrical system. Guidance and payload items would come to 1,500 lb. Avco is occupied with means of magnetic acceleration of gases, and Giannini is working on ion-plasma jets.

Some investigators have come up with schemes for electronic and ionic propulsion systems where 10 million–sec specific impulses are linked with figures of 312,000 kilowatts of power; 10,000 lb of thrust for 100 sec, and perhaps more than 130,000 farads capacity for the electron-gas storage condenser. These are assuredly formidable parameters.

Others ponder photon rockets, driven by parallel beams formed by properly designed reflectors. Here, of course, the exhaust velocity would be equal to the familiar c, the velocity of light in a vacuum, but to pick up a pound of thrust (someone has figured) over one million kilowatts of power would be needed! If thrust built up to a moderate 10,000 lb, we would be dealing with over 13 billion kilowatts, 13 million volts, and 1 million amperes of current, assuming an electric-power source!

Sänger and others have made rather detailed studies of the photon principle, wherein thrust would be produced by radiation pressure. They all point out that, in order to obtain sufficient radiation intensity, the temperature source—possibly a radiating gas plasma produced by a stationary nuclear reaction—would have to be very high. They also point out that we have no notion of how to begin to develop an effective reflecting surface to collimate the photon stream. Mirrors would need a reflecting power of 0.99999999. Furthermore, unless the chamber walls in which the photons were created were not so reflective, they would vaporize instantly.

Since photon rocket exhausts would be identical with light speed, theoretically the vehicle could eventually approach this limiting velocity. This immediately would bring us into the realm of relativistic mechanics. Man, even today, can dimly perceive the shadow of what may come thousands of years hence.

Chemical, atomic, ion, and photon rockets are the four main categories that are either practical today or hold theoretical implications for future developments. Atomic rocket motors are reportedly being developed by the Atomic Energy Commission's laboratories at Livermore and Los Alamos, and presumably Sandia Corporation is doing the same thing. Cosmic ramjets which use "scooped up" interstellar matter for fuel have been suggested by German authors, but they have yet to be subjected to wide analysis. Antigravity systems look good on paper, and there are research laboratories investigating the problem, but nothing is known today that would suggest any immediate or foreseeable prospect of neutralizing gravity. So the best we can do is to base our calculations on highly developed systems using atomic, ionic, or photonic particles (but mainly atomic), accept the speed of light as a practical limit, and consider how to approach it.

It should not be assumed, however, that all will be easy once velocities in the neighborhood of optic (light) speed are attained. Interstellar particles and gases striking a rocket moving at 0.9 c may tend to decelerate the rocket, damage its surfaces, or even subject it to the equivalent of a cyclotron nuclear bombardment. Secondary cosmic radiations might cause a serious human hazard. Temperature may well increase. These are indications of the practical problems to be considered before true interstellar travel becomes feasible.

We have studied the implications of relativity on bodies traveling at near-optic speeds. Mass increases, apparent time elapse violently changes, and dimensions shorten. Photons, ions, or atomic particles may be our thrust-producing agents. There is nothing theoretically impossible about a trip to the stars; it is merely that the mind of man reels at the task of trying to tie the whole proposition into a mental framework. And man somehow feels that, since light is, at least apparently, a limiting speed, limits are placed on what man can ultimately do in the universe. And limitations, even of this magnitude, tend to frustrate him.

One who is not frustrated in regard to distance is Eugen Sänger, who startled an audience at the Seventh Congress of the International Astronautical Federation with a discussion of internebular journeys. Relativistic mechanics considered, his ship would take us to Andromeda in 25 years' time and across the universe in 41.9 years, from the voyager's point of view. From the reference point of earth, three billion years would have passed.

Shepherd, in his article on interstellar flight, believes that this should not worry us.

It is clear . . . that the limiting nature of the velocity of light is not necessarily the most serious barrier in the attainment of interstellar flight, in fact in most respects it is no barrier at all. [Here he is referring to the time-dilation effect or "time paradox," which would allow man to go practically anywhere within his lifetime provided he were able to closely approach light speed.] The real difficulty, always assuming that we can find suitable energy sources for the job, lies in the unfavorable ratio of power dissipation to acceleration as soon as we become involved with high relative velocities. The problem is fundamental to any forces [e.g., the thrust of a rocket jet] to produce the necessary acceleration. The only method of acceleration which one can conceive that would not be subject to this difficulty would be that caused by an external field of force.

Science has not yet reached the point where the application of an external field of force can be considered in other than highly speculative terms, and the problem of power supply for more conventional systems is staggering. Yet the stars that beckon us are within our theoretical reach. If man and science continue to advance for hundreds and thousands of years without destroying themselves and without serious interruption, there is probably no reason not to assume that someday our insatiable curiosity will lead us into the spaces beyond our native solar system.

L'expérience ayant cependant prouvé qu'il est parfois dangereux d'assigner trop précipitamment des limites absolues au pouvoir de la Science, j'aurai la prudence de terminer en remarquant que la physiologie doit continuer à progresser comme le reste et qu'il ne semble pas absurde de songer qu'elle puisse peut-être un jour fournir un procédé de narcose ralentissant la vie et simultanément l'usure de l'organisme; elle permittrait alors aux hommes de passer outre au veto que les lois de la relativité leur opposent.

Robert Esnault-Pelterie
L'Astronautique, 1930

BIBLIOGRAPHY

Aller, L. H.: "Astrophysics: Nuclear Transformations, Stellar Interiors, and Nebulae," The Ronald Press Company, New York, 1954. (Especially the chapter entitled The Interstellar Medium.)

White, H. E.: "Classical and Modern Physics," D. Van Nostrand Company, Inc., Princeton, N.J., 1940. (Especially the chapter entitled The Theory of Relativity.)

Serviss, G. P.: "The Einstein Theory of Relativity," Fadman, New York, 1923.

Einstein, A., and L. Infeld: "The Evolution of Physics," Simon and Schuster, Inc., New York, 1952.

Clarke, A. C.: "Exploration of Space," Temple Press, Ltd., London, 1951. (Especially the chapter entitled To the Stars.)

Freundlich, E.: "The Foundations of Einstein's Theory of Gravitation," E. P. Dutton & Co., Inc., New York, 1920 (translation).

Carr, H. W.: "The General Principle of Relativity," Macmillan & Co., Ltd., London, 1922.

Bolton, L.: "An Introduction to the Theory of Relativity," E. P. Dutton & Co., Inc., New York, 1922.

Einstein, A.: "Relativity," Hartsdale House, New York, 1947 (translation).

Frank, P.: "Relativity and its Astronomical Implications," Sky Publishing Corporation, Cambridge, Mass., 1952.

Gatland, K. W., and A. M. Kunesch: "Space Travel," Philosophical Library, Inc., New York, 1953. (See especially chapter entitled The Stars Beckon.)

ARTICLES IN THE *Journal of the British Interplanetary Society*

Shepherd, L. R.: Interstellar Flight, vol. 11, no. 4, p. 149, 1952.
———: Note on Shielding of Atomic Rockets, vol. 8, no. 4, p. 149, 1949.
——— and A. V. Cleaver: The Atomic Rocket, Parts I–IV, vol. 7, no. 6, 1948, to vol. 8, no. 2, 1949.

Clarke, A. C.: The Challenge of the Spaceship, vol. 6, no. 3, p. 66, 1947.

Bussard, R. W.: A Nuclear-electric Propulsion, vol. 15, no. 6, p. 297, 1956.

Rowland, E. N.: A Note on Space Travel in a Gravitational Field, vol. 16, no. 4, p. 216, 1957.

ARTICLES IN THE *Journal of the American Rocket Society*

Monroe, W. D.: Random Thoughts on Atomic Power, no. 65, March–April, 1946.

McCarthy: On a Nuclear Rocket Motor, vol. 24, no. 1, 1954.

Kaeppeler, H. J.: On Cooling of Nuclear Rockets, vol. 24, no. 5, 1954.

What to Expect in Atomic Energy Rockets, no. 84, March–April, 1951.

ARTICLES IN THE *Journal of Astronautics*

Stuhlinger, E.: Electrical Propulsion System for Space Ships with Nuclear Power Source, vol. 2, no. 4, 1955; vol. 3, nos. 1 and 2, 1956.

H. E. Prew: Space Exploration: The New Challenge to the Electronics Industry, *J. Astronautics,* vol. 4, no. 1, p. 9, 1957.

Kaeppeler, H. J.: Aspects of Nuclear Power Application for Jet Propulsion, vol. 2, nos. 2 and 3, 1955.

OTHER LITERATURE

Stuhlinger, E.: Possibilities of Electrical Space Ship Propulsion, Bericht über den V. Internationalen Astronautischen Kongress, Springer-Verlag, Berlin, Vienna, 1955.

Kreuse, H. G. L.: Relativistische Raketenmechanik, *Astronaut. Acta,* vol. 11, no. 1, 1956.

Romick, D. C.: Basic Design Principles Applicable to Reaction-propelled Space Vehicles, Bericht über den V. Internationalen Astronautischen Kongress, Springer-Verlag, Berlin, Vienna, 1955.

Michielsen, H. F.: The Case for the Low Acceleration Spaceship, *Astronaut. Acta,* vol. 3, no. 2, p. 130, 1957.

Bade, W. L.: Relativistic Rocket Theory, *Am. J. Phys.,* vol. 21, p. 310, 1953.

Esnault-Pelterie, R.: "Astronautique et relativité," pp. 228–241, "L'Astronautique" Imprimerie A. Lehure, Paris, 1930.

Elliott, D. G.: Interstellar Flight, *R R S News,* no. 83, p. 1, Winter, 1955–1956.

Space Flight Notes: Space Travel and Relativity, *Jet Propulsion,* vol. 26, no. 12, p. 1105, 1956.

The Possibility of Interstellar Flight, *Jet Propulsion,* vol. 27, no. 1, p. 69, 1957.

The Slowing Down of Time, *Jet Propulsion*, vol. 27, no. 6, p. 665, 1957.

Time Dilatation in Space Flight, *Jet Propulsion*, vol. 27, no. 6, p. 665, 1957.

Evolution et incertitude de la théorie du champ unifié, *Fusées et recherche aéronaut.*, vol. 1, no. 3, p. 209, 1956.

Singer, S. F.: "Relativity and Space Travel," *University of Maryland Physics Department Tech. Rept.* 61, January, 1957.

Brewster, W. R., Jr. et al.: The Rate Processes of Life and the Special Relativity Theory, American Rocket Society Preprint, 376–56, 1956.

Zaehringer, A. J.: Fuels for the Atomic Rocket, *Missiles and Rockets*, vol. 2, no. 6, p. 93, 1957.

Reichel, R. H.: Nuclear Powered Rockets, *Missiles and Rockets*, vol. 2, no. 6, p. 96, 1957.

Fusion for Flight, *Missiles and Rockets*, vol. 2, no. 6, p. 65, 1957.

Shechtman, I., and E. Larisch: Comments on Thermonuclear Power Plants, *Jet Propulsion*, vol. 27, no. 2, p. 176, 1957.

Gustavson, J.: Nuclear Fusion—Energy of the Future, *Jet Propulsion*, vol. 27, no. 5, p. 570, 1957.

Sanger-Bredt, I.: A Propos des fusées nucléaires thermodynamiques, *Fusées et recherche aéronaut.*, vol. 1, no. 2, p. 11, 1956.

Sänger, E.: La Mecanique du vol des fusées à photons, *Fusées et recherche aéronaut.*, vol. 1, no. 3, p. 253, 1956.

———: Flight Mechanics of Photon Rockets, *Aero Digest*, vol. 73, no. 1, p. 68, 1956.

Ducrocq, A.: L'Energie atomique et la propulsion par reaction, *Fusées*, vol. 1, no. 3, p. 213, 1956.

Winterberg, F.: Situation presente du probleme des fusées propulsees au moyen de l'energie nucléaire, *Fusées et recherche aéronaut.*, vol. 2, no. 1, p. 9, 1957.

Reis, T., and P. Ageron: Quelques aspects de la propulsion par l'energie nucléaire, *Fusées et recherche aéronaut.*, vol. 2, no. 1, p. 23, 1957.

Nuclear Rocket Race On, *Missiles and Rockets*, p. 33, October, 1956.

Gerardin, L. A. A.: La Propulsion electro-gravitationelle, *Interavia*, p. 992, December, 1956.

Stuhlinger, E.: Flight Path of an Ion-propelled Space Ship, *Jet Propulsion*, vol. 27, no. 4, p. 410, 1957.

———: Outlook to Space Travel, *Space Journal*, vol. 1, no. 1, p. 17, 1957.

———: Ion Propulsion and Why, *Missiles and Rockets*, vol. 2, no. 6, p. 82, 1957.

Naugle, J. E.: The Ion Rocket, *Missiles and Rockets*, vol. 2, no. 6, p. 87, 1957.

Simmons, H. T.: Air Force Studies Ion Power, *Missiles and Rockets*, vol. 2, no. 6, p. 76, 1957.

Ion, Photon Power Space Travel Hope, *Missile Eng.,* vol. 1, no. 3, p. 15, 1957.

Ehricke, K. A.: Solar Power for Spacecraft, *Missiles and Rockets,* vol. 1, no. 2, p. 44, 1956.

————: The Solar-powered Space Ship, American Rocket Society Preprint, 310–56, 1956.

15

The Reality of the Irrational

The Prelude

The prelude of today's rational reality is the photostat of the "irrational" dreams of yesteryears. These dreams and achievements of the past are evidence that man must, by nature, move onward and outward, ever conquering new frontiers, ever expanding, never being quite satisfied with things as they are, even though his soul harbors the inherent fear of change.

The Four Elements

Empedocles maintained that all matter was derived from four elements—earth, air, fire, and water. These are essential to man's survival as a civilized being, but each has proved to be, in its own way, a thing to be conquered, harnessed, and put to use.

Earth. Now, let us consider first the element earth. Man looks upon earth as his mother. As a matter of fact, many early religions believed that man was, in actuality, derived from the earth. "And the Lord God formed man of the dust of the ground and breathed into his nostrils the breath of life; and man became a living soul." [1] "For dust thou art, and unto dust shalt thou return." [2] The early Greeks believed that Prometheus formed man out of clay.

Although the earth nourished and sustained man in his infancy, freely producing wild berries and fruits for his consumption and

[1] Genesis 2:7.
[2] *Ibid.,* 3:19.

354

wild herbs for his medications, the actual conquest of the earth for man's use at will, the science of agriculture, was a relatively recent achievement. While man is thought to have made his appearance about one million years ago, the beginning of agriculture is estimated at about 18,000 B.C. The first notable advances in agriculture, however, were made by the Egyptians about 5000 B.C.: they utilized the science of irrigation to develop the valley of the Nile.

Even through today's mechanized culture, agriculture continues to be a challenge to man's ingenuity. Our civilization, with its large cities and broad industries, depends upon an ever-abundant food supply. Man's conquest of the earth has been realized, but his responsibility to the earth, his mother, continues; what he draws from the earth he must replenish, to prevent diminution of the supply of nourishment for his ever-increasing demands.

Yes, man has conquered the element earth. He has moved it, tilled it, and changed its face. But he has never ceased to love it. It is his mother, his home. And even as he lifts his eyes to dream of space and the conquest of other earths, there is a fear in him, a fear of breaking the bond, of severing the umbilical cord, to reach for the stars. For other worlds may not be so kind, so long-suffering, so indulgent.

The waters deluge man with rain, oppress him with hail, and drown him with inundations; the air rushes in storms, prepares the tempest, or lights up the volcano; but the earth, gentle and indulgent, ever subservient to the wants of man, spreads his walks with flowers and his table with plenty; returns, with interest, every good committed to her care; and though she produced the poison, she still supplies the antidote; though constantly teased more to furnish the luxuries of man than his necessities, yet even to the last she continues her kind indulgence, and, when life is over, she piously covers his remains in her bosom.[3]

Fire. The second element mentioned, fire, was present on earth long before man appeared, and man probably saw a good deal of fire before he took it for himself and put it to use. Man alone was little more than an animal. He had hands, he formed weapons and tools. But he forged no metals, cooked no bread, created no light,

---

[3] Pliny.

and he shivered in the cold. Greek mythology recognized the importance of fire to man's development and told of Prometheus, the Son of Earth, who stole fire from the gods and gave it to man, and who, for this offense, was bound to a rock by Zeus to suffer eternal pain.

Fire was indeed a gift of the gods, for early man saw it descend from the skies in bolts of lightning to ignite whole forests. But man was young and bold, and he took the gift of fire for his own hearth and forge.

Fire is the basis of mechanization and industry; it is the instigator of motion; it is the source of light. Man conquered it early in his history, but he is still devising new avenues for its use. When man enters space, he will ascend upon fire.

Water. Water is one of the most essential elements for man's survival; he can exist only a few days without it. When the waters descended upon the earth, animal life began in the water. When creatures emerged from the seas to become land animals, they carried the water with them, for the plasma that bathes the cells of living creatures differs little in composition from the water of the ocean in which the creatures originated.

But water, too, had to be conquered. It separated man from new lands yet unseen. It was not until the New Stone Age that man fashioned boats out of the skins of animals and hollow logs and learned to direct his craft over rivers and streams. Some men were bold enough to float out into the ocean, but always within sight of land. It was not until much later, with the development of navigational skills, that man dared cross large bodies of water.

And many, like the poet Horace, felt that man was doing a great wrong, even committing sacrilege, to dare to cross the seas.

Oak and triple bronze must have girt the breast of him who first committed his frail bark to the angry sea, and who feared not the furious southwest wind battling with the blasts of the north, nor the gloomy Hyades, nor the rage of Notus [the south wind], than whom there is no mightier master of the Adriatic, whether he choose to raise or calm the waves. What form of death's approach feared he who with dry eyes gazed on the swimming monsters, on the stormy sea, and the ill-famed cliffs of Acroceraunia? Vain was the purpose of the god in severing the lands by the estranging main, if in spite of him our impious ships dash across the depths he meant should not be touched. Bold to endure all things, mankind rushes even through forbidden wrong.[4]

However, in spite of such forebodings, man over the years did conquer the water. He sailed it, charted it, fished it, dammed it, and diverted it for his own use. He is still looking into its depths and finding new wonders.

Air. Our most "irrational" dreams of today find their source in the fourth element, air, but even in bygone centuries early man looked at the soaring birds and envied their power of flight. Many dreamed of ways to fly. The angels had wings and thus could fly to and from heaven. The early Greeks told of Daedalus and Icarus and their daring ascent into the air on wings manufactured of birds' feathers and wax. But Icarus flew too near the sun, and his wings melted. He fell to his death into what was later named the Icarian sea, in his honor, a mythological warning against daring to "fly too high." It is encouraging, however, that Daedalus landed safely.

Throughout the ages man dreamed of the power of flight. Leonardo da Vinci made intricate drawings of a flying machine. But the conquest of the air was to be the achievement of the twentieth century. The success of the Wright brothers at Kittyhawk marked the beginning of the Air Age. And once man had realized his long ambition of flight through the air, he turned his dreams to space, to flight beyond the enveloping and protective atmosphere to still uncharted skies.

The Drive

In the midst of all this planning and speculation about flight into space, there arises the question why? What drive forges reality from these "irrational" dreams? Why should man attempt to reach other worlds just when he has made himself comfortable on this one? There are many superficial answers—for national protection ("The nation that controls the moon and planets controls the earth."), to search for more abundant natural resources, to satisfy innate curiosity, etc. But actually one must look much deeper than this into the scheme of things to arrive at the true answer. One must look at life itself.

[4] Horace, "Odes," book I, iii, Loeb Classical Library.

Life on earth began in the water. It was only after the great seas and oceans were formed that life began in the small unicellular organisms known as protozoa. Then life evolved in the sea. Each new species which came into being as a tentative improvement over an older and simpler one was a marine species. Its environment was aqueous; it was bathed by fluid abounding in nourishment; its locomotion depended upon the water surrounding it.

But then occurred an event which was really more advanced, more hazardous, indeed more daring, from the human point of view, than man's proposed extension of himself into space: A life form completely changed its environment; life left the sea and came upon the land. Why? Competition for food became too great in the oceans. The oceans receded and left these life forms stranded. But why struggle through the evolutionary processes required to develop new structures for the adaptation to an environment of air rather than water? Why did these early creatures refuse to die when subjected to such overwhelming change? To be sure, the process involved millions of years, but even so, there was a choice involved. Either change or nonexistence. Life chose to exist. Life chose change.

Life itself involves a drive—a drive onward to a better existence, toward the best conditions possible for future progeny. This drive has spurred on most of the advances made by all species. Its failure resulted in extinction. It was the basis of man's upward ascent from the savage. It caused him to seek new frontiers. It caused him to look upward and outward to the new boundaries of space.

One of the best descriptions of this drive and the reasons behind man's desire to project himself to new worlds is given by Ray Bradbury in "The Strawberry Window." In this short story about a future in which the colonization of Mars is a reality, the hero describes to his family his ideas of the reasons behind it all.

"I believe in Mars," he began quietly. "I guess I believe some day it'll belong to us. We'll nail it down. We'll settle in. We won't turn tail and run. It came to me one day a year ago, right after we first arrived. 'Why did we come?' I asked myself. 'Because,' I said, 'because. It's the same thing with the salmon every year. The salmon don't know why they go where they go, but they go, anyway. Up rivers they don't remember, up streams, jumping waterfalls, but finally making it to where they propagate and die, and the whole thing starts again. Call it racial memory, instinct, call it nothing, but there it is.' And here we are."

They walked in the silent morning with the great sky watching them and the strange blue and steam-white sands sifting about their feet on the new highway.

"So here we are. And from Mars where? Jupiter, Neptune, Pluto and on out? Right. *And on out.* Why? Someday the sun will blow up like a leaky furnace. Boom—there goes Earth. But maybe Mars won't be hurt. Or if Mars is hurt maybe Pluto won't be, or if Pluto's hurt, then where'll *we* be, our son's sons, that is?"

He gazed steadily up into that flawless shell of plum-colored sky.

"Why, we'll be on some world with a number maybe; planet 6 of star system 97, planet 2 of system 99: So damn far off from here you need a nightmare to take it in! We'll be gone, do you see, gone off away and safe! And I thought to myself, ah, ah. So that's the reason men shoot off their rockets!"

"Will—"

"Let me finish. Not to make money, no. Not to see the sights, no. Those are lies men tell, the fancy reasons they give themselves. Get rich, get famous, they say. Have fun, jump around, they say. But all the while, inside, something else is ticking along the way it ticks in salmon or whales, the way it ticks, by God, in the smallest microbe you want to name. And that little clock that ticks in everything living, you know what it says? It says get away, spread out, move along, keep swimming. Run to so many worlds and build so many towns that *nothing* can ever kill man. You *see,* Carrie? It's not just us come to Mars, it's the race, the whole darn human race, depending on how we make out in our lifetime. This thing is so big I want to laugh, I'm so scared stiff of it."

He felt the boys walking steadily behind him and he felt Carrie beside him and he wanted to see her face and how she was taking all this but he didn't look there, either.

"All this is no different than me and Dad walking the fields when I was a boy, casting seed by hand when our seeder broke down and we'd no money to fix it. It had to be done somehow, for the later crops. My God, Carrie, my God, you *remember* those Sunday-supplement articles, "The Earth Will Freeze in a Million Years!" I bawled once, as a boy, reading articles like that. My mother asked why. 'I'm bawlin' for all those poor people up ahead,' I said. 'Don't worry about them,' Mother said. But, Carrie, that's my whole point; we *are* worrying about them. Or we wouldn't be here. It matters if Man with a capital M keeps going. There's nothing better than Man with a capital M in my book. I'm prejudiced, of course, because I'm one of the breed. But if there's any way to get hold of that immortality men are always talking about, this is the way—spread out—seed the Universe. Then you got a harvest against crop failures anywhere down the line. No matter if Earth has famines or the rust comes in. You got the new wheat lifting on Pluto or where-in-hell-ever man gets to in the next thousand years. I'm crazy with the idea, Carrie, crazy. When I finally hit on it I got so excited I wanted to grab people, you, the boys, and tell them. But, hell, I knew that wasn't necessary. I knew a day or night would come when you'd hear that ticking in yourselves, too, and then you'd see, and no one'd have to say anything again about all this. It's big talk, Carrie, I know, and big thoughts for a man just short of five feet five, but by all that's holy, its true." [5]

Farfetched Ideas

Speculation on the details of a future in which space flight is a fact has been the meat of a relatively new department of literary endeavor known as science fiction-fantasy. While the settings and situations of most of these stories will probably never be approached in reality (although today's television, rocket ships, atom bomb, electronic brain, etc. were prophesied in detail by earlier writers of science fiction), they do reflect the general train of thought, the aspirations and fears, of a group of individuals who have accepted the conquest of space as a rational and necessary next step in human achievement. In this way, science fiction is today's prophet warning against tomorrow's problems, or, at times, today's critic of today's morals, ethics, and philosophy by means of its projection against the larger screen of tomorrow's universe.

And what are the dooms and glories foreseen for the children of the third planet when they venture into the unknown realms of space? Or what dangers await the earth when contacted by beings from other worlds?

The Other Worlds. By far the majority of science-fiction writers betray the basic fear of the unknown when depicting the worlds with which the travelers through space might come into contact. Sometimes the danger lies in the hostility of the planet itself, sometimes in the woefully inadequate personalities of the human beings

[5] R. Bradbury, The Strawberry Window, in F. Pohl, ed., "Star Science Fiction Stories No. 3," pp. 30–32, Ballantine Books, New York, 1954.

deposited upon it, sometimes in both. Ray Bradbury is the accepted master of this theme in "Here There Be Tygers." He creates a living planet with a personality of its own, dangerous to the overly materialistic Chatterton, who expresses the underlying theme of many a science-fiction drama—"You can't trust planets. They're bound to be different, bound to be bad, bound to be out to get you. . . ." But the planet is benevolent toward the other, more philosophically inclined members of the interstellar expedition, who accept its bounties with gratitude. And in "The Martian Chronicles," Bradbury elaborates at length and in many directions upon the effects of the planet Mars on the people of earth, and vice versa. The ethical Captain Wilder, the idealist Spender, the materialist Parkhill, all see Mars in a different light, all receive their just rewards at its hands.

The Other People. The forms of life, the cultures, morals, and ideals of the beings from other worlds contacted via space flight have been debated and examined from almost every conceivable angle by science-fiction writers. And again a fear of mankind is the basic theme—the fear of inferiority. Although the forms depicted are often the most repulsive imaginable, the superiority of the other people of the galaxy is always evident, in technological aspects at least. Man is often given the final edge only on the basis of his fighting spirit or dogged refusal to give up, even in the face of seemingly overwhelming odds. And while these other beings are strange in themselves, the science-fiction writers often use them to enable man to look at himself through their eyes, from an entirely new and alien point of view, to realize his own inadequacies, eccentricities, and repulsiveness.

Once flight into space has been achieved and earth becomes a member of a galactic or universal civilization, the next rational step will be the establishment of "colonies" upon other planets or satellites. Environmental difficulties must be overcome, to be sure, but the science-fiction writers usually display great ingenuity in describing ways and means of controlling a variety of situations.

Imagining Earth, then, as only one of many inhabited worlds, what situations of an interplanetary or intergalactic nature might arise? A multitude of these have been suggested and expounded. The "other people," once contacted, may begin to entertain ideas of earth's conquest. The other people may be assimilated into earth's way of life, thereby creating new opportunities and difficulties. The distant colonies of earth might assert their independence, with or without resulting earth-colony warfare. The earth-people of the distant colonies might undergo a variety of mutations, producing the next step in man's evolution. Earth may find herself to be only one of a multitude of civilized worlds, all greatly advanced scientifically and philosophically.

One of the natural questions that arises when one contemplates the vastness of the universe and realizes the submicroscopic stature of man in the scheme of things is that of the actual scope of the universe itself. Are our solar systems merely atoms and our galaxies merely molecules in a universe immensely larger than we can conceive, as Donald Wandrei suggests in "Colossus"? Are we the infinitesimal creations of some macroscopic scientist, as Edmond Hamilton suggests in "Fessenden's Worlds"? What actually is man's status in the universe?

Perhaps we shall know when we make manifest the "irrational" dreams and apparent fears of men like Horace, who said, "No thing is too high for the daring of mortals: We storm heaven itself in our folly." Yet Horace was not alone in his day nor in the present in his concern regarding the consequence of man's daring and dream fulfillment. There are many today who fear the realization of our dream of space flight; all have questions and are anxious of answer. There are those who are concerned with the sociological effects of man's flight into space, those concerned with the complex political ramifications, with the philosophical aspect, with the purely religious, moral, and ethical consequences of man as he "storms heaven itself."

Man's Place in the Universe

So now man realizes he is on the horns of the ultimate dilemma. The vital drive which propels all life has brought life, on this planet, to the point of a cosmic awareness, and the implacable instinct to express life's basic motility has brought the knowledge that action must have its consequences. The racial memory, of which Bradbury spoke, reminds man that the drive leads to the encounter of obstacles, the conquest of which brings him face to face with the unknown.

The racial instinct to recoil from obstacle has been termed by Freud the "original instinct" and cosmically transcends the sexual urges with which his writings are popularly identified. Encounters with the unknown usually have drastic and violent consequences for man, and this knowledge leads him to believe that such violence is symbolic of evil—since tranquillity is identified with happiness. The further knowledge that intelligence alone brings order out of chaos has resulted in the universal conviction that the order of the universe is the result of intelligent planning; and the magnitude of the universe implies a colossal intelligence, so immense that any attempt to deny its supremacy is disastrous. Since purposive intelligence has thus far been observed only in man, it is not unnatural that the colossal intelligence is associated with manlike attributes—and hence the existence of religion and the feeling that the colossal intelligence is either on his side or must be so persuaded. Robert Jungk recognizes all these things and notes with horror that man aspires to total conquest of the universe. "The stake," he says, "is nothing less than the Throne of God."

And here is the crux of the ultimate dilemma: Man is terrified by the prospect of a deity who is jealous of his command of the universe, not so much because of the element of apparent omnipotence (which could also be kindly) but because he, man, will himself not rest until *he* attains all within his awareness. This is the program set in motion when the symbolic progenitors, Adam and Eve, ate of the tree of knowledge. They were cast out of Eden (tranquillity) when they did not agree to yield completely to God's will. They immediately were face to face with the unknown. Violence ensued, and man conquered it with an artifact, the ark, and began a slow climb to a nominal state of order.

But there was never any doubt, once man ate of the forbidden tree of knowledge, that there would someday be a day of reckoning. The Last Judgment represents the cataclysmic climax in the battle between man's instinctive drive to total mastery (ambition) and the "desire" of the universe to maintain the status quo.

Maybe the odds, when they are known, will prove to be hopeless.

The part is less than the whole, and it may develop that the whole will prove conclusively that might makes right. "For we see now, as it were, in a glass, darkly, but then face to face." We will not know until we finally are face to face with the infinite. In the depths of our being, we must feel that we have a chance or we would not try.

We try today, and we will keep on trying. In the day of reckoning we may discover that we never had command, or we may find that God had endowed us with it from the beginning, and we were merely in the process of making it more and more complete. In the meantime, let us pray that man's striving to find his place in the universe will so satisfy his "aggressive drive" for "conquest and empire" that he will no longer contemplate his own destruction with nuclear weapons, but instead find in his fellowman a brother with whom he may sojourn to Heaven itself.

Index

365